Residence Time Distribution Theory in Chemical Engineering

Edited by
A. Pethö and R. D. Noble

verlag chemie

Residence Time Distribution Theory in Chemical Engineering

Proceedings of a Summer School held at
Bad Honnef, August 15-25, 1982

Edited by
A. Pethö and R. D. Noble

verlag chemie

Weinheim · Deerfield Beach, Florida · Basel · 1982

Prof. Dr. Árpád Pethö
Institut für Technische Chemie
der TU Hannover
Callinstr. 3
D-3000 Hannover 1
Federal Republic of Germany

Dr. Richard D. Noble
Center for Chemical Engineering
National Bureau of Standards
Boulder, CO 80303
USA

The Summer School was organized by the Institut für Technische Chemie der Universität Hannover, took place at Bad Honnef in the Physikzentrum der Deutschen Physikalischen Gesellschaft, and was sponsored by the Stiftung Volkswagenwerk (all addresses in the Federal Republic of Germany).

This book contains 85 figures and 26 tables

CIP-Kurztitelaufnahme der Deutschen Bibliothek

Residence time distribution theory in chemical engineering: proceedings of a summer school held in Bad Honnef, August 15 – 25, 1982/[the summer school was organized by the Inst. für Techn. Chemie d. Univ. Hannover and was sponsored by the Stiftung Volkswagenwerk]. Ed. by A. Pethö and R. D. Noble. – Weinheim; Deerfield Beach, Florida; Basel: Verlag Chemie, 1982.

ISBN 3-527-26025-0 (Weinheim, Basel)

ISBN 0-89573-061-8 (Deerfield Beach, Florida)

NE: Pethö, Árpád [Hrsg.]; Institut für Technische Chemie « Hannover »

Printing and Bookbinding: Krebs-Gehlen Druck, D-6944 Hemsbach
Printed in the Federal Republic of Germany

In Memoriam

Chin-Yung Wen
1928-1982

Preface

In the last two or three decades a new branch of chemical engineering has been synthesized. “This transition from descriptive technology to modern engineering came ... at the First Symposium on Chemical Reaction Engineering (1957), where a number of earlier developments were brought together ... into a discipline ... called Chemical Reaction Engineering” [O. Levenspiel, Chem. Engng. Sci. *35* (1980) p. 1821].

Physical effects in chemical reactors, however, are difficult to separate from the chemical rate processes. In trying to do so one usually distinguishes between chemical kinetics and fluid dynamics, putting down the “performance equation” of a chemical reactor as follows:

$$\text{output} = f\,(\text{input, kinetics, flow pattern})$$

When constructing a flow model for a given reactor, we must know the pattern of fluid passage through the reactor. This flow behavior could be determined by finding the complete history of each fluid element. However, Danckwerts pointed out in his famous paper (1953) that, instead of this complexity of the flow pattern, it is enough to know how long the fluid elements stay in the reactor, in other words, to determine the residence time distribution of the fluid particles in the exit stream. We can then select a model to represent the real process which has the same or similar type of residence time distribution.

The primary goal of the Bad Honnef Summer School 1982 is to offer the possibility of basic unterstanding of the above system identification process, which is, however, by far not as simple as it may seem, through lecturers who are experts of world niveau in the field. General mathematical background, both deterministic and stochastic, are being taught besides the more sophisticated, newly developed techniques. However, another principal aim of the Summer School is to draw attention to the various fields of application.

A. Pethö
R. D. Noble

Contents

The Scope of R. T. D. Theory 1
R. Aris

Residence Time Distribution with Many Reactions and in Several Environments 23
R. Aris

Measurement of Binary Gaseous Diffusion Coefficients Within Porous Catalysts 41
D. L. Cresswell, N. H. Orr

Stochastic Flow Reactor Modeling: A General Continuous Time Compartmental Model with First-order Reactions 75
L. T. Fan, J. R. Too, R. Nassar

Fixed Bed Reactors, Flow and Chemical Reaction 103
V. Hlavacek

A Spectral-Theoretic View of Axial Dispersion Models 113
S. J. Parulekar, D. Ramkrishna

Nonlinear Adsorption, Reaction, Diffusion and Intraparticle Convection Phenomena in Flow Systems 147
A. E. Rodrigues

Influence of Bed Structure and Tracer Sorption on the R. T. D. in Fluidized Bed Reactors 181
H. Schlingmann, M. Thoma, D. Wippern, H. Helmrich, K. Schügerl

Measurement of Liquid and Solid Residence Time Distribution in Biological Reactors 217
S. Elmaleh, S. Papaconstantinou

Pseudorandom Technique for Measuring Residence Time Distributions 223
A. Lübbert, J. Diekmann, G. Rotzoll

Simulation of the Performance of a Flow System Consisting of Interconnected Reactors by Markov Processes 229
R. Nassar, J. R. Too, L. T. Fan

Simulation of the Performance of a Flow Chemical Reactor by Markov Chains 237
J. R. Too, R. Nassar, L. T. Fan

A Macroscopic Model of a Continuous Emulsion Liquid Membrane Extraction System 247
J. D. Way, R. D. Noble

Models for Flow Systems and Chemical Reactors 255
C. Y. Wen

Two Abstracts 283
E. B. Nauman

Subject Index 285

List of Contributors

(Invited lecturers are printed in italics)

R. Aris, Department of Chemical Engineering and Materials Science, University of Minnesota, Minneapolis, MN 55455, USA

D. L. Cresswell, Swiss Federal Institute of Technology, Technisch-Chemisches Labor, E. T. H. Zentrum, CH-8092 Zürich, Switzerland

J. Diekmann, Institut für Technische Chemie, Universität Hannover, D-3000 Hannover, Federal Republic of Germany

S. Elmaleh, Laboratoire de Génie Chimique Appliqué aux Biotechnologies, Université des Sciences et Techniques du Languedoc, F-34060 Montpellier Cedex, France

L. T. Fan, Department of Chemical Engineering, Kansas State University, Manhattan, KS 66506, USA

*I. Halász**, Angewandte Physik. Chemie, Universität des Saarlandes, D-6600 Saarbrücken, Federal Republic of Germany

H. Helmrich, Lurgi-Gesellschaften, Abt. LV-E, D-6000 Frankfurt 2, Federal Republic of Germany

V. Hlavacek, Department of Chemical Engineering, State University of New York at Buffalo, Buffalo, NY 14260, USA

A. Lübbert, Institut für Technische Chemie, Universität Hannover, D-3000 Hannover, Federal Republic of Germany

R. Nassar, Department of Statistics, Kansas State University, Manhattan, KS 66506, USA

E. B. Nauman, Department of Chemical Engineering, Rensselaer Polytechnic Institute, Troy, NY 12181, USA

---

* no manuscript has been submitted

R. D. Noble, National Bureau of Standards, Center for Chemical Engineering, 773.1, Boulder, CO 80303, USA

N. H. Orr, Research and Development Department, B. P. Chemicals, Grangemouth, Scotland

S. Papaconstantinou, Laboratoire de Génie Chimique Appliqué aux Biotechnologies, Université des Sciences et Techniques du Languedoc, F-34060 Montpellier Cedex, France

S. J. Parulekar, School of Chemical Engineering, Purdue University, West Lafayette, IN 47907, USA

D. Ramkrishna, School of Chemical Engineering, Purdue University, West Lafayette, IN 47907, USA

A. E. Rodrigues, Department of Chemical Engineering, University of Porto, P-4099 Porto Codex, Portugal

G. Rotzoll, Institut für Technische Chemie, Universität Hannover, D-3000 Hannover, Federal Republic of Germany

H. Schlingmann, Hoechst AG, Abtl. Verfahrenstechnik, D-6230 Frankfurt, Federal Republic of Germany

K. Schügerl, Institut für Technische Chemie, Universität Hannover, D-3000 Hannover, Federal Republic of Germany

M. Thoma, Institut für Regelungstechnik, Universität Hannover, D-3000 Hannover, Federal Republic of Germany

J. R. Too, Department of Chemical Engineering, Kansas State University, Manhattan, KS 66506, USA

J. D. Way, National Bureau of Standards, Center for Chemical Engineering, 773.1, Boulder, CO 80303, USA

C. Y. Wen, Department of Chemical Engineering, West Virginia University, Morgantown, WV 26505, USA

D. Wippern, Dr.-Ing. Bender & Wippern, D-2000 Hamburg, Federal Republic of Germany

The Scope of R.T.D. Theory

R. Aris

Department of Chemical Engineering and Materials Science, University of Minnesota, Minneapolis, MN 55455

SUMMARY

An attempt is made to survey the scope of RTD theory discussing first the general concepts and broad principles, the looking at some of the systems considered and their applications to mixing, reaction. The stochastic approach and the direct derivation of moments are discussed.

1. Introduction- general concepts

This workshop is the lineal descendent of that oldest of symposia, the English tea-break. For it was during such an interlude of praiseworthy academic indolence that the central idea of Danckwerts' paper on continuous flow systems came to him [1]. The paper that he subsequently wrote [2] is not as often cited as it might be for it has become so primary a reference, that like ignorance of Latin, it is usually taken for granted.

In it he defined the internal and external age distributions, $I(t)$ and $E(t)$, and related them to the F-diagram, the fraction of material introduced after a given instant that emerges at a time t later. This is the response of the system to a step change of tracer concentration in the input. The C-diagram is the response to an impulse of tracer at the inlet and thus gives $E(t)$ directly on normalization. The relations between these functions and the intensity function $\Lambda(t)$, later introduced by Shinnar and Naor [3], are given by:

$$E(t) = F'(t) = -\theta I'(t) = \Lambda(t) \exp -\left[\int_0^t \Lambda(t')dt'\right] \quad (1)$$

$$\int_0^t E(t')dt' = F(t) = 1 - \theta I(t) = 1 - \exp -\left[\int_0^t \Lambda(t')dt'\right] \quad (2)$$

$$\theta^{-1} \int_t^\infty E(t')dt' = \theta^{-1}\big(1-F(t)\big) = I(t) = \theta^{-1} \exp -\left[\int_0^t \Lambda(t')dt'\right] \quad (3)$$

$$E(t)/\int_t^\infty E(t')dt' = -\frac{d}{dt} \ell n\{1-F(t)\} = -\frac{d}{dt} \ell n\ \theta I(t) = \Lambda(t) \quad (4)$$

where $\theta = V/q$ = volume of system/perfusion rate. We note in passing that

$$\mu = \int_0^\infty tE(t)dt = -\theta \int_0^\infty tI'(t)dt = \theta \int_0^\infty I(t)dt = \theta \quad (5)$$

Danckwerts went on to discuss two parameters which might give indications of the physical situation from the inspection of the F or E curves. The first is the hold-back

$$H = \frac{1}{2} \int_0^\theta F(t)dt \quad (6)$$

which is zero for plug flow and might approach 1 if there is much dead space in the system. Thus it is a comparison of the residence time distribution with the plug-flow system. The other parameter compares the F-curve with that of the perfectly mixed single stage by the integral

$$S = \frac{1}{2} \int_0^\infty \left| F(t) - 1 + e^{-t/\theta} \right| dt \quad (7)$$

He called this the segregation and gave it the sign of $\{1 - e^{-t/\theta} - F(t)\}$ for small t. He then discussed flow through a bed of solids with longitudinal dispersion obtaining

$$F(t) = \frac{1}{2} \operatorname{erfc} \frac{(L-vt)}{2\sqrt{Dt}} = \frac{1}{2} \operatorname{erfc} \frac{1-(t/\theta)}{2\sqrt{\Delta t/\theta}}, \quad \Delta = D\theta/L^2, \quad (8)$$

and laminar flow in pipes for which

$$F(t) = \begin{cases} 0 & t < \tfrac{1}{2}\theta \\ 1 - \theta^2/4t^2 & t > \tfrac{1}{2}\theta \end{cases} \quad (9)$$

In a later paper [4] Danckwerts used the idea of local residence times based on the observation of Spalding [5] that in a tracer test the $\int_0^\infty c\, dt$ is constant throughout the system and equal to Q/q, where Q is the total quantity of tracer and q the volumetric flow rate. This gives a local average age of particles

$$\mu(\mathbf{x}) = \int_0^\infty tc(\mathbf{x},t)dt/\int_0^\infty c(\mathbf{x},t)dt \quad (10)$$

In 1963, Shinnar and Naor [3] introduced the escape probability or intensity function, $\Lambda(t)dt$, or the fraction of material of age t that will leave the system in the interval $(t,t+dt)$ to give a clearer insight into stagnancy. A system with stagnancy has an escape probability that decreases over some interval for in such an interval the longer a particle stays the less likely is it to leave. The intensity function shows a maximum when there is stagnancy both in experimental and model situations.

As probability densities the functions E(t) etc. have their characteristic functions and the Laplace transform has often been used in this one. It serves usefully as a moment generating function for $\bar{E}(s)$, the Laplace transform of E(t), is analytic in the right half plane. Denoting by μ and σ^2 the mean residence time and the variance of residence times

$$\mu = \int_0^\infty tE(t)dt \quad , \quad \sigma^2 = \int_0^\infty (t-\mu)2E(t)dt \tag{10}$$

we have

$$\bar{E}(s) = 1 - \mu s + \frac{1}{2}(\sigma^2 + \mu^2)s^2 - \cdots \tag{11}$$

and

$$\mu = -\bar{E}'(0) = -\frac{d}{ds}\left[\ell n\ E(s)\right]_{s=0} \tag{12}$$

$$\sigma^2 = \bar{E}''(0) - \left[\bar{E}'(0)\right]^2 = \frac{d^2}{ds^2}\left[\ell n\ \bar{E}(s)\right]_{s=0} \tag{13}$$

When a model is governed by linear equations the Laplace transform can be used to obtain E(t) and if only the moments are required a difficult inversion may often be avoided. Matching moments is one technique that can be used for parameter estimation though it needs to be used with care (Seinfeld and Lapidus give a careful treatment in their text [5]).

Following Spalding [6] it is worth commenting on the general structure of the linear process. Let the system of volume V occupy a region Ω with boundary $\partial\Omega$, which consists of three types of region: $\partial\Omega_o$, over which no transport takes place; $\partial\Omega_i$, over which fluid enters the system; and $\partial\Omega_e$, over which it leaves the system. Thus if $c(\mathbf{x},t)$ is the concentration of tracer at a point $\mathbf{x}$ within Ω

$$\frac{\partial c}{\partial t} = \nabla\cdot D\nabla c - \nabla\cdot\mathbf{v}c \tag{14}$$

where D is a local Fickian coefficient and $\mathbf{v}$ the local velocity. Both of these can be functions of position but we assume the fluid is incompressible.

$$\nabla\cdot\mathbf{v} = 0$$

and that there are no density partitions in the system — a condition that can be relaxed — so that c = constant is a solution of the equations. Then (14) has to be solved subject to

$$c(\mathbf{x},0) = 0 \tag{15}$$

$$\mathbf{v}\cdot\mathbf{n} = 0 \text{ and } D(\partial c/\partial n) = 0 \text{ on } \partial\Omega_o \tag{16}$$

$$D(\partial c/\partial n) - \mathbf{n}\cdot\mathbf{v}c = f \text{ on } \partial\Omega_i \tag{17}$$

$$\partial c/\partial n = 0 \text{ on } \partial\Omega_e \tag{18}$$

where $\mathbf{n}$ is the outward normal to $\partial\Omega$. The function f is the local flux into the system over $\partial\Omega_i$ and

$$\iint_{\partial\Omega_i} - \mathbf{n}\cdot\mathbf{v}\, dS = q \tag{19}$$

$$\iint_{\partial\Omega_i} - f\, dS = q\,\delta(t) \tag{20}$$

$\delta(t)$ being the unit Dirac measure. Then

$$E(t) = \frac{1}{q}\iint_{\partial\Omega_e} \mathbf{n}\cdot\mathbf{v}\, c\, dS \tag{21}$$

Of these equations we take the Laplace transform and use the expansion

$$\overline{c}(\mathbf{x},s) = \overline{c}_o(\mathbf{x}) - s\overline{c}_1(\mathbf{x}) + \frac{1}{2}\, s^2\overline{c}^2(\mathbf{x}) - \cdots \tag{22}$$

Then

$$\nabla\cdot(D\nabla\overline{c}_o) - \nabla\cdot\mathbf{v}\overline{c}_o = 0 \tag{23}$$

$$\nabla\cdot(D\nabla\overline{c}_1) - \nabla\cdot\mathbf{v}\overline{c}_1 = -\,\overline{c}_o \tag{24}$$

$$\nabla\cdot(D\nabla\overline{c}_2) - \nabla\cdot\mathbf{v}\overline{c}_2 = -\,2\overline{c}_1 \tag{25}$$

and the boundary conditions (16) and (18) carry over immediately whilst (17) becomes

$$D(\partial\overline{c}_o/\partial n) - \mathbf{n}\cdot\mathbf{v}\overline{c}_o = -\,\mathbf{n}\cdot\mathbf{v} \tag{26}$$

$$D(\partial\overline{c}_i/\partial n) - \mathbf{n}\cdot\mathbf{v}\overline{c}_i = 0 \quad ,\ i = 1,2 \tag{27}$$

Now

$$\overline{E}(s) = \frac{1}{q}\iint_{\partial\Omega_e} \mathbf{n}\cdot\mathbf{v}c\,dS$$

$$= 1 - \mu s + \frac{1}{2}(\sigma^2 + \mu^2)s^2 - \cdots$$

so we should find

$$\frac{1}{q}\iint_{\partial\Omega_e} \overline{c}_o\mathbf{n}\cdot\mathbf{v}dS = 1 \ ,\ \frac{1}{q}\iint_{\partial\Omega_e} \overline{c}_1\mathbf{n}\cdot\mathbf{v}dS = \mu \ ,\ \frac{1}{q}\iint_{\partial\Omega_e} \overline{c}_2\mathbf{n}\cdot\mathbf{v}dS = \sigma^2 + \mu^2 \tag{28}$$

The first follows from the fact that $\overline{c}_o \equiv 1$ is a solution of (23), (16), (26) and (18). Then integrating (24) over Ω and using Green's theorem and the boundary conditions, gives

$$V = \iiint_\Omega \bar{c}_o dV = - \iiint_\Omega (\nabla \cdot D\nabla \bar{c}_1 - \nabla \cdot \mathbf{v}\bar{c}_1) dV$$

$$= \iint_{\partial\Omega_e} \mathbf{n} \cdot \mathbf{v}\bar{c}_1 dS = q\mu$$

Thus

$$\mu = \theta = V/q \tag{29}$$

Now the partial differential equation (24)

$$\nabla \cdot (D\nabla \bar{c}_1) - \nabla \cdot \mathbf{v}\bar{c}_1 = -1 \tag{30}$$

has to be solved before we can calculate the second moment. Again the use of (25) and Green's theorem gives

$$q(\sigma^2 + \mu^2) = \iint_{\partial\Omega_e} \mathbf{n} \cdot \mathbf{v}\bar{c}_2 dS = 2 \iiint_\Omega \bar{c}_1 dV$$

$$= -2 \iiint \{\bar{c}_1 \nabla \cdot D\nabla \bar{c}_1 - \bar{c}_1 \nabla \cdot \mathbf{v}\bar{c}_1\} dV$$

$$= 2 \iiint D(\nabla \bar{c}_1)^2 dV - \iint \bar{c}_1^2 \mathbf{v} \cdot \mathbf{n} dS \tag{31}$$

Horn [7] has shown how important the modification to a positive integrand can be for accurate computation of dispersion coefficients. If the system has internal partitions the volume is weighted according to the equilibrium concentration of each [24].

Independent of the linearity however is the additivity of moments of systems in series, for if these have individual distributions $E_1(t)$ and $E_2(t)$ their joint distribution is

$$E(t) = \int_0^t E_1(\tau) E_2(t-\tau) d\tau \tag{32}$$

Thus

$$\bar{E}(s) = \bar{E}_1(s) \bar{E}_2(s) \tag{33}$$

and by (12) and (13)

$$\mu = \mu_1 + \mu_2 \quad , \quad \sigma^2 = \sigma_1^2 + \sigma_2^2 \quad . \tag{34}$$

If the systems are in parallel with probability p_i that an incoming particle goes to the system with R.T.D. $E_i(t)$, then

$$E(t) = \lambda_1 E_1(t) + \lambda_2 E_2(t) \quad , \quad \lambda_1 + \lambda_2 = 1 \quad . \tag{35}$$

Thus

$$\mu = \lambda_1 \mu_1 + \lambda_2 \mu_2 \quad , \quad \sigma^2 = \lambda_1 \sigma_1^2 + \lambda_2 \sigma_2^2 + \lambda_1 \lambda_2 (\mu_1 - \mu_2)^2 \tag{36}$$

If the stream passing through the first system is recycled in such a way that $\lambda/(1+\lambda)$ is the probability of passing through the second system and round to the first again, then

$$E(t) = \frac{1}{1+\lambda} E_1(t) + \frac{\lambda}{(1+\lambda)^2} \int_0^t \int_0^{t'} E_1(t-t') \int_0^{t'} E_2(t'-t'') E_1(t'')dt''dt' + \frac{\lambda^2}{(1+\lambda)^3} \int \cdots$$

or

$$\overline{E}(s) = \frac{1}{1+\lambda} \overline{E}_1(s)\{1 + \frac{\lambda}{1+\lambda} \overline{E}_2(s)\overline{E}_1(s) + \frac{\lambda^2}{(1+\lambda)^2} \overline{E}_2^2(s)\overline{E}_1^2(s) + \cdots\} = \frac{\overline{E}_1(s)}{1+\lambda-\lambda\overline{E}_1(s)\overline{E}_2(s)} \quad (37)$$

Hence

$$\mu = \mu_1 + \lambda(\mu_1 + \mu_2) \quad , \quad \sigma^2 = \sigma_1^2 + \lambda(\sigma_1^2 + \sigma_2^2) + \lambda(1+\lambda)(\mu_1 + \mu_2)^2 \quad , \quad (38)$$

Note that $\mu_1 = V_1/q_1 = V_1/(t+\lambda)q$, $\mu_2 = V_2/q_2 = V_2/\lambda q$ so that $\mu = (V_1+V_2)/q = \theta_1 + \theta_2$. Note also that $\lambda \to \infty$

$$\overline{E}(s) \longrightarrow \frac{1}{1+(\theta_1 + \theta_2)s} \quad (39)$$

Systems Considered

So many possible systems have been considered that it is almost impossible to organize them, let alone record them in detail. The table which follows is but the very roughest outline and makes no claim to completeness. A worth-while task would be to compile a reference list of systems together with what is known of their distributions and moments. This has been done for certain subclasses [16] or for systems that might be relevant in particular contexts [8,60,61], but not comprehensively. In particular the connection has never been well made to the very considerable biological literature on compartmental analysis [24,54,62]. When Sheppard's book was published in 1962, the chemical engineer would probably have recognized but one of its references, Taylor's 1953 paper on longitudinal dispersion in laminar flow through a tube and the overlap is still not a large one though such a distinguished worker as K. B. Bischoff has made important contributions in both areas.

System		References
Single stirred tank or Plug flow with no diffusion		2, everybody!
Sequences of stirred tanks,		
	with by pass	3,5,8,9,46,48
	in parallel	5,9,60,61
	with cross-flow	3,53,60,61
	with back mixing	5,8,11,19,47
	with end reflux	5,61
	with stagnant regions	45,61
	with transport delay	5,10,12,44
Arrays of stirred tanks		8,14,15
General networks		6,13,17,19,28,30,43,49,50,52
Systems of compartments		24,54-59,62
Stochastic flows		13,58
Recycle systems		31-40
Zone models		6,17,23
Plug-flow with diffusion		2,5,8,16
Flow in helical coils		41,42,51
Combined stirred tanks and plug flow		10,13,18,21

Zweitering's concept of the degree of mixing

Zweitering [18] noted that two very different systems might have the same residence time distribution. For example a plug-flow tubular reactor of holding time θ_1 followed by a mixed reactor of holding time θ_2 would give

$$E(t) = \begin{cases} 0 & 0 \leqslant t \leqslant \theta_1 \\ \frac{1}{\theta_2} e^{-\frac{t-\theta_1}{\theta_2}} & , t > \theta_1 \end{cases} \tag{40}$$

If the tank preceeded the tube then R.T.D. would be exactly the same, yet the conversions in the two schemes for anything but a first-order reaction would be different. Zweitering observed that the residence time t was the sum of the age, α, and the life expectancy, β. Now during $(t,t+\delta t)$ a volume $q\delta t$ leaves the system of which a fraction $\{1-F(\beta)\}$ were already in the system at time $t-\beta = \alpha$. These had a life expectancy of β so that if $I^*(\beta)\delta\beta$ = fraction within the system with expectancy $(\beta,\beta+\delta\beta)$, $VI^*(\beta)\delta\beta = \{1-F(\beta)\}q\delta t$. But $\delta\beta = \delta t$ so $\theta I^*(\beta) = 1-F(\beta) = \theta I(\beta)$ and α and β are distributed in the same way. We note in passing that $\bar{\alpha} = \int_0^\infty \alpha I(\alpha)d\alpha = (\mu^2+\sigma^2)/2\mu$ so that the average residence time of all particle <u>in</u> the system is $\mu + (\sigma^2/\mu)$, which is greater than μ, the average residence time of those entering or leaving the system.

We have noted above that, since, in a tracer test, $\int_0^\infty c(\mathbf{x},t)dt = 1$ everywhere, a local mean age; $\mu(\mathbf{x})$, can be defined by

$$\mu_a(\mathbf{x}) = \int_0^\infty tc(\mathbf{x},t)dt \; . \tag{10 bis}$$

Now except in the case of complete mixing $\mu_a(\mathbf{x})$ will vary and this variation may be measured by

$$\Sigma_a^2 = \langle(\mu_a(\mathbf{x}) - \bar{\alpha})^2\rangle = \frac{1}{V}\iiint (\mu_a(\mathbf{x}) - \bar{\alpha})^2 dV \tag{41}$$

This is called the age variance between points. The age variance within points is

$$\Sigma_a^2 = \langle \int_0^\infty \{t - \mu_a(\mathbf{x})\}^2 c(\mathbf{x},t)dt\rangle \tag{42}$$

and it can be shown that

$$\sigma_a^2 = \int_0^\infty (\alpha-\bar{\alpha})^2 \; I(\alpha)d\alpha = s_a^2 + \Sigma_a^2 \tag{43}$$

Zweitering shows how to attain any required residence time distribution in a plug-flow reactor with side-stream take off. Then the section of the tubular reactor which contains material of ages in $(\alpha, \alpha+d\alpha)$ has a volume = $dV \; VI(\alpha)d\alpha$ =

$[1-F(\alpha)]d\alpha$. The volume drawn off must contribute that moiety of effluent with residence time in $(\alpha, \alpha+d\alpha)$ i.e. $qE(\alpha)d\alpha$, so that the flow rate at α is $q - \int_0^\infty qE(t)dt = q(1-F(\alpha))$. If $c(\alpha)$ is the concentration of a reactant disappearing by reaction at a rate $r(c)$

$$q[1-F(\alpha)]c(\alpha) - q[1-F(\alpha+d\alpha)]c(\alpha+d\alpha) = qE(\alpha)d\alpha c(\alpha) + r(c(\alpha))dV$$

which reduces to

$$\frac{dc}{d\alpha} = - r(c) \tag{44}$$

with an effluent concentration

$$\overline{c} = \int_0^\infty E(\alpha)c(\alpha)d\alpha \tag{45}$$

This is the condition of complete segregation; eqn. (44) is solved subject to $c(0) = c_f$.

On the other hand Zweitering claimed maximum mixedness for the scheme whereby the residence time distribution is attained by a sidestream of flow rate $qE(\beta)d\beta$ being added to a plug flow reactor at a point of life expectancy β. Since the distribution of expectancy is the same the volume element is the same as before and a balance gives

$$q[1-F(\beta+d\beta)]c(\beta+d\beta) - q[1-F(\beta)]c(\beta) = qE(\beta)d\beta c_f - r(c(\beta))dV$$

or

$$\frac{dc}{d\beta} = r(c(\beta)) - \Lambda(\beta)[c_f - c(\beta)] \tag{46}$$

This equation should be solved subject to the condition

$$\frac{dc}{d\beta} \to 0 \qquad \beta \to \infty \quad ,$$

since c is bounded. Thus in the limit

$$c_f - c_\infty = \left[\underset{\beta\to\infty}{\mathrm{Lt}} \ \frac{1-F(\beta)}{E(\beta)}\right] r(c_\infty) \tag{47}$$

which for a stirred tank is

$$c_f - c_\infty = \theta r(c_\infty) \ . \tag{48}$$

Since $\Lambda(\beta)$ is constant for the stirred tank, the solution of (46) is a constant and $c(0) = c_\infty$ satisfies (48).

For first order reaction $r(c) = kc$

$$\frac{dc}{d\beta} = kc - \Lambda(\beta)(c_f-c)$$

or

$$c(\beta) = \frac{c_o \; e^{k_\beta}}{1-F(\beta)} \int_\beta^\infty E(t)\; e^{-kt}\; dt \tag{49}$$

whence

$$c(0) = c_o \int_0^\infty E(t)e^{-kt}\; dt \tag{50}$$

Zweitering showed that $J = \Sigma_a^2/\sigma_a^2$, Danckwert's segregation parameter [20], would be minimized under conditions of maximum mixedness.

Combinations of these models have been made by Weinstein and Adler [21], Villermaux and Zoulalian [22] and Ng and Rippin [23]. Asbjørnsen [15] has used a network model and Kranbeck, Shinnar and Katz [13] a general assemblage of units in their stochastic model (vide inra).

Reaction transforms

If c is the concentration of a reactant disappearing at a rate r(c), the fraction remaining after time t is $\gamma(t)$ the solution of

$$\frac{d\gamma}{dt} = -\; k\; R(\gamma) \tag{51}$$

$$k = R(c_o)/c_o \quad , \quad R(\gamma) = r(c_o\gamma)/r(c_o) \tag{52}$$

Then, by (44) and (45) a completely segregated reactor will give a product with a fraction of

$$\Gamma = \int_0^\infty \gamma(t)\; E(t)dt$$

$$= \int_0^1 \frac{\gamma}{kR(\gamma)}\; E\left(\frac{1}{k}\int_\gamma^1 \frac{d\gamma'}{R(\gamma')}\right)d\gamma \quad . \tag{53}$$

This may be regarded as an integral transform of the residence time distribution which is best expressed in dimensionless form. Let θ be the mean residence time and

$$\tau = t/\theta \;,\quad f(\tau) = \theta E(\theta\tau) \;,\quad \kappa = k\theta = R(c_o)\theta/c_o \tag{54}$$

Then $\gamma(\tau) = \gamma(\tau;\kappa,R)$ satisfies

$$\frac{d\gamma}{d\tau} = -\; \kappa R(\gamma) \quad , \; \gamma(0) = 1 \tag{55}$$

and

$$\Gamma(\kappa) = \int_0^\infty \gamma(\tau)f(\tau)d\tau \quad . \tag{56}$$

For example, a pth order reaction with $R(\gamma) = \gamma^p$ gives

$$\gamma(\tau) = \{1 + (p-1)\kappa\tau\}^{-1} \tag{57}$$

when

$$q = 1/(p-1), \; k = k\, c_o^{p-1} \tag{58}$$

we can unite

$$\Gamma(\rho) = p^q \int_0^\infty \frac{f(\tau)}{(\rho+\tau)^q} d\tau \tag{59}$$

with

$$\rho^{-1} = (p-1)\kappa \tag{60}$$

and $\Gamma(\rho)$ is the generalized Stieltjes transform of f. Cf. [25,26]. When p = 1 this degenerates into the Laplace transform as $\gamma(\tau) = \exp{-\kappa\tau}$.

Some generalized Stieltjes transform pairs are given in [26]. The most important one for our purposes is given by the formula

$$\int_0^\infty x^\lambda e^{-\alpha x}(x+y)^{-\mu}dx = \Gamma(\lambda+1)\alpha^{(\mu-\lambda-2)/2}\, y^{(\lambda-\mu)/2}\, e^{\alpha y/2}\, e^{\alpha 7/2} W_{k,m}(\alpha y) \tag{61}$$

where $2k = -\lambda - \mu$, $2m = \lambda - \mu + 1$. The Whittaker function

$$W_{k,m}(\alpha y) = \frac{\Gamma(-2m)}{\Gamma(\frac{1}{2}-m-k)} M_{k,m}(\alpha y) + \frac{\Gamma(2m)}{\Gamma(\frac{1}{2}+m-k)} M_{k,-m}(\alpha y)$$

$$= \frac{\Gamma(\mu-\lambda-1)}{\Gamma(\mu)} M_{k,m}(\alpha y) + \frac{\Gamma(\lambda-\mu+1)}{\Gamma(\lambda+1)} M_{k,-m}(\alpha y) \tag{62}$$

and

$$M_{k,m}(\alpha y) = (\alpha y)^{\frac{1}{2}+m} e^{-\alpha y/2}\, {}_1F_1(\tfrac{1}{2}+m-k;\; 2m+1;\; \alpha y) \quad . \tag{63}$$

Combining these formulae gives

$$\int_0^\infty x^\lambda e^{-\alpha x}(x+y)^{-\mu}dx = \frac{\Gamma(\lambda+1)\Gamma(\mu-\lambda-1)}{\Gamma(\mu)} y^{\lambda-\mu+1}\, {}_1F_1(\lambda+1;\; \lambda-\mu+2;\; \alpha y)$$

$$+ \Gamma(\lambda-\mu+1)\, \alpha^{\mu-\lambda-1}\, {}_1F_1(\mu;\; \mu-\lambda;\; \alpha y) \tag{64}$$

where

$${}_1F_1(\alpha;\beta;z) = 1 + \frac{\alpha}{\beta}\frac{z}{1!} + \frac{\alpha(\alpha+1)}{\beta(\beta+1)}\frac{z^2}{2!} + - + \frac{(\alpha)^n}{(\beta)^n}\frac{z^n}{n!} + \cdots \tag{65}$$

is Kummer's hypergeometric function

A key step in the Hirschman-Widder treatment is the expression of the general transform in convolution form. Let

$$\rho = e^{-r} \quad , \quad \tau = e^{-t} \quad , \quad \phi(t) = f(e^{-t}) \quad , \quad \Phi(r) = e^{r}\Gamma(e^{-r}) \tag{66}$$

then (50) becomes

$$e^{r}\Gamma(e^{-r}) = \int_{-\infty}^{\infty} f(e^{-t})e^{r-t}(1+e^{-t+r})^{-q}dt$$

or (67)

$$\Phi(r) = \int_{-\infty}^{\infty} \phi(t)G(r-t)dt$$

where the convolution kernel is

$$G(t) = \{1 + et\}^{-q}\, e^{t} \tag{68}$$

Much turns on the nature of E(s) where

$$\frac{1}{E(s)} = \int_{-\infty}^{\infty} e^{-st}G(t)dt$$

(69)

$$= \int_{-\infty}^{\infty} e^{-(s-1)t}\{1 + e^{t}\}^{-q}dt$$

Let $\mu = \dfrac{e^{t}}{1 + e^{t}}$, so that $1 - \mu = \dfrac{e^{t}}{1 + e^{t}}$ and $d\mu = \mu(1 - \mu)dt$ giving

$$\frac{1}{E(s)} = \int_{0}^{\infty} \left(\frac{\mu}{1 - \mu}\right)^{1-s} (1-\mu)^{q} \frac{d\mu}{\mu(1 - \mu)}$$

$$= \int_{0}^{1} \mu^{-s}(1 - \mu)^{s+q-2}d\mu \tag{70}$$

$$= B(1 - s,\ s + q - 1)$$

or

$$E(s) = \Gamma(q)/\Gamma(1 - s)\Gamma(s + q - 1) \tag{71}$$

In this last form E(s) is defined so long as q is not zero or a negative integer. As $q \to \infty$, $\Gamma(q)/\Gamma(q + s - 1) \to q^{-s+1}$, hence

$$E(s) \sim q^{1 - s}/\Gamma(1 - s)$$

which is the correct first order expression.

Using the formula

$$\frac{1}{\Gamma(s+\alpha)} = \frac{1}{\Gamma(\alpha)} e^{\alpha\gamma - s\psi(\alpha)} \prod_{r=0}^{\infty} \left(1 + \frac{s}{r+\alpha}\right) e^{-\frac{s}{r+\alpha}} \tag{72}$$

where γ is Euler's constant and $\psi(\alpha) = \Gamma'(\alpha)/\Gamma(\alpha)$ and setting

$$a_k = \begin{cases} 1 - q + k , & -\infty < k \leqslant 0 \\ k , & 0 \leqslant k < \infty \end{cases}$$

$$b = \psi(1) - \psi(q-1) ,$$

$$c = (q-1) \exp \gamma q , \tag{73}$$

we have

$$E(s) = ce^{bs} \prod_{-\infty}^{\infty} \left(1 - \frac{s}{a_k}\right) e^{s/a_k} \tag{74}$$

which is the key form used by Hirschman and Widder. The kernel is of Class I [25, p. 14].

Shinnar's stochastic approach

Shinnar's introduction of the intensity function has been mentioned above [3]; his work with Naor [19] and Krambeck and Katz [13] was critical in introducing probability considerations in a more general way. Their most general formulation is of n stirred tanks connected quite arbitrarily with four types of flow:

w_{ij} = flow from ith to jth tank

w_{oj} = flow of feed to jth tank

$w_{i,n+1}$ = flow from ith tank to effluent

$w_{o,n+1}$ = flow completely by-passing the system

The volumes, V_i, of the tanks are constant so

$$\sum_{\substack{i=1 \\ i \neq j}}^{n} w_{ij} = \sum_{\substack{k=1 \\ k \neq j}}^{n} w_{jk} , \quad j = 1,2,\ldots n \tag{75}$$

and

$$\sum_{i=0}^{n} w_{i,n+1} \sum_{j=0}^{n+1} w_{oj} = w \tag{76}$$

By defining $-w_{jj}$ as the common value of the two sides of (75) an (n+1)x(n+1) matrix is obtained whose last n rows and first n columns sum to zero, the first row and last column having sums of w. These flows can fluctuate taking on a set of values subject to (75) and (76) but indexed by a random variable α. The fluctuation can now be described by $p\alpha(t)$ the probability that the state is α at time t. These evolve by the Markov equations

$$\frac{dp_\beta}{dt} = \sum_\alpha \lambda_{\alpha\beta}\, p_\alpha \tag{77}$$

where $\lambda_{\alpha\beta}$, $\alpha \neq \beta$, are the switching rates and $\sum_{\beta\neq\alpha} \lambda_{\alpha\beta} = -\lambda_{\alpha\alpha}$.

If zero is a simple eigenvalue there is a steady-state or statistical equilibrium vector $\overline{p}_\alpha$ such that

$$\Sigma_a\, \lambda_{\alpha\beta}\overline{p}_\alpha = 0 \quad , \quad \Sigma_\alpha \overline{p}_\alpha = 1 \tag{78}$$

Shinnar's great idea was to treat both α and i as indexes of state with $\pi(\alpha,i \rightarrow \beta,j,\tau)$ = probability of transition from i to j in time τ, thus giving an overall Markov process. For Poissonian conditions,

$$\pi(\alpha,i \rightarrow \beta,j;\tau) = \delta_{\alpha\beta}\delta_{ij} + \{\lambda_{\alpha\beta}\delta_{ij} + \delta_{\alpha\beta}(w_{ij\alpha}/V_i)\}\tau + o(\tau)$$
$$\pi(\alpha,n+1 \rightarrow \beta,j;\tau) = (\delta_{\alpha\beta} + \delta_{\alpha\beta}\tau)\delta_{n+1,j} + o(\tau) \tag{79}$$

For a Markov process

$$p_{\beta j}(t + \tau) = \sum_\alpha \sum_i p_{\alpha i}(t)\, \pi(\alpha,i \rightarrow \beta,j;\tau) \tag{80}$$

and in the limit $\tau \rightarrow 0$,

$$\frac{dp_{\beta j}}{dt} = \sum_{i=1}^{n} \frac{w_{ij\beta}}{V_i} p_{\beta i} + \sum_\alpha \lambda_{\alpha\beta} p_{\beta j} \tag{81}$$

The initial condition is obtained by distributing the location according to the feed rates

$$p_{\beta j}(0) = \overline{p}_\beta (w_{oj\beta}/w_\beta) \tag{82}$$

it can be shown that

$$\sum_{j=1}^{n+1} p_{\beta j} = \overline{p}_\beta \tag{83}$$

and

$$_j(t) = \Sigma_\beta\, p_{\beta j}(t)/\int_0^\infty \Sigma_\beta\, p_{\beta j}(t)dt \tag{84}$$

is the age distribution of material in stage j. Also

$$F(t) = \Sigma_\beta\, p_{\beta,n+1}(t) \tag{85}$$

is the cumulative residence time distribution

This analysis is used as the basis for the interpretation of tracer experiment with fluctuating throughput [27]. In another paper Shinnar and Naor [19] looked at the chain of stirred tanks with internal reflux. If these are of volumes $V_i = q\theta_i$ with a flow of q into the first and out of the Nth and u_i from ith to (i+1)th and w_i from ith to (i-1)th so that

$$u_{i-1} - w_i = u_i - w_{i+1} = q$$

The total flow rate to stage i is $u_{i-1} + w_{i+1} = u_i + w_i = \lambda_i q$ then the sojourn time (i.e. period of uninterrupted residence is distributed exponentially

$$E_i(t) = \frac{\lambda_i}{\theta_i} \exp - \frac{\lambda_i t}{\theta_i} \quad . \tag{86}$$

Moreover the probability of moving to the left is

$$\tilde{\omega}_1 = 0 \quad , \quad \tilde{\omega}_i = w_i/(u_i + w_i) \ , \ i = 2,\cdots N \quad . \tag{87}$$

Now, we have seen that age and life-expectancy (Shinnar calls the latter 'anti-age') are distributed in the same way and we denote this distribution for stage i by $I_i(t)$. Thus for stages 1 and 2

$$I_1(t) = \int_0^t E_1(t-\tau)I_2(\tau)d\tau = E_1 * I_2 \tag{88}$$

For $i = 2,\cdots N-1$,

$$I_i(t) = \tilde{\omega}_i I_{i-1} * E_i + (1-\tilde{\omega}_i)I_{i+1} * E_i \tag{89}$$

Also

$$I_N(t) = \tilde{\omega}_N E_N * I_{N-1} + (1-\tilde{\omega}_N)E_N \tag{90}$$

The Laplace transforms of these equations give the equations

$$\begin{bmatrix} 1 & -A_1 & \cdot & & & & \\ -B_2 & 1 & -A_2 & & & & \\ \cdot & -B_3 & 1 & -A_3 & & & \\ & & & & & & \\ & & & & -B_{N-1} & 1 & -A_{N-1} \\ & & & & \cdot & -B_N & 1 \end{bmatrix} \begin{bmatrix} \bar{I}_1(s) \\ \bar{I}_2(s) \\ \bar{I}_3(s) \\ \cdot \\ \bar{I}_{N-1}(s) \\ \bar{I}_N(s) \end{bmatrix} = \begin{bmatrix} 0 \\ 0 \\ 0 \\ \cdot \\ \cdot \\ 0 \\ A_N \end{bmatrix} \tag{91}$$

where $A_i = (1-\tilde{\omega}_i)\lambda_i/(\lambda_i + \theta_i s)$, $B_i = \tilde{\omega}_i\lambda_i/(\lambda_i + \theta_i s)$.

The residence time of a particle is the life expectancy of a particle in the first stage i.e.

$$E(t) = I_1(t) = \mathcal{L}^{-1}[\bar{I}_1(s)] = \mathcal{L}^{-1}[\Pi A_i/\Delta] \tag{92}$$

where Δ is the determinant of the tridiagonal matrix. The Laplace transform is not easy to invert except for special cases, but the moments can be calculated.

In case of identical tanks and flows we set

$$\eta = N\,\lambda/\theta \ , \ \xi = \eta(1-\tilde{\omega}) \tag{93}$$

Thus $\tilde{\omega}$ $1-(\xi/\eta)$ is the probability of a particle going back from i to i-1, i=2,•••N-1 for i=N it is $\Pi = w/u = (\eta/\xi)-1$; for i=1, it is zero. Note

$$\frac{1}{\tilde{\omega}} - \frac{1}{\pi} = 1 \tag{94}$$

with $0 \leqslant \pi < 1$, $0 \leqslant \tilde{\omega} < 1/2$. The expected residence time $V/q = N/(1-\pi)\xi$. For N = 2

$$I_1(t) = \frac{1-\pi}{\sqrt{\pi}}\,\xi\, e^{-\xi t}\, \sinh(\xi\sqrt{\pi}\,t) \tag{95}$$

Derivation of moments

Even though the inversion of an equation like (92) is generally difficult the moments can often be obtained. Thus if we take equations such as (88)-(90) and multiply by t and integrate we have for the first moments

$$\bar{\mu}_i = \int_0^\infty t I_i(t)dt \tag{96}$$

the equations

$$\bar{\mu}_1 - \bar{\mu}_2 = \theta_1/\lambda_1 \tag{97}$$

$$\bar{\mu}_i - \tilde{\omega}_i\, \bar{\mu}_{i-1} - (1-\tilde{\omega}_i)\bar{\mu}_{i+1} = \theta_i/\lambda_i \tag{98}$$

$$\bar{\mu}_N - \tilde{\omega}_N\bar{\mu}_N = \theta_N/\lambda_N \tag{99}$$

$$\begin{bmatrix} 1 & -1 & \cdot & \cdot & \cdot & \cdot \\ -\tilde{\omega}_2 & 1 & -(1-\tilde{\omega}_2) & \cdot & \cdot & \cdot \\ \cdot & -\tilde{\omega}_3 & 1 & -(1-\tilde{\omega}_3) & \cdot & \cdot \\ \cdot & \cdot & - & & & \\ \cdot & \cdot & & & 1 & -(1-\tilde{\omega}_{N-1}) \\ \cdot & \cdot & & & -\tilde{\omega}_N & 1 \end{bmatrix} \begin{bmatrix} \bar{\mu}_1 \\ \bar{\mu}_2 \\ \bar{\mu}_3 \\ \\ \bar{\mu}_{N-1} \\ \bar{\mu}_N \end{bmatrix} = \begin{bmatrix} \Theta_1/\lambda_1 \\ \Theta_2/\lambda_2 \\ \Theta_3/\lambda_3 \\ \\ \Theta_{N-1}/\lambda_{N-1} \\ \Theta_N/\lambda_N \end{bmatrix} \tag{100}$$

It is usually simpler to work from the Laplace transformed equations and to show this we will consider again the case of equal tanks with total holding time θ. Then (91) can be written

$$\begin{bmatrix} 1+\theta s/N & -1 & \cdot & \cdot & \cdot \\ -\tilde{\omega} & 1+\theta s/N & -(1-\tilde{\omega}) & \cdot & \cdot \\ \cdot & -\tilde{\omega} & 1+\theta s/N & \cdot & \cdot \\ & & & & \\ \cdot & \cdot & \cdot & 1+\theta s/N & -(1-\tilde{\omega}) \\ \cdot & \cdot & \cdot & -\tilde{\omega} & 1+\theta s/N \end{bmatrix} \begin{bmatrix} \bar{I}_1 \\ \bar{I}_2 \\ \bar{I}_3 \\ \\ \bar{I}_{N-1} \\ \bar{I}_N \end{bmatrix} = \begin{bmatrix} 0 \\ 0 \\ 0 \\ \\ 0 \\ 1-\tilde{\omega} \end{bmatrix} \tag{101}$$

Setting s=0 we see immediately that $\bar{I}_i(0) = 1$ as normalization requires. Either by differentiation or by setting $I_i = 1 - \bar{\mu}_i s + (\bar{\sigma}_i^2 + \mu_i^2)s^2/2 \cdots$ we have equations (98) with all $\tilde{\omega}_i = \tilde{\omega}$ and $\theta_i/\lambda_i = 1/\eta$. But

$$\bar{\mu}_1 = \theta = N/(1-\pi)\xi = N/(1-p)(1-\pi)\xi \tag{102}$$

and by recursion

$$\bar{\mu}_i = \frac{1}{\xi}\left\{\sum_{j=0}^{i-1}(N-j)\Pi^{i-j-1} + \frac{N\pi^i}{1-\pi}\right\}, \quad i=1, \cdots N \tag{103}$$

The average life expectancy is the same as the average age, namely

$$\bar{\alpha} = \frac{1}{N}\sum_{i=1}^{N}\bar{\mu}_i = \frac{\theta}{N^2}\left\{\frac{1}{2}N(N+1) + \frac{\pi}{(1-\pi)^2}(N-1 - N\pi + \pi^N)\right\} \quad . \tag{104}$$

But by the relation $\bar{\alpha} = (\mu^2 + \sigma^2)/2\mu$ noted above we have

$$\frac{\sigma^2}{\mu^2} = \frac{1}{N} + \frac{2}{N^2}\left(\sum_{1}^{N-1} k\pi^{N-k}\right) \tag{105}$$

giving the variance of the residence times.

Conclusions

This is necessarily a very imperfect survey neither touching on all aspects nor delving very deeply into any. After it was written I came on Nauman's excellent review [30] which will repair some of my omissions, and I understand we may hope for a book by him and Buffham in the near future. It is clear that the subject is by no means exhausted and the present workshop will no doubt be productive of further ideas and developments.

References

1. P. V. Danckwerts. "Insights into chemical engineering," p. 217. Pergamon Press. Oxford. 1981.

2. P. V. Danckwerts. "Continuous flow systems. Distribution of residence times." Chem. Engng. Sci. 2, 1, 1953.

3. P. Naor and R. Shinnar. "Representation and evaluation of residence time distributions." Ind. Eng. Chem. Fundamentals 2, 278, 1963.

4. P. V. Danckwerts. "Local residence-times in continuous-flow systems." Chem. Engng. Sci. 9, 78, 1958.

5. J. H. Seinfeld and L. Lapidus. "Mathematical Methods in Chemical Engineering. Process modelling, estimation and identification. Prentice-Hall. Englewood Cliffs. 1974.

6. D. B. Spalding. "A note on mean residence-times in steady flows of arbitrary complexity." Chem. Engng. Sci. 9, 74, 1958.

7. F. J. M. Horn. "Calculation of dispersion coefficients by means of moments." AIChE Journal 17, 613, 1971.

8. C. Y. Wen and L. T. Fan. "Models for flow systems and chemical reactors." Marcel Dekker. New York. 1975.

9. D. Chiang and A Cholette. "Performance of tanks in series of non-ideal mixing." Can. J. Chem. Eng. 48, 286, 1970.

10. D. Wolf and W. Resnick. "Residence time distribution in real systems." Ind. Eng. Chem. Fund. 2, 287, 1963.

11. A. Klinkenberg. "Distribution of residence times in a cascade of mixed vessels with back-mixking." Ind. Eng. Chem. Fund. 5, 283, 1966.

12. S. Sundaresan, N. R. Amundson and R. Aris. "Observations on fixed-bed dispersion models: the role of interstitital fluid." A.I.Ch.E. Journal 26, 529, 1980.

13. F. J. Krambeck, R. J. Shinnar and S. Katz. "Stochastic mixing models for chemical reactors." Ind. Eng. Chem. Fund. 6, 276, 1967.

14. H. A. Deans and L. Lapidus. "A computational model for predicting and correlating the behavior of fixed bed reactors." AIChE Journal 6, 656, 1960.

15. O. A. Asbjørnsen. "Incomplete mixing simulated by fluid-flow networks."

16. K. B. Bischoff and O. Levenspiel. "Patterns of flow in chemical process vessels." Advances in Chem. Eng. 4, 95, 1963.

17. J. A. Van der Vusse. "A new model for the stirred tank reactor." Chem. Engng. Sci. 17, 507, 1962.

18. T. N. Zweitering. "The degree of mixing in continuous flow systems." Chem. Engng. Sci. 11, 1, 1959.

19. R. Shinnar and P. Naor. "Residence time distributions in systems with internal reflux." Chem. Engng. Sci. 22, 1369, 1967.

20. P. V. Danckwerts. "The effect of incomplete mixing on homogeneous reactions." Chem. Engng. Sci. 8, 93, 1958.

21. H. Weinstein and R. J. Adler. "Micromixing effects in continuous chemical reactors." Chem. Engng. Sci. 22, 65, 1967.

22. J. Villermaux and A. Zoulalian. "Etat de mélange du fluide dans un reácteur continu." Chem. Engng. Sci. 24, 1513, 1969.

23. D. Y. C. Ng and D. W. T. Rippin. "The effect of incomplete mixing on conversion in homogeneous reactions." Proc. 3rd Eur. Symp. on Chem. Reac. Eng. Amsterdam. 1964.

24. R. Aris. "Compartmental analysis and the theory of residence time distributions." in "Intracellular Transport." Ed. K. Warren, Academic Press. New York. 1966.

25. D. V. Widder and I. Hirschman. "The convolution transform." Princeton Univ. Press. Princeton. 1955.

26. A. Erdelyi et al. "Tables of Integral Transforms." McGraw-Hill. New York. 1954.

27. F. J. Krambeck, R. Shinnar and S. Katz. "Interpretation of tracer experiments in systems with fluctuating throughput." Ind. Eng. Chem. Fund. 8, 431, 1969.

28. R. H. S. Mah. "Residence time distributions in discrete recycle systems with cross-mixing." Chem. Engng. Sci. 26, 201, 1971.

29. J. M. Hochman and J. R. McCord. "Residence time distributions in recycle systems with crossmixing." Chem. Engng. Sci. 25, 97, 1970.

30. E. B. Nauman. "Residence time distributions and micromixing." Chem. Eng. Commun. 8, 53, 1981.

31. J. C. Mecklenburgh and S. Hartland. "The Theory of Backmixing." Wiley. 1975.

32. M. P. Dudukovic. "On the use of the generalized recycle model to interpret micromixing in chemical reactors." Ind. Eng. Chem. Fund. 16, 385-388, 1977.

33. D. W. T. Rippin. "The recycle reactor as a model of incomplete mixing." Ind. Eng. Chem. Fund. 6, 488-492, 1967.

34. B. Fu, H. Weinstein, B. Berstein and A. B. Shaffer. "Residence time distributions of recycle systems — integral equation formulation." Ind. Eng. Proc. Des. Dev. 10, 501-508, 1971.

35. E. B. Nauman. "Residence times and cycle times in recycle systems." Chem. Engng. Sci. 29, 1883-1888, 1974.

36. M. Rubinovitch and U. Mann. "The limiting residence time distribution of continuous recycle systems." Chem. Engng. Sci. 34, 1309-1317, 1979.

37. B. A. Buffham and E. B. Nauman. "On the limiting form of the residence time distribution for a constant volume recycle system." Chem. Engng. Sci. 30, 1519-1524 (1975).

38. E. B. Nauman and B. A. Buffham. "Limiting forms of the residence time distribution for recycle systems." Chem. Engng. Sci. 32, 1233-1236, 1977.

39. E. B. Nauman and B. A. Buffham. "A note on residence time distributions in recycle systems." Chem. Engng. Sci. 34, 1057-1058, 1979.

40. U. Mann and E. J. Crosby. "Cycle time distribution in circulating systems." Chem. Engng. Sci. 28, 623-627, 1973.

41. E. B. Nauman. "The residence time distribution for laminar flow in helically coiled tubes." Chem. Engng. Sci. 32, 287-298, 1977.

42. D. M. Ruthven. "The residence time distribution for ideal laminar flow in a helical tube." Chem. Engng. Sci. 26, 113-1121, 1971.

43. B. W. Ritchie and A. H. Tobgy. "Residence time analysis in systems having many connections with their environment." Ind. Eng. Chem. Fund. 17, 287-291, 1978.

44. B. A. Buffham and L. G. Gibilaro. "A unified time delay model for dispersion in flowing media." Chem. Eng. J. 1, 31-35, 1970.

45. J. Ragnauraman and Y. B. G. Varma. "A model for residence time distribution in multistage systems with cross-flow between active and dead regions. Chem. Engng. Sci. 28, 585-591, 1973.

46. R. L. Stokes and E. B. Nauman. "Residence time distribution functions for stirred tanks-in-series." Can. J. Chem. Eng. 48, 723-725, 1970.

47. A. H. Haddad and D. Wolf. "Residence time distribution function for multistage systems with backmixing." Can. J. Chem. Eng. 45, 100-104, 1967.

48. L. T. Fan, M. S. K. Chen, K. Ahn, and C. Y. Wen. "Mixing models with varying stage size." Can. J. Chem. Eng. 47, 141-148, 1969.

49. L. G. Gibilaro. "Mean residence times in continuous flow systems." Nature 270, 47-48, 1977.

50. B. A. Buffham. "Mean residence times in steady-flow and some non-flow systems." Nature 274, 879-880, 1978.

51. V. R. Ranade and J. J. Ulbrecht. "The residence time distribution for laminar flow of non-Newtonian liquids through helical tubes." Chem. Eng. Commun. 8, 165, 1981.

52. B. A. Buffham and H. W. Kropholler. "Tracer kinetics: general properties, the mean residence time, and applications to phase and chemical equilibriums." Chem. Engng. Sci. 28, 1081-1089, 1973.

53. M. Moo-Young and K. W. Chan. "Nonideal flow parameters for viscous fluids flowing through stirred tanks." Can. J. Chem. Eng. 49, 187-194, 1971.

54. J. A. Jacquez. "Compartmental analysis in biology and medicine" Elsevier. Amsterdam. 1972.

55. J. Z. Hearon. "Residence times in compartmental systems and the moments of a certain distribution." Math. Biosci. 15, 69, 1972.

56. D. H. Anderson. "Structural properties of compartmental models." Math. Biosci. 58, 61, 1982.

57. D. Fife. "Which linear compartmental systems contain traps?" Math. Biosci. 14, 311, 1972.

58. J. Eisenfeld. "Relationship between stochastic and differential models of compartmental systems." Math. Biosci. 43, 289, 1979.

59. J. Eisenfeld. "On mean residence times in compartments." Math. Biosci. 57, 265, 1981.

60. Y. T. Shah. "Gas-liquid-solid reactor design." McGraw-Hill. New York. 1979.

61. M. Crine and G. A. l'Homme. "Recent trends in the modelling of catalytic trickle bed reactors" in "Mass transfer with chemical reaction in multiphase systems." NATO Advanced Study Series. Sijthoff and Noordhof Int. Pub.

62. C. W. Sheppard. "Basic principles of the tracer method." Wiley. New York. 1962.

Residence Time Distribution with Many Reactions and in Several Environments

R. Aris

Department of Chemical Engineering and Materials Science, University of Minnesota, Minneapolis, Minnesota 55455, U.S.A.

SUMMARY

The combination of a large number of parallel reactions into a so-called 'lumped' system is combined with a residence time distribution to describe the conversion of a complex mixture. The joint residence time distribution when there are several environments is also discussed.

1. Lumping and Residence Time Distributions

The art of chemical engineering is to simplify complex situations and to make them amenable first to analysis and ultimately to design. The notion of a residence time distribution is undoubtedly one of the most important of such ideas and vast is the literature that has evolved from Danckwerts' fundamental insight (1). In the hands of a skillful practitioner, such as Shinnar, it shows both theoretical eleganc and practical utility (2), for it takes the complexities of the physical situation of flow and mixing and reduces them to tractable form without discarding their essential complexity.

Another bold simplification, this time in the realm of kinetics, is that of lumping (3,4) or, as it was originally called, aliasing (5). Here a complex mixture of chemical species is made into a putative continuum of reacting species and the kinetics of a "lump" or segment of this continuum are examined. The well-known phenomenon of a mixture of hydrocarbons appearing to crack by a second-order reactio can be accounted for in this way. The idea has physical origins in the earlier work on distillation of complex mixtures (6) and was only later applied to reactive situations (7).

Now the physico-chemical properties of a species that affect its mixing and hence its residence time distribution may well be correlated with those that affect its reaction rate. For example, molecular weight will have something to say both to diffusivity and to reactivity. Thus in general if α is the parameter of the continuum (simulated boiling point or whatever), so that we think of $A(\alpha)d\alpha$ as the "species" in the parameter interval $(\alpha,\alpha+d\alpha)$, both

$$f(t;\alpha)dt = \text{probability of residence time being in } (t,t+dt) \tag{1}$$

and

$$r(c;\alpha)d\alpha = \text{rate of disappearence of } A(\alpha)d\alpha \text{ by reaction} \tag{2}$$

are functions of the parameter α. The variable $c(t;\alpha)d\alpha$ is the concentration of $A(\alpha)d\alpha$ and, for complete segregation,

$$\frac{dc}{dt} = -r(c;\alpha) . \tag{3}$$

Thus, integrating (3), we have

$$t = \int_{c(t;\alpha)}^{c(0;\alpha)} \frac{dc}{r(c;\alpha)} \tag{4}$$

which in principal can be inverted to give

$$c(t;\alpha) = \Gamma(t;\alpha;c(0;\alpha)) \tag{5}$$

Then the total concentration emerging from the reactor is

$$C = \int_0^\infty\int_0^\infty f(t;\alpha)\Gamma(t;\alpha;c(0;\alpha))dtd\alpha \tag{6}$$

This is a functional of $c(0;\alpha)$ and $f(t;\alpha)$.

It may be useful to exploit the monotonicity of c and write

$$C = \int_0^\infty d\alpha \int_0^{c(0;\alpha)} f(t;\alpha) \frac{cdc}{r(c;\alpha)} \tag{7}$$

where the t in $f(t;\alpha)$ is $\int_c^{c(0;\alpha)} dc/r(c;\alpha)$ (8)

2. An Example

A well-known example of kinetic lumping (4) is given when α is the rate of first-order cracking and

$$c(0;\alpha) = C_o(\lambda/\beta)^\lambda \alpha^{\lambda-1} e^{-\lambda\alpha/\beta}/\Gamma(\lambda) \tag{9}$$

This gives an overall reaction which is ostensibly of order $(\lambda+1)/\lambda$ and may account for the success of fitting cracking data with second order kinetics ($\lambda \doteq 0$). The parameter β is the mean value of α and the variance of the distribution is β^2/λ. Thus as λ varies from 1 to ∞ the spectrum of crackabilities is narrowed to the pure component of rate constant β. Then

$$\Gamma(t;\alpha;c(0,\alpha)) = c(0;\alpha)e^{-\alpha t}$$

and

$$C = \int_0^\infty\int_0^\infty f(t;\alpha)c(0;\alpha)e^{-\alpha t}\, d\alpha dt \tag{10}$$

$$= \mathcal{L}_\alpha[\mathcal{L}_t\{f(t;\alpha);\alpha\}c(0;\alpha);0]$$

where

$$\mathcal{L}_t\{h(t);s\} = \int_0^\infty h(t)e^{-st}\,dt .$$

A residence time distributin with a considerable degree of flexibility is the n-tank in series, which indeed has the same form. We will suppose it to be independent of α for the moment so that

$$f(t;\alpha) = \frac{t^{n-1}\,n^n}{(n-1)!\,\theta^n}\,e^{-nt/\theta} \tag{11}$$

and this would give

$$\frac{C}{C_o} = \mathcal{F}(\lambda,\beta;n,\theta) = (\tfrac{\lambda}{\beta})\,(\tfrac{n}{\theta})^n\,\frac{1}{(n-1)!\,\Gamma(\lambda)}\int_0^\infty\!\!\int_0^\infty t^{n-1}\alpha^{\lambda-1}e^{-\alpha t-nt/\theta-\lambda\alpha/\beta}\,dt\,d\alpha$$

$$= (\tfrac{\lambda}{\beta})^\lambda\,\frac{1}{\Gamma(\lambda)}\int_0^\infty \alpha^{\lambda-1}\left\{1+\alpha\,\frac{\theta}{n}\right\}^{-n} e^{-\lambda\alpha/\beta}\,d\alpha$$

$$= \frac{1}{\Gamma(\lambda)}\int_0^\infty z^{\lambda-1}\left\{1+\frac{\beta\theta}{\lambda n}\,z\right\}^{-n} e^{-z}\,dz$$

$$= \mathcal{G}(\lambda,n;\beta\theta) . \tag{12}$$

Note that

$$\mathcal{G}(x,\infty;\beta\theta) = \frac{1}{\Gamma(\lambda)}\int_0^\infty z^{\lambda-1}\,e^{-(1+\frac{\beta\theta}{\lambda})z}\,dz = (1+\frac{\beta\theta}{\lambda})^{-\lambda} \tag{13}$$

and that by symmetry

$$\mathcal{G}(\infty,n;\beta\theta) = (1+\frac{\beta\theta}{n})^{-n} . \tag{14}$$

The last is a well-known result and both give the pure component, plug-flow limit

$$\mathcal{G}(\infty,\infty;\beta\theta) = e^{-\beta\theta} \tag{15}$$

To calculate the complete integral we observe that

$$(1+\mu z)^{-n} = \sum_{r=0}^{\infty}(-)^r\binom{n+r-1}{r}\mu^r z^r = \sum_{r=0}^{\infty}(-)^r\binom{n+r-1}{r}(\mu z)^{-n-r}$$

according as μz is less or greater than 1. Applying this to (12) with $\mu = \beta\theta/\lambda n$ gives

$$\mathcal{G}(\lambda,n,\beta\theta) = \frac{1}{\Gamma(\lambda)} \sum_{r=0}^{\infty} (-)^r \binom{n+r-1}{r} \left\{ \left(\frac{\beta\theta}{\lambda n}\right)^r \int_0^{1/\mu} z^{\lambda-1+r} e^{-z} dz + \left(\frac{\lambda n}{\beta\theta}\right)^{n+r} \int_{1/\mu}^{\infty} z^{\lambda-1-n-r} e^{-z} \right\}$$

$$= \frac{1}{\Gamma(\lambda)} \sum_{r=0}^{\infty} (-)^r \binom{n+r-1)}{r} \left\{ \left(\frac{\beta\theta}{\lambda n}\right)^r \gamma\left(\lambda+r, \frac{\lambda n}{\beta\theta}\right) + \left(\frac{\lambda n}{\beta\theta}\right)^{n+r} \Gamma\left(\lambda-n-r; \frac{\lambda n}{\beta\theta}\right) \right\} \tag{16}$$

where

$$\gamma(a,x) = \int_0^x t^{a-1} e^{-t} dt \qquad \Gamma(a,x) = \int_x^{\infty} t^{-1} e^{-t} dt = \Gamma(a) - \gamma(a,x) \tag{17}$$

When λ is an integer, say ℓ, we may profitably go back to (12) and write

$$1 + \frac{\beta\theta}{\lambda n} z = y$$

for then

$$\mathcal{G} = \frac{1}{(\ell-1)!} \int_1^{\infty} y^{-n} \left(\frac{\lambda n}{\beta\theta}\right)^{\ell} (y-1)^{\ell-1} e^{-\frac{\lambda n}{\beta\theta}(y-1)} dy$$

$$= \left(\frac{\ell n}{\beta\theta}\right)^{\ell} e^{\lambda n/\beta\theta} \sum_{k=0}^{\ell-1} \frac{(-1)^{\ell-1-k}}{k!(\ell-1-k)!} \int_1^{\infty} y^{-n+k} e^{-y/\mu} dy$$

$$= \mu^{-\ell} e^{1/\mu} \sum_{k=0}^{\ell-1} \frac{(-)^{\ell-1-k}}{k!(\ell-1-k)!} E_{n-k}(1/\mu) , \tag{18}$$

where

$$E_r(z) = \int_1^{\infty} t^{-r} e^{-zt} dt , \quad r>0$$

$$E_o = e^{-z}/z , \quad E_{-r} = e^{-z} \sum_{q=0}^{r} (r!/q!) z^{q-r-1} , \quad r>0 . \tag{19}$$

Thus

$$\mathcal{G}(1,n;\beta\theta) = \mu^{-1} e^{1/\mu} E_n(1/\mu) , \quad \mu = \beta\theta/n \tag{20}$$

$$\mathcal{G}(2,n;\beta\theta) = \mu^{-2} e^{1/\mu} \{E_{n-1}(1/\mu) - E_n(1/\mu) , \quad \mu = \beta\theta/2n \tag{21}$$

Since $E_n(1/\mu) \sim (-1/\mu)^{n-1} \dfrac{\ell n\mu+\psi(n)}{(n-1)!} - \sum_{\substack{m=0 \\ m\neq n-1}}^{\infty}{}' \dfrac{(-1/\mu)^m}{m!(m-n+1)}$, as $\mu \to \infty$, where

$\psi(n) = - \;\; + \sum_{m=1}^{n-1} \frac{1}{m}$, $\gamma = .57721$, we have such formulae as

$$\mathcal{G}(1,n;\beta\theta) \sim \left\{\frac{n}{\beta\theta}\,\frac{1}{n-1} + \sum_{\substack{m=1\\ m\neq n-1}}^{\infty}{}' (-)^{m-1}\left(\frac{n}{\beta\theta}\right)^{m+1} \frac{1}{m!\,(m-n+1)}\,(-)^{n-1}\left(\frac{n}{\beta\theta}\right)^{n}\left[\ell n\,\frac{\beta\theta}{n} + \psi(n)\right]\right\} e^{\frac{n}{\beta\theta}} \tag{22}$$

and

$$\mathcal{G}(1,1;\beta\theta) \sim \frac{1}{\beta\theta}\, e^{\frac{1}{\beta\theta}}\left[\ell n\beta\theta - \gamma + \frac{1}{\beta\theta} - \frac{1}{4\beta^2\theta^2} + \cdots\right] \tag{23}$$

In particular as $\beta\theta \longrightarrow \infty$,

$$\mathcal{G}(1,1;\beta\theta) \sim \frac{n}{\beta\theta}\left\{\ell n\,\frac{\beta\theta}{n} - 0{\cdot}57721\right\} \tag{24}$$

$$\mathcal{G}(1,n;\beta\theta) \sim \frac{n}{n-1}\,\frac{1}{\beta\theta} \qquad n>1 \tag{25}$$

$$\mathcal{G}(2;n;\beta\theta) \sim \frac{n^2}{(n-1)(n-2)}\,\frac{4}{\beta^2\theta^2} \qquad n>1 \tag{26}$$

Since $E_n(x) \quad \frac{e^{-x}}{x+n}$ as n and $x \longrightarrow \infty$ we have

$$\mathcal{G}(1,\infty;\beta\theta) = (1+\beta\theta)^{-1} , \quad \mathcal{G}(2,\infty;\beta\theta) = \left(1+\frac{\beta\theta}{2}\right)^{-2} \tag{27}$$

in agreement with (13).

3. Correlated Physical and Chemical Properties

If the material which cracks more easily moves with less dispersion, as is possible with a Taylorian mechanism, we might correlate this by setting $n = N + \nu\alpha$. Then

$$\frac{C}{C_o} = \left(\frac{\lambda}{\beta}\right)^{\lambda} \frac{1}{\Gamma(\lambda)} \int_o^{\infty}\!\!\int_o^{\infty} \alpha^{\lambda-1}\,\frac{t^{N-1+\nu\alpha}}{\Gamma(N+\nu\alpha)}\left(\frac{N+\nu\alpha}{\theta}\right)^{N+\nu\alpha} e^{-\frac{\lambda\alpha}{\beta} - \frac{N+\nu\alpha+\theta\alpha}{\theta}t}\, dt\, d\alpha$$

$$= \left(\frac{\lambda}{\beta}\right)^{\lambda} \frac{1}{\Gamma(\lambda)} \int_o^{\infty} \left\{\frac{N+\nu\alpha}{N+(\nu+\theta)\alpha}\right\}^{N+\nu\alpha} \alpha^{\lambda-1}\, e^{-\lambda\alpha/\beta}\, d\alpha \tag{28}$$

Let us define

$$\mathcal{H}(\kappa,\lambda,\omega,\sigma) = \frac{\omega^{\lambda}}{\Gamma(\lambda)} \int^{\infty} \left\{1 + \frac{\kappa x}{1+x}\right\}^{-\sigma(1+x)} x^{\lambda-1} e^{-\omega x} dx \tag{29}$$

so that

$$C/C_o = \mathcal{H}(\theta/\nu, \lambda, \lambda N/\beta\nu, N) \tag{30}$$

This integral will have to be evaluated numerically. We note that if $\nu \rightarrow 0$, κ and ω both go to infinity with $\kappa/\omega = \beta\theta/N$ and

$$\mathcal{H} \sim \mathcal{G}(\lambda, N; \beta\theta) \ . \tag{31}$$

This line of reasoning will be developed elsewhere and we now turn to the problem of several environments.

4. Residence Times in Several Environments

In the case of the single residence time distribution there are two methods of determining $f_1(t_1)$. Experimentally, one can trace the system with a unit impulse in the feed and the fraction of tracer emerging in the interval (τ_1, T_1) is

$$\int_{\tau_1}^{T_1} f_1(t_1)dt_1 = F_1(\tau_1, T_1) \ . \tag{32}$$

Inversion is given by

$$f_1(t_1) = \left(\frac{\partial F_1}{\partial T_1}\right)_{T_1=t_1} = \left(-\frac{\partial F_1}{\partial \tau_1}\right)_{\tau_1=t_1} \tag{33}$$

Alternatively, it may be supposed that a first order reaction destroys a substance with a rate constant k_1 and that a steady concentration of this substance is fed to the system. The fraction emerging is

$$\int_o^{\infty} e^{-k_1 t_1} f_1(t_1)dt_1 = \bar{f}_1(k_1) \tag{34}$$

and the inversion of this transform gives

$$f_1(t_1) = \frac{1}{2\pi i} \int_{-i\infty}^{i\infty} f_1(k_1) e^{k_1 t_1} dk_1 \tag{35}$$

For the completely mixed tank of volume V through which fluid flows at a rate q, for example, the first experiment gives

$$V \frac{df_1}{dt_1} = q(\delta(t_1) - f_1(t_1)) , \quad f_1(0) = 0 , \tag{36}$$

or

$$f_1(t_1) = \frac{q}{V} \exp - \frac{qt_1}{V} . \tag{37}$$

The second experiment gives

$$0 = q(1 - \bar{f}_1(k_1)) - Vk_1\bar{f}_1(k_1) \tag{38}$$

or

$$\bar{f}_1(k_1) = \frac{1}{1 + Vk_1/q} \tag{39}$$

and (39) is the Laplace transform of (37).

To illustrate the idea of two environments we might consider two stirred tanks in sequence and suppose that it is of interest to have the joint residence time distribution of spending a time t_1 in the first and t_2 in the second. If k_1 is the rate constant in the first tank and k_2 that in the second, we can write for the concentrations c_1 and c_2

$$\begin{aligned} 0 &= q(1 - c_1) - V_1k_1c_1 \\ 0 &= q(c_1 - c_2) - V_2k_2c_2 . \end{aligned} \tag{40}$$

Thus

$$c_2 = \frac{1}{(1 + k_1\theta_1)(1 + k_2\theta_2)} \tag{41}$$

where

$$\theta_i = V_i/q . \tag{42}$$

This is $\bar{f}_2(k_1,k_2)$ and its inversion gives

$$f_2(t_1,t_2) = \frac{1}{\theta_1\theta_2} e^{-(t_1/\theta_1)-(t_2/\theta_2)} . \tag{43}$$

If t is the local residence time $t_1 + t_2$ it is distributed as

$$f(t) = \int_0^t f_2(t-s,s)ds .$$

To use the first method is to write

$$\theta_1 \frac{df_1}{dt_1} = \delta(t_1) - f_1(t_1)$$

$$\theta_2 \frac{df_2}{dt_2} = f_1(t_1)\delta(t_2) - f_2(t_1,t_2) \tag{44}$$

and this gives $f_1(t_1) = \frac{1}{\theta_1} e^{-t_1/\theta_1}$ and recovers equation (43) for $f_2(t_1,t_2)$. The $\delta(t_2)$ of the second equation arises since everything that enters the second stage has $t_2 = 0$.

5. Distributions and Moments

Let us look at the structure of the distributions more generally. f_n is normalized so that

$$\int_0^\infty\int_0^\infty \cdots \int_0^\infty f_n(t_1,t_2,\cdots,t_n)dt_1dt_2,\cdots,dt_n = 1 \tag{45}$$

The marginal distributions $f_{1i}(t_i)$ giving the probability density of a time t_i in the ith environment are

$$f_{1i}(t_i) = \int_0^\infty \cdots \int_0^\infty f_n(t_1,\cdots,t_{i-1},t_{i+1},\cdots,t_n)dt_1,\cdots,dt_{i-1}dt_{i+1},\cdots,dt_n \tag{46}$$

where the integration is over all the t_j's except t_i. The total time $t = t_1 + t_2 + \cdots + t_n$ is distributed as

$$f(t) = \int \cdots \int f_n(t-t_2-,\cdots,-t_n,t_2,\cdots,t_n)dt_2,\cdots,dt_n \tag{47}$$

where the integral is over the positive orthant $t_i \geq 0$ and the hyperplane $\sum_1^n t_j = t$. There are other marginal distributions of two, three,$\cdots$,(n-1) variables but they are not of immediate interest.

The expected values of t_i give the mean times spent in each environment, while the variances and correlation coefficients are also important. These are

$$\mu_i = \int_0^\infty t_i f_{1i}(t_i)dt_i = \int_0^\infty\int_0^\infty \cdots \int_0^\infty t_i f_n(t_1,t_2,\cdots,t_n)dt_1 dt_2,\cdots,dt_n \tag{48}$$

$$\sigma_i^2 = \int_0^\infty (t_i-\mu_i)^2 f_{1i}(t_i)dt_i = \int_0^\infty\int_0^\infty \cdots \int_0^\infty (t_i-\mu_i)^2 f_n(t_1,\cdots,t_n)dt_1,\cdots,dt_n \tag{49}$$

and

$$\sigma_i\sigma_j\rho_{ij} = \int_0^\infty\int_0^\infty \cdots \int_0^\infty (t_i-\mu_i)(t_j-\mu_j)f_n(t_1,t_2,\cdots,t_n)dt_1 dt_2,\cdots,dt_n \tag{50}$$

The mean and variance of the total residence times are

$$\mu = \sum_{i=1}^n \mu_i$$

$$\sigma^2 = \sum_{i=1}^n \sum_{j=1}^n \rho_{ij}\sigma_i\sigma_j \tag{51}$$

It is often useful to use the Laplace transforms of these probability density functions as characteristic functions, for, when the moments exist,

$$\bar{f}(k) = \int_0^\infty e^{-kt}f(t)dt = \int_0^\infty f(t)dt - k\int_0^\infty t\,f(t)dt + \frac{1}{2}k^2\int_0^\infty t^2 f(t)dt - \cdots$$

$$= 1 - k\mu + \frac{1}{2}k^2(\sigma^2+\mu^2) - \cdots \tag{52}$$

for a properly normalized distribution. Thus

$$\bar{f}(0) = 1\ ,\quad \bar{f}'(0) = -\mu\ ,\quad \bar{f}''(0) - \bar{f}'^2(0) = \sigma^2\ . \tag{53}$$

or

$$\bar{g}(0) = 0\ ,\quad \bar{g}'(0) = -\mu\ ,\quad \bar{g}''(0) = \sigma^2 \quad \text{with} \quad \bar{g}(k) = \ln f(k)\ .$$

Some useful formulae arise when we apply this to the multivariable transform

$$\bar{f}_n(k_1,\cdots,k_n) = \int_0^\infty \cdots \int_0^\infty e^{-k_1t_1-\cdots-k_nt_n} f_n(t_1,\cdots,t_n)dt_1,\cdots,dt_n\ . \tag{54}$$

We observe first that

$$\bar{f}_{1i}(k_i) = \bar{f}_n(0,\cdots,k_i,\cdots,0) \tag{55}$$

in which all but one k has been put equal to zero. For the total holding time $t = \Sigma\, t_i$,

$$\bar{f}(k) = \int_0^\infty e^{-kt}\, \bar{f}(t)dt = f_n(k,k,\cdots,k) \tag{56}$$

where the k_i are no longer distinguished but all are identified with the transform variable k. Similarly

$$\begin{aligned} f_n(0,0,\cdots,0) &= 1\,, \quad \mu_i = -\frac{\partial \bar{f}_n}{\partial k_i}(0,\cdots,0) \\ \sigma_i\sigma_j\rho_{ij} + \mu_i\mu_j &= \frac{\partial^2 \bar{f}_n}{\partial k_i\, \partial k_j}(0,0,\cdots,0) \end{aligned} \tag{57}$$

6. Two Examples

Before attempting any further general theorems it will be instructive to look at two examples less trivial than that of the introductory paragraph. We will use the second method and seek the output of the system for a steady input of the first order reactant. For simplicity of notation the concentrations in the various environments will be denoted by c_i and

$$\bar{f}_n(k_1,\cdots,k_n) = \Sigma\, \nu_i c_i \tag{58}$$

where ν_i is the fraction of effluent coming directly from the ith environment. k_i or κ_i will be retained for the Laplace transform variable rather than the s_i or p_i which would be more familiar to the mathematician or engineer. Since k_i often occurs in the product $k_i\theta_i$ an elementary theorem of Laplace transforms is worth remarking, namely

$$\mathcal{L}^{-1}\{\bar{f}_n(k_1\theta_1,k_2\theta_2,\cdots,k_n\theta_n)\} = \frac{1}{\theta_1\theta_2,\cdots,\theta_n} f_n\left(\frac{t_1}{\theta_1}, \frac{t_2}{\theta_2}, \cdots, \frac{t_n}{\theta_n}\right) \tag{59}$$

The first case will be that of two communicating well-mixed vessels through only one of which is there a flow. We note that the limiting cases of no exchange and complete exchange are stirred tanks of holding times θ_1 and $(\theta_1 + \theta_2)$ respectively. Thus, if the volumes are $V_i = q\theta_i$, $i=1,2$, and the flow is through the vessel for which $i=1$,

$$1 - c_1 - \lambda(c_1 - c_2) - k_1\theta_1 c_1 = 0 \tag{60}$$

$$\lambda(c_1 - c_2) - k_2\theta_2 c_2 = 0 \tag{61}$$

where λ is the exchange coefficient between the two compartments. In this case

$$\nu_1 = 1 , \quad \nu_2 = 0 \tag{62}$$

and

$$f_2(k_1, k_2) = \frac{\lambda + k_2\theta_2}{(1 + \lambda + k_1\theta_1)(\lambda + k_2\theta_2) - \lambda^2} \tag{63}$$

We observe that the total time distribution has a characteristic function

$$\bar{f}(k) = \frac{\lambda + \ _2k}{\lambda + \theta_2 k + (\theta_1 + \theta_2)k + \theta_1\theta_2 k^2} \tag{64}$$

If we let

$$\begin{aligned} \alpha &= \frac{1+\lambda}{2\theta_1} + \frac{\lambda}{2\theta_2} , \quad \beta = \frac{1}{2\theta_1\theta_2} \sqrt{\lambda^2\theta_1^2 + 2\lambda(\lambda-1)\theta_1\theta_2 + (1+\lambda)^2\theta_2^2} \\ \gamma &= -\frac{1+\lambda}{2\theta_1} + \frac{\lambda}{2\theta_2} , \end{aligned} \tag{65}$$

then

$$f(t) = \frac{1}{\theta_1}\left[\cosh\beta t + \frac{\gamma}{\beta}\sinh\beta t\right] e^{-\alpha t} \tag{66}$$

In the limiting cases $\lambda=0$ and $\lambda \to \infty$ we have, of course, the single stirred tank with $\theta=\theta$, or $\theta = \theta_1 + \theta_2$.

The marginal distributions are given by

$$\bar{f}_{11} = \frac{1}{1+k_1\theta_1} \quad \text{and} \quad \bar{f}_{12} = \frac{\lambda + k_2\theta_2}{\lambda + (1+\lambda)k_2\theta_2} = \frac{1}{1+\lambda} + \frac{\lambda^2/(1+\lambda)}{\lambda + (1+\lambda)k_2\theta_2} \tag{67}$$

or

$$f_n(t_1) = \frac{1}{\theta_1} e^{-t_1/\theta_1} , \quad f_{12}(t_2) = \frac{\delta(t_2)}{1+\lambda} + \frac{\lambda}{1+\lambda}\,\frac{1}{\theta_2'} e^{-t_2/\theta_2'} , \quad \theta' = \left(\frac{1+\lambda}{\lambda}\right)\theta_2 . \tag{68}$$

The first makes eminently good sense for it says that the distribution of residence time in the first vessel is simply that of a stirred tank of holding time θ_1. The second is also sensible for it shows that there is a non-zero probability of $(1+\lambda)^{-1}$ that a molecule does not even enter the second environment, while if it does the second environment acts as a stirred vessel with holding time θ_2', namely θ_2 with a factor of $(1+\lambda)/\lambda$.

The moments are easily calculable too from eqs. (18)-(20); these give:

$$\mu_1 = \theta_1 \ , \ \mu_2 = \theta_2 \ , \ \sigma_1^2 = \theta_1^2 \ , \ \sigma_2^2 = \theta_2^2 \ (1 + \tfrac{2}{\lambda}) \ , \ \rho_{12} = (1 + \tfrac{2}{\lambda})^{-1/2} \tag{69}$$

To invert the two variable distributions given by (33) we first invoke equation (29) and consider

$$\bar{f}_2 = \frac{\lambda+\kappa_2}{(1+\lambda+\kappa_1)(\lambda+\kappa_2) - \lambda^2} = \frac{1}{\kappa_1 + \{1 + \lambda - \lambda^2/(\lambda+\kappa_2)\}} \tag{70}$$

where $\kappa_i = k_i\theta_i$. This inversion is easy with respect to κ_1 and gives

$$f_2(\tau_1,\tau_2) = \mathcal{L}_2^{-1}\left[\exp\left\{(1+\lambda)\tau_1 + \frac{\lambda^2\tau_1}{\lambda+\kappa_2}\right\}\right] \tag{71}$$

where $\mathcal{L}_2^{-1}$ denotes the inversion with respect to the second variable. We use the transform pair

$$\mathcal{L}\left\{(\tfrac{\beta}{t})^{1/2}\ I_1(2\sqrt{\beta t})\right\} = e^{\beta/s} - 1 \tag{72}$$

see e.g. (2) eqn. 5.5.31, and using equation (29)

$$f_2(t_1,t_2) = \frac{1}{\theta_1}\, e^{-(1+\lambda)t_1/\theta_1}\left\{\delta(t_2) + e^{-\lambda t_2/\theta_2}\, \frac{\lambda}{t_2}\sqrt{\frac{t_1t_2}{\theta_1\theta_2}}\ I_1\left(2\lambda\sqrt{\frac{t_1t_2}{\theta_1\theta_2}}\right)\right\} . \tag{73}$$

That this has marginal distributions in agreement with those found in equation (38) may be confirmed by integration using the formulae

$$\int_0^\infty e^{-p^2z^2}\, I_1(z)dz = e^{1/4p^2} - 1 \ , \quad \int_0^\infty z^2e^{-p^2z^2}\, I_1(z)dz = e^{1/4p^2}/4p^4 \ . \tag{74}$$

The continuouous part of the distribution can be expressed by means of the function

$$g(\tau_1,\tau_2) = \frac{1+\lambda}{\lambda}\left\{\theta_1\theta_2 f_2 - e^{-(1+\lambda)\tau_1}\delta(\tau_2)\right\} = (1+\lambda)\sqrt{\frac{\tau_1}{\tau_2}}\, e^{-(1+\lambda)\tau_1-\lambda\tau_2} I_1(2\lambda\sqrt{\tau_1\tau_2}) \tag{75}$$

A similar system at the other end of the mixing scale would be obtained by assuming plug flow in one environment and complete stagnancy in the other. Then

$$\frac{\partial c_1}{\partial \xi} = -\lambda(c_1-c_2) - \kappa_1 c_1 \ , \quad c_1(0) = 1 \tag{76}$$

$$0 = \lambda(c_2-c_1) + \kappa_2 c_2 \tag{77}$$

where $\kappa_i = k_i\theta_i$, λ is again a dimensionless exchange coefficient and $\xi=1$ at the exit. Thus

$$f_2(\kappa_1,\kappa_2) = c_1(1) = \exp -\left\{\frac{\lambda\kappa_2}{\lambda+\kappa_2} + \kappa_1\right\} = e^{-\lambda-\kappa_1+\lambda_2/(\lambda+\kappa_2)} \tag{78}$$

or

$$f_2(\tau_1,\tau_2) = e^{-\lambda}\delta(\tau_1-1)\left\{\delta(\tau_2) + \lambda\tau_2^{-1/2} I_1(2\lambda\tau_2^{1/2})\right\} e^{-\lambda\tau_2} .$$

In terms of the variables t_1 and t_2 this gives

$$f_2(t_1,t_2) = \delta(t_1-\theta_1)e^{-\lambda[1+(t_2/\theta_2)]}\left\{\delta(t_2) + \frac{\lambda}{(t_2\theta_2)^{1/2}} I_1(2\lambda(t_2/\theta_2)^{1/2})\right\} . \tag{79}$$

The marginal distributions are

$$f_{11}(t_1) = \delta(t_1-\theta_1) \text{ and } f_{12}(t_2) = e^{-\lambda[1+(t_2/\theta_2)]}\left\{\delta(t_2) + \frac{\lambda}{(t_2\theta_2)^{1/2}} I_1\left(2\lambda\sqrt{\frac{t_2}{\theta_2}}\right)\right\} \tag{80}$$

and the total time distribution

$$f(t) = e^{\left[1+\frac{t-\theta_1}{\theta_2}\right]}\left\{\delta(t-\theta_1) + \frac{\lambda}{\sqrt{(t-\theta_1)\theta_2}} I_1\left(2\lambda\sqrt{\frac{t-\theta_1}{\theta_2}}\right)\right\} H(t-\theta_1) . \tag{81}$$

The moments are:

$$\mu_1 = \theta_1 \ , \quad \mu_2 = \theta_2 \ , \quad \sigma_1^2 = 0 \ , \quad \sigma_2^2 = 2\theta_2^2/\lambda \ , \quad \rho_{12} = 0 . \tag{82}$$

The part of the marginal t_2 distribution that is continuous is given in normalized form as the function

$$h(\tau) = \lambda(e^{\lambda}-1)^{-1} \tau^{-1/2} I_1(2\lambda\tau^{1/2})e^{-\lambda\tau} \tag{83}$$

7. Moments From Cases Where Inversion is Difficult

There are cases where the inversion of the double transform is difficult. Such is the case where the moving phase is in plug flow and the stationary is well mixed. The equations will be

$$\frac{dc_1}{d\xi} = -(\theta_1 k_1+\lambda)c_1 + \lambda c_2, \quad c_1(0) = 1 \tag{84}$$

$$0 = -(\theta_2 k_2+\lambda)c_2 + \lambda \int_o^1 c_1(\xi)\,d\xi \tag{85}$$

where ξ is the fractional length on the plug flow side. Thus

$$\bar{f}_2(k_1,k_2) = c_1(1) = e^{-(\theta_1 k_1+\lambda)} + \frac{\lambda}{\theta_1 k_1+\lambda} c_2 \left\{1-e^{-(\theta_1 k_1+\lambda)}\right\}$$

$$c_2 = \frac{\lambda}{\theta_2 k_2+\lambda} \int_o^1 c_1(\xi)\,d\xi = \left\{\frac{1-e^{-(\theta_1 k_1+\lambda)}}{\theta_1 k_1+\lambda} + \frac{\lambda}{\theta_1 k_1+\lambda} c_2\left[1 - \frac{1-e^{-(\theta_1 k_1+\lambda)}}{\theta_1 k_1 \lambda}\right]\right\} \frac{\lambda}{\theta_2 k_2+\lambda}$$

giving

$$\bar{f}_2 = \bar{e}_1 + \lambda^2 E_2^2/\{\nu_2 - \lambda^2 E_3\} \tag{86}$$

where

$$\nu_i = \theta_i k_i+\lambda, \quad E_1 = e^{-\nu_1}, \quad E_2 = \frac{1}{\nu_1}(1-e^{-\nu_1}), \quad E_3 = \frac{1}{\nu_1}(1-E_2) \tag{87}$$

The inversion with respect to k_2 follows familiar lines giving

$$f_2(k_1,t_2) = E_1\delta(t_2) + \frac{1}{\theta_2}\lambda^2 E_2^2\, e^{-(1+\lambda)t_2/\theta_2+\lambda^2 E_3} \tag{88}$$

but the inversion of this does not appear to be easy.

However we may seek the moments directly by writing $\kappa_i = k_i\theta_i$ and seeking the expansion

$$C_1(1) = 1 - A_1\kappa_1 - A_2\kappa_2 + \frac{1}{2} B_{11}\kappa_1^2 + B_{12}\kappa_1\kappa_2 + \frac{1}{2} B_{22}\kappa_2^2, + \cdots \tag{89}$$

whence

$$\mu_1 = \theta_1 A_1,\ \mu_2 = \theta_2 A_2,\ \sigma_1^2 = \theta_1^2(B_{11}-A_1^2),\ \sigma_1\sigma_2\rho_{12} = \theta_1\theta_2(B_{12}-A_1A_2),\ \sigma_2^2 = \theta_2^2(B_{22}-A_2^2) \tag{90}$$

To do this we expand each concentration in the form

$$\begin{aligned} C_1(\xi) &= 1 - \alpha_1(\xi)\kappa_1 - \alpha_2(\xi)\kappa_2 + \frac{1}{2}\beta_{11}(\xi)\kappa_1^2 + \beta_{12}(\xi)\kappa_1\kappa_2 + \frac{1}{2}\beta_{22}(\xi)\kappa_2^2 \cdot\cdot \\ C_2(\xi) &= 1 - a_1(\xi)\kappa_1 - a_2(\xi)\kappa_2 + \frac{1}{2} b_{11}(\xi)\kappa_1^2 + b_{12}(\xi)\kappa_1\kappa_2 + \frac{1}{2} b_{22}(\xi)\kappa_2 \cdot\cdot \end{aligned} \tag{91}$$

and obtain a sequence of equations of the form

$$\begin{aligned} u' &= -\lambda u + \lambda v + f(\xi) \qquad u(0) = 0 \\ 0 &= \lambda \int_o^1 u d\xi - \lambda v + g(\xi) \end{aligned} \tag{92}$$

These equations give immediately that

$$u(1) = \int_o^1 [f(\xi) + g(\xi)]d\xi \tag{93}$$

but since f and g will come from solutions of the equation we need to solve them more completely. Thus

$$u' + \lambda u = \lambda \int_o^1 u d\xi' + f(\xi) + g(\xi) \tag{94}$$

or

$$u(\xi) = (1-e^{-\lambda\xi}) \int_o^1 u d\xi' + e^{-\lambda\xi} \int_o^{\xi} e^{\lambda\xi'}[f(\xi')+\xi(\xi')]d\xi' \tag{95}$$

Then

$$\int_o^1 u d\xi = (1-E)\int_o^1 u d\xi + \left[-\frac{1}{\lambda} e^{-\lambda\xi} \int_o^{\xi} e^{\lambda\xi'}(f+g)d\xi'\right]_o^1 + \frac{1}{\lambda}\int_o^1 \{f(\xi)+g(\xi)\}d\xi$$

or

$$E\int_0^1 u\,d\xi = \frac{1}{\lambda}\int_0^1 (1-e^{-\lambda+\lambda\xi})\{f(\xi)+g(\xi)\}d\xi \tag{96}$$

where

$$E = \frac{1}{\lambda}(1-e^{-\lambda}) \tag{97}$$

when (f+g) is a constant this gives

$$E\int_0^1 u\,d\xi = \frac{1}{\lambda}(1-E)(f+g) \tag{98}$$

and

$$E\int_0^1 u\,d\xi = \frac{1}{\lambda}(1-E)f + \frac{1}{\lambda}g\ .$$

Substituting from (91) into (84) and (85) gives five pairs of equations of the form (92) with the following interpretations:

Coefficient of:	u	v	f	g	Coefficient in $C_1(1)$
$-\kappa_1$	α_1	a_1	1	0	$A_1 = 1$
$-\kappa_2$	α_2	a_2	0	1	$A_2 = 2$
$\frac{1}{2}\kappa_1^2$	β_{11}	b_{11}	$2\alpha 1$	0	$B_{11} = 2\int_0^1 \alpha_1(\xi)d\xi$
$\kappa_1\kappa_2$	β_{12}	b_{12}	α_2	a_1	$B_{12} = \int_0^1(\alpha_2+a_1)d\xi$
$\frac{1}{2}\kappa_2^2$	β_{22}	b_{22}	0	$2a_2$	$B_{22} = 2\int_0^1 a_2(\xi)d\xi$

But using (98) and (99) with the realization that α_1, α_2, a_1, a_2 satisfy equations with constant f and g gives immediately

$$\int_0^1 \alpha_1(\xi)d\xi = (1-E)/\lambda E\ ,\quad \int_0^1 a_1(\xi)d\xi = (1-E)/\lambda E$$
$$\int_0^1 \alpha_2(\xi)d\xi = (1-E)/\lambda E\ ,\quad \int_0^1 a_2(\xi)d\xi = 1/\lambda E \tag{99}$$

Thus

$$\mu_1 = \theta_1 , \quad \mu_2 = \theta_2$$

$$\sigma_1^2 = \left(\frac{2(1-E)}{\lambda E} - 1\right)\theta_1^2 = \sigma_1\sigma_2\rho_{12}(\theta_1/\theta_2) , \quad \sigma_2^2 = \left(\frac{2}{\lambda E} - 1\right)\theta_2^2$$

or

$$\rho_{12} = \left\{\frac{2(1-E)-\lambda E}{2-\lambda E}\right\}^{1/2}$$

These can be written

$$\sigma_1^2 = \left\{\coth\frac{\lambda}{2} - \frac{2}{\lambda}\right\}\theta_1^2 , \quad \sigma_2^2 = \left\{\coth\frac{\lambda}{2}\right\}\theta_2^2$$

$$\rho_{12}^2 = \left\{1 - \frac{2}{\lambda}\tanh\frac{\lambda}{2}\right\} \tag{100}$$

References

1. P. V. Danckwerts, "Continuous flow systems. Distribution of residence times," Chem. Engng. Sci. 2 (1953).
2. R. Shinnar, "Tracer experiments in chemical reactor design," Proc. 1st. Levich Conference, Oxford (1977).
3. V. W. Weekman, "Lumps, models and kinetics in practice," AIChE Monograph Series 11 75 (1979).
4. D. Luss and P. Hutchinson, "lumping of mixtures with many parallel reactions," Chem. Eng. J. 2 (1971), 172.
5. R. Aris, "Prolegomena to the rational analysis of systems of chemical reactions. II. Some addenda," Arch. Rat. Mech. Anal. 27 (1968), 356.
6. N. R. Amundson and A. Acrivos, "On the steady state fractionation of multicomponent and complex mixtures in an ideal cascade," Chem. Engng. Sci. 4 (1955), 29.
7. G. R. Gavalas and R. Aris, "On the theory of reactions in continuous mixtures," Phil. Trans. Roy. Soc. A260 (1966), 351.

Measurement of Binary Gaseous Diffusion Coefficients Within Porous Catalysts

D. L. Cresswell, N. H. Orr*

Swiss Federal Institute of Technology,
Technisch-Chemisches Labor, E.T.H. Zentrum
CH-8092 Zürich, Switzerland.

SUMMARY

The simplest theoretical treatments for packed beds of porous particles and for single particles, for the case of a transient of non-adsorbing tracer, are utilised to determine a coefficient of diffusion in the pores.

The dimensions of and flows through packed beds of technical preparations of catalyst which yield good pore diffusion data are determined through a combination of modelling and experimental work.

Working methods for a diffusion cell housing a miniature catalyst particle are described. Finally, an experimental comparison is made between packed bed and single particle techniques.

OBJECTIVES

The paper is intended to help colleagues who wish to apply more science to catalytic process development and who may need to elaborate the treatments herein explained and illustrated.

The main uses of the techniques described here lie in the following areas:

- as one of the tools needed to optimise the lay-down of active species on the support during catalyst formulation.
- for providing a simple and quick testing method to be used as a screening or quality control procedure during catalyst manufacture.
- in reactor design for determining the catalyst effectiveness factor.

---

*Research and Development Department, B.P. Chemicals, Grangemouth, Scotland.

INTRODUCTION

Diffusive resistance within the pores of a catalyst particle is a factor which must be considered at some stage of process development work. Models of diffusion and flow within porous media rarely allow a reliable prediction of the transport resistance to be made and firm argument only comes through experimental measurement. There is clearly a demand for a simple, fast method of evaluating meaningful effective diffusivities in porous solids and the purpose of this paper is to develop methods which could meet this need.

Attention has been deliberately confined to binary systems and dilute tracer concentrations, so that simple models can be used to describe transient diffusion within a porous pellet. It must be remembered, however, that ultimately concern may rest with the modelling of multi-component diffusion of reacting molecules present in concentrated mixtures. The final objective, however, would involve careful synthesis of the individual mechanistic feactures making up the problem, and one of these involves binary effective diffusion. The ability of the final "complex" model to interpret real experimental data is usually severely limited; often too many unknown, or inaccurately known, parameters are present and the experiments can seldom be conducted with sufficient accuracy or discrimination to define them. As in many other areas of engineering an enormous gulf separates the theoretician from the practitioner concerned with real process systems.

1. The Packed Bed

Packed beds offer the attraction of simplicity of design. They can be used for technical preparations of catalyst particles and can closely reproduce the flow pattern to be met under reaction conditions. However, the design and operation of the bed requires the following five conditions to be met simultaneously:

(1) No radial variations in flow or composition.
(2) An open-ended bed.
(3) Carrier gas velocity independent of axial position.
(4) No bulk flow through the particles.
(5) Negligible mass transfer resistance at the external surface of the particles.

Juggling with these conditions while at the same time seeking to accentuate pore diffusion is not trivial.

Packed bed systems come in two extreme forms - the conventional wide-bodied shallow bed (Fig. 1a) and the single pellet string (Fig. 1b). Each system offers certain features for exploitation, but neither is ideal (Table 1).

TABLE 1: PACKED BED FEATURES

wide-bodied bed	single pellet string
• "in-house" detection minimises delays and additional pulse spreading.	• external detection necessary.
• complicated injection system needed to satisfy condition (1).	• straightforward injection into narrow feed pipe.
• low bed porosity (∿0.4) limits attainable carrier gas velocity - accentuates axial mixing relative to pore diffusion.	• high inter-particle porosity (∿0.6) permits higher carrier gas velocities - accentuates pore diffusion relative to axial mixing.

Our experience suggests that the single pellet string system, first developed by Scott, Lee and Papa (1) in 1974, is the preferred type of column. The problems associated with external signal measurement can be largely overcome by using micro--katharometers as detectors (∿200 μl volume) and by minimising the volumes of sample lines. Care should be taken to measure the column pressure accurately so that the measured volumetric flow rate can be corrected to give an independent estimate of the carrier gas velocity. It is also important that the ratio of column diameter/particle diameter should lie in the range 1.1 - 1.4 to eliminate the possibility of fluid by-passing along the wall.

1.1 Model of the packed bed

In writing down equations describing the packed bed it is assumed that compositions are smooth functions of position - both inter-particle voids and intra-particle pores are thoroughly cross-linked. The case considered in Fig. 2 is appropriate to a carrier gas passing at constant superficial (i.e. empty tube) velocity U_G through a packed bed of spheres of radius R, held at fixed T and P. A transient composition disturbance is imposed by injecting a small quantity of tracer, and its concentrations in the carrier gas are observed as functions of time at points in the bed a distance L apart.

Material balances on inter-particle and intra-particle tracer lead to the pair of equations

$$\alpha \frac{\partial c_G}{\partial t} = D_G \frac{\partial^2 c_G}{\partial z^2} - U_G \frac{\partial c_G}{\partial z} - \frac{3(1-\alpha)}{R} D_p \frac{\partial c_p}{\partial r}\Big|_{r=R} \qquad (1)$$

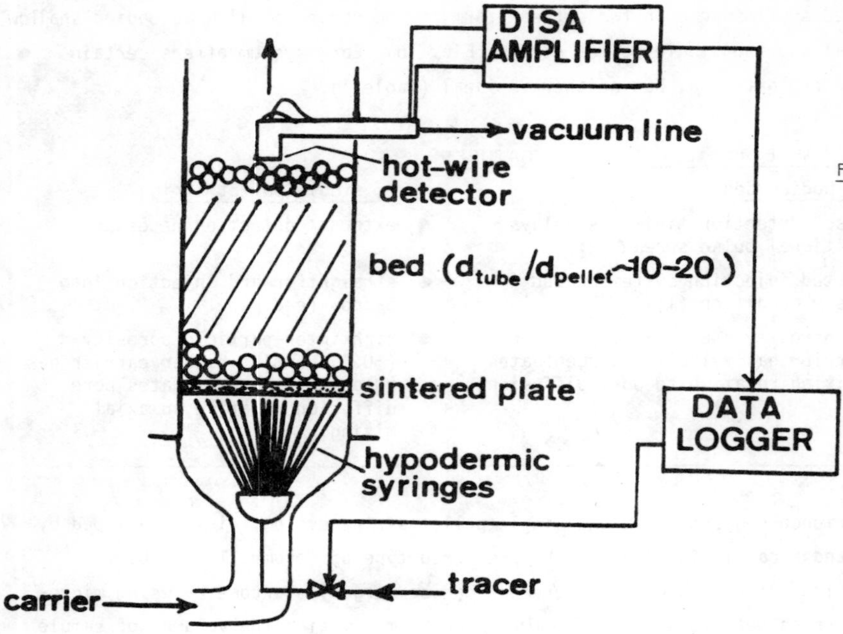

FIG. 1A

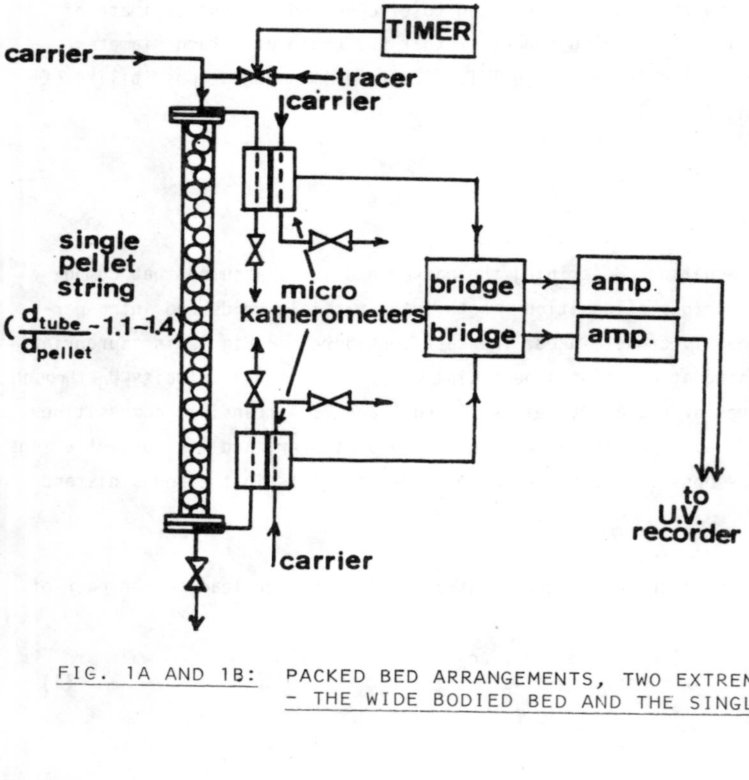

FIG. 1B

FIG. 1A AND 1B: PACKED BED ARRANGEMENTS, TWO EXTREME FORMS:
- THE WIDE BODIED BED AND THE SINGLE PELLET STRING

$$r^2\beta \frac{\partial c_p}{\partial t} = D_p \frac{\partial}{\partial r}\left(r^2 \frac{\partial c_p}{\partial r}\right) ; \qquad c_p\Big|_{r=R} = c_G \tag{2}$$

The diffusion coefficients are based on unit cross section of bed and particle respectively, normal to the direction of diffusion. Concentrations, on the other hand, are interstitial local averages, based on the respective void volume, rather than the total volume, since these are more closely related to the properties of bulk gases.

Eqns. (1) and (2) can be easily solved in the Laplace domain and decoupled to give the transfer function

$$\overline{E} = \frac{\overline{c}_G\Big|_{z=L}}{\overline{c}_G\Big|_{z=0}} = \exp\left[N - q^{1/2}\right]$$

where $N = \frac{U_G\, L}{2\, D_G}$, $\quad q = N^2 + \frac{L^2\,\sigma}{D_G}$

and $\sigma = \alpha s + \frac{3(1-\alpha)\, D_p}{R^2}\left(\frac{R\eta \cosh R\eta}{\sinh R\eta} - 1\right)$ (3)

$\eta = \left(\frac{\beta s}{D_p}\right)^{1/2}$

with $\overline{c_G} = \int_0^\infty c_G\, e^{-st}\, dt.$

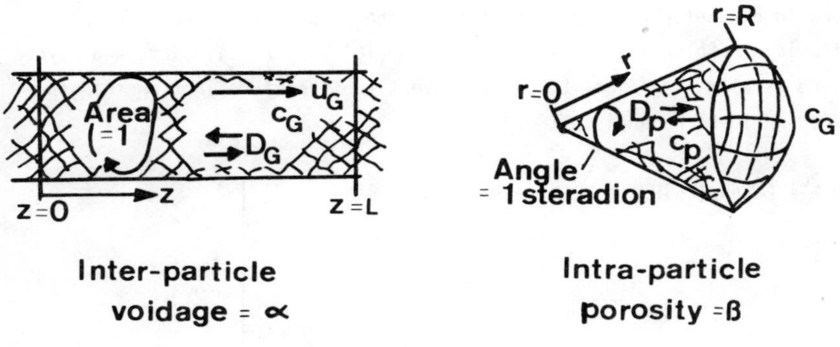

FIG. 2: SCHEMATICS OF THE PACKED BED AND SINGLE PELLET

1.2 Equations for estimating the pore diffusion coefficient

(a) Moments of the weighting function E(t)

The required moments, matchable with observation, are

$$E_1 = [\int_0^\infty t\,E\,dt \,/ \int_0^\infty E\,dt] \qquad \text{- the mean}$$

and

$$E_2' = [\int_0^\infty t^2 E\,dt \,/ \int_0^\infty E\,dt - E_1^2] \qquad \text{- the variance,}$$

and are given by

$$\left.\begin{aligned} E_1 &= -\left.\frac{d\bar{E}}{ds}\right|_{s\to o} \qquad (\text{since} \int_0^\infty E dt = \bar{E}\big|_{s\to o} = 1) \\ E_2' &= \left.\frac{d^2\bar{E}}{ds^2}\right|_{s\to o} - E_1^2 \end{aligned}\right\} \qquad (4)$$

It follows from eqns. (3) and (4) that

$$\left.\begin{aligned} E_1 &= \frac{L}{U_G}[\alpha + \beta(1-\alpha)] \\ \frac{E_2^1}{E_1} &= \frac{E_1}{N} + \frac{2\ \beta^2(1-\alpha)R^2}{15\ \{\alpha+\beta(1-\alpha)\}D_p} \end{aligned}\right\} \qquad (5)$$

The means and variances of the two traces, measured a distance L apart, are computed, and their differences (E_1 and E_2^1, respectively) characterise the behaviour of the bed.

(b) Time domain solutions

Solutions in the time domain can be found for idealised inputs, but they are rarely used in parameter estimation because of their complexity. For a problem involving diffusion in molecular sieves, where $D_p \sim O(10^{-10}\ cm^2/sec)$, Sarma and Haynes (2) could ignore axial mixing (i.e. $D_G=0$) and invert the transfer function into the time domain. For an ideal pulse input

$$\left.\begin{aligned} E &= \frac{2C_1}{\pi}\int_0^\infty \exp(-C_2H_1)\cos(C_1\lambda^2\theta - C_2H_2)\,\lambda\,d\lambda \\ &\text{where} \qquad C_1 = 2D_p / \beta R^2 \\ &\qquad\qquad C_2 = \frac{3D_p(1-\alpha)L}{R^2U_G} \\ &\qquad\qquad \theta = t - \alpha L / U_G \end{aligned}\right\} \qquad (6)$$

$$H_1 = \lambda\left(\frac{\sinh 2\lambda + \sin 2\lambda}{\cosh 2\lambda - \cos 2\lambda}\right) - 1; \qquad H_2 = \lambda\left(\frac{\sinh 2\lambda - \sin 2\lambda}{\cosh 2\lambda - \cos 2\lambda}\right)$$

When $C_2 \leq 0.2$, the infinite integral may be accurately approximated by the more useful closed-form RTD function

$$E = \frac{C_1 C_2}{(2\pi\ C_1^3\ \theta^3)^{1/2}} \exp\{-C_2\ (\frac{C_2}{2C_1\theta} - 1)\} \tag{7}$$

When $\hat{C}_2 < 2.0$, the frontal part of the chromatogram may be analysed using Eqn. (7) to give an estimate of D_p. Alternatively the time-to-peak may be matched with observation, giving

$$D_p = \frac{\frac{2}{3} \cdot t_{RT} \cdot R^2 \cdot U_G^2}{\beta(1-\alpha)^2\ L^2} \tag{8}$$

where t_{RT} is the rise time of the trace at z=L - i.e. the time elapsed between the start of the frontal wave and the peak.

(c) Other methods

Various ad hoc methods of reducing the emphasis of response tails on the estimated value of D_p have been suggested. These include weighted moments (Anderssen and White (3)) and Fourier analysis (Gangwal et al. (4)). More recently, an approximate time-domain solution was obtained by taking the intra-particle concentration profile to be parabolic (Rice (5)).

It should be emphasized that criteria which match properties of the RTD with observables to give an estimate of D_p do not provide a test of the mathematical model. If such methods are used, it is particularly important to look for model deficiencies by checking to see if D_p is correlated with carrier gas velocity or particle diameter, for example.

1.3 Optimising packed bed experiments

Three criteria are presented here to guide the investigator towards an optimal choice of 'design' variables L, R and U_G. Satisfaction of these criteria should guarantee that pore diffusion is the main contributor to pulse broadening, at the expense of axial dispersion, and, secondly, the chromatograms will be near-Gaussian, enabling a reliable estimate of the pore diffusion coefficient D_p to be extracted from 1st and 2nd moments, together with independent axial mixing data.

CRITERION I

Pore-Diffusion Enhancement:

$$U_G R \geq \frac{4}{k} D_p(1-\alpha) \left[1 + \frac{\alpha}{\beta(1-\alpha)}\right]^2 \tag{9}$$

CRITERIA II & III

Anti-Tailing: $L/R \geq 200$ (10)

$$U_G R \leq 3\left(\frac{L}{R}\right) D_p(1-\alpha) \qquad (11)$$

Inequality (9) is derived directly from 1st and 2nd moments in Eqn. (5) by requiring that the second term (due to pore diffusion) outweighs the first (due to axial dispersion) in the equation giving the difference in 2nd moments, E_2^1. It is noted in Fig. 3 that the minimum value of the Peclet group, $Pe = 2U_G R/D_G$, characterising axial dispersion, exceeds 1.0 over the working range of Reynolds Number. Thus, D_G is eliminated from (5) by setting it to its upper bound $2U_G R$. Various shape factors k for use in inequality (9) are summarised in Table 2 below.

TABLE 2: SHAPE FACTORS (WALDRAM AND CO-WORKERS (7), (8))

Geometry of particle	Shape factor (k)	R
sphere	2/15	radius
flat plate	1/6	thickness
cylinder	$\frac{64}{\pi^2} \sum_{m=1}^{\infty} \sum_{n=0}^{\infty} \frac{1}{[(2n+1)^2 J_m^2 \cdot (J_m^2+(2n+1)^2 p^2\pi^2)]}$	radius
(a) ends sealed	1/4	p=aspect ratio
(b) sides sealed	$1/(6p^2)$	R/1
long hollow cylinder	∿ 1/6 (as for flat plate)	$\frac{R_{outer}}{R_{inner}} \leq 5$

Two anti-tailing criteria are required. The first (Eqn. (10)) guarantees a Gaussian distribution for the "blank" run using "identical" non-porous particles, from which D_G can be determined.

The second is derived for spherical porous particles via simulation studies. These reveal that, for a sharp input pulse, the parameter C_2 in Eqn. (6) is the main variable affecting the shape of the exit trace, when $L/R \geq 200$. Two parameters are computed for this comparison: $\frac{C_1\theta_1}{C_2}$, the time between the peak of the exit trace, and the start of the trace (1% of peak height) and $\frac{C_1\theta_2}{C_2}$, the time between the end of the exit trace (1% of peak height) and the start of the trace. These reduced times are shown in Table 3 as a function of C_2.

The threshold for severe tailing is arbitrarily set at $\theta_2/\theta_1 \simeq 10$, in which case $C_2 \geq 1.0$, approximately. This condition leads directly to inequality (11). More detailed simulation studies are reported by Haynes (6).

TABLE 3: ASYMMETRY OF EXIT TRACE (θ_2/θ_1) VS. C_2. PARAMETERS C_1, C_2 AND θ GIVEN IN EQN. (6)

C_2	$\frac{C_1\theta_1}{C_2}$	$\frac{C_1\theta_2}{C_2}$	θ_2/θ_1
40	0.175	0.405	2.3
20	0.23	0.555	2.4
5	0.37	1.1	3.0
2.5	0.41	1.51	3.7
1.5	0.385	1.9	4.9
1.0	0.28	2.28	8.1
0.5	0.13	2.88	22.2
0.2	0.075	3.1	41.3

In order to use these criteria to plan experiments a preliminary estimate of D_p is required. It is normal that prior measurements of the pore size distribution and particle porosity will be made and from these data an estimate of D_p can be furnished. Rapid tuning of the experiment can take place as confidence in the estimated value of D_p grows.

Two outstanding points require checking before the experimenter can feel confident over his selection of experimental conditions, namely the pressure drop and external mass transfer intrusion. The bed pressure drop must be a small fraction of the total pressure, otherwise U_G will vary along the bed, and the absolute pressure drop per particle must be absolutely small for condition (4) to hold, in general. Too low a Reynolds number, with laminar flow, will introduce external mass transfer resistance.

1.3.1 Bed pressure drop

The most widely used correlation for pressure drop in packed beds is due to Ergun (9), and has the form for random packed beds,

$$\left(\frac{\Delta P}{L}\right)\frac{d_p}{\rho U_G^2}\frac{\alpha^3}{(1-\alpha)} = \frac{k_1(1-\alpha)}{\left(\frac{\rho U_G d_p}{\mu}\right)} + k_2 \qquad (12)$$

where k_1 and k_2 are constants (150 and 1.75, respectively), and d_p is an equivalent particle diameter, defined as $d_p = 6/S_v$, where S_v is the specific solid surface per unit volume of solid. There have been many criticisms and minor modifications of this equation over the years. It seems to be appropriate to wide-bodied beds ($d_t/d_p \geq 20$)

of uniform "spheroidal-like" particles.

The Ergun equation is also appropriate to the single pellet string column (1) in the range $1.16 < \frac{d_t}{d_p} < 1.35$, if the equivalent particle diameter d_p in Eqn. (12) is modified to include also the specific surface of the wall per unit volume of solid:

$$d_{p,mod} = \frac{d_p}{\left[1 + \frac{2d_p}{3(1-\alpha)d_t}\right]} \tag{13}$$

1.3.2 External mass transfer

Incorporation of external mass transfer into the packed bed model adds a third term $2(1-\alpha)\beta^2 R/[3k_f\{\alpha+\beta(1-\alpha)\}]$ to the right hand side of the difference of 2nd moments E_2^1 in Eqn. (5). In order that pore diffusion outweighs external mass transfer in broadening the pulse input it is necessary that

$$\frac{k_f\ R}{D_p} \gg 5 \tag{14}$$

The external mass transfer coefficient k_f depends on the gas velocity, the particle diameter, the inter-particle voidage and physical properties of the binary gas pair, such as viscosity, density and molecular diffusivity. An elegant analysis of the inter-relations is given by Gunn (10) in the form of a wide-ranging correlation

$$N_{Sh} = (7-10\alpha+5\alpha^2)\ (1+0.7\ N_{Re}^{0.2}\ N_{Sc}^{1/3}) + (1.33 - 2.4\alpha + 1.2\alpha^2) \times N_{Re}^{0.7} \cdot N_{Sc}^{1/3} \tag{15}$$

applicable for <u>all</u> values of N_{Re} and the range of bed voidage $0.35 \leq \alpha \leq 1$. In Eqn. (15), the following dimensionless groups are defined:

N_{Sh}	=	$k_f\ d_p\ /\ D_{AB}$	(Sherwood number)
N_{Re}	=	$\rho U_G d_p/\mu$	(Reynolds number)
N_{Sc}	=	$\mu/\rho D_{AB}$	(Schmidt number)

1.4 Applications of the design criteria

Two examples are given here which clearly show the limitations of the packed bed for furnishing reliable pore diffusion data. They cover the two extremes of cases encountered in practice - namely Knudsen diffusion in small particles containing fine pores, and bulk diffusion in large coarsely porous particles.

Example 1: Knudsen diffusion in finely porous particles

SiO_2/Al_2O_3 xylenes isomerisation catalyst: (Q17/3)

d_p = 3.3 mms, β = 0.5
mean pore radius (r_p) $\cong$ 40 Å(4×10^{-7}cms)
He diffusion in N_2 at NTP.

The Knudsen diffusion coefficient of He in a straight cylindrical pore of radius r_p cms. is given by

$$D_{SP} = 9.70 \times 10^3\ r_p\sqrt{T/M}\quad cm^2/sec. \qquad (16)$$

$$= 9.70 \times 10^3 \times 4 \times 10^{-7}\sqrt{\frac{298}{4}}$$

$$= 3.35 \times 10^{-2}\ cm^2/sec.$$

The bulk diffusion coefficient of He in N_2 is approximately twenty times greater than D_{SP} and it is therefore safe to assume that Knudsen diffusion prevails.

For a catalyst particle it is necessary to correct D_{SP} to account for porosity and tortuosity of the diffusion path:

$$D_P = \frac{\beta}{\tau}\ D_{SP} \qquad (17)$$

Taking τ=3 as a rough guess gives an initial estimate of $D_p = 5.6\times10^{-3}$ cm²/sec. The results of applying the experimental design criteria (9) - (15) are given in Table 4.

A shorter bed length is chosen in the wide-bodied case to reflect a purely practical, but important, constraint of availability of the catalyst support, which is usually in short supply during process development work.

Both alternatives can satisfy simultaneously the three desired conditions (9) - (11) although, given the shorter bed length, the wide-bodied bed is much more restrictive in the permitted range of gas velocity. In neither case is pressure drop nor external mass transfer a factor.

TABLE 4: SUMMARY OF THE EXPERIMENTAL DESIGN CRITERIA FOR A FINELY POROUS PARTICLE

	wide-bodied bed (WBB)	single pellet string (SPS)	Criterion
L (cm)	50	200	
d_t (cm)	∞	0.44	
α	0.4	0.6	
U_G (cm/sec)	≥ 3.3	≥ 6.5	Pore diffusion enhancement criterion (9).
L/R	300	1200	Anti-tailing criterion (10)
U_G (cm/sec)	≤ 18.3	≤ 49	Anti-tailing criterion (11)
k_f (cm/sec), based on U_G = 12 cm/sec (WBB) U_G = 30 cm/sec (SPS)	20.7	40.3	Eqn. (15)
$(\frac{k_f R}{D_p})$	610	1187	Eqn. (14)
ΔP (cm H_2O)	1.29	10.43	Eqns. (12) - (13)

Example 2: Bulk diffusion in coarsely porous particles

α-alumina support for A_g catalyst in ethylene oxide manufacture (ALC 182)

d_p = 7.7 mm (sphere), $\beta = 0.7$
mean porous radius (r_p) = 2×10^4 Å (2×10^{-4} cms)
He diffusion in N_2 at NTP.
D_p(estimated) = 0.16 cm^2/sec.

Both types of packed bed can be readily operated and should permit reliable estimation of the pore diffusion coefficient over a wide range of gas velocity (Table 5). Higher gas velocities are required to minimise axial dispersion effects than was the case previously. Carrier gas velocities should now be chosen as large as possible to eliminate external mass transfer intrusions. Pressure drop over the larger particles is unlikely to be a significant factor.

These two examples, which span the range of effective diffusion coefficients $D_p = 5 \times 10^{-3}$ to 0.16 cm^2/sec, indicate that reliable determination of pore diffusivities is possible, using packed bed methods, providing care is exercised in the choice of experimental variables L, R and U_G. The design criteria do not consider optimisation of the tracer-carrier gas pair, but this interesting idea has been taken up by Chou (11).

TABLE 5: DESIGN CRITERIA FOR A COARSELY POROUS PARTICLE

	wide-bodied bed (WBB)	single pellet string (SPS)	Criterion
L (cm)	120	200	
d_t (cm)	∞	1.11	
α	0.4	0.6	
U_G (cm/sec)	≥ 28	≥ 47.5	Pore diffusion enhancement criterion (9)
L/R	312	520	Anti-tailing criterion (10)
U_G (cm/sec)	≤ 90	≤ 100	Anti-tailing criterion (11)
k_f (cm/sec), based on U_G = 70 cm/sec.	25.5	16	Eqn. (15)
$(k_f R/D_p)$	61	38	Eqn. (14)
ΔP(cm H_2O)	17	13	Eqns. (12) - (13)

1.5 Axial dispersion in packed beds

It would be inappropriate to finish this review of packed beds without discussing inter-particle axial dispersion, since its effect must be invariably considered when interpreting the residence time distribution. A direct measurement of the axial dispersion coefficient D_G can be made over, say, glass particles of similar size and shape to the porous particles of interest. This is certainly to be preferred to estimation of D_G from empirical correlations. Nevertheless, the latter are useful in giving an indication of the relative importance of axial dispersion.

Edwards and Richardson (12) provide extensive axial dispersion data for the wide--bodied bed randomly packed with uniform spheres. Scott, Lee and Papa (1) present similar data for the single pellet string. Rather surprisingly, the two extremes show very similar axial dispersion characteristics. An equation of the form

$$N_{Pe}^{-1} = \frac{\alpha\gamma}{N_{Re}\, N_{SC}} + \frac{\lambda}{1 + \frac{\alpha\beta'}{N_{Re}\, N_{SC}}} \qquad (18)$$

$$\left(N_{Pe} = \frac{U_G\, d_p}{D_G}\right)$$

where γ, λ and β' are constants related to various dispersive mechanisms, has been found to interpolate properly between lower and upper limits on D_G, set by molecular diffusion and turbulent mixing. The constants appear to depend to some extent on the tracer-carrier gas combination and vary considerably between different workers, as indicated in Table 6.

Our own axial dispersion data, gathered on three different "single pellet string" columns, are shown in Fig. 3, together with the "best-fit" of Eqn. (18). The data show broad support for this type of correlating equation but, at the same time, show a fair amount of scatter. Uncertainty as to the precise value of D_G will, of course, have a considerable impact on the reliability of estimated pore diffusion coefficients D_p, obtained from similar experiments on porous particles unless, that is, the experiments are designed along the lines suggested in Section 1.3. Even then, this impact cannot be completely removed.

TABLE 6: SUMMARY OF PARAMETER VALUES γ, λ, β' OBTAINED BY VARIOUS WORKERS (± INDICATES MARGINAL 95% CONFIDENCE INTERVAL).

	System Tracer-Carrier	γ	λ	β'	N_{Sc}	α
Wide-bodied bed						
- Edwards/Richardson (12)	Air-Argon	0.73	0.5	9.7	0.72	≃0.4
- Urban/Gomezplata (13)	He - N_2	0.73	0.5	14.1	0.35	
Single pellet string						
- Scott Lee, Papa (1)	H_2-N_2	0.753	0.5	22.0	0.205	0.515
	N_2-He	0.64	0.5	25.0	1.662	0.424
	He-N_2	0.57	0.5	24.1	0.22	0.424
This work	He-N_2 }	0.43±0.16	0.78	12.8	0.22	0.58-
	N_2-He		±0.16	±6.5	1.662	0.63

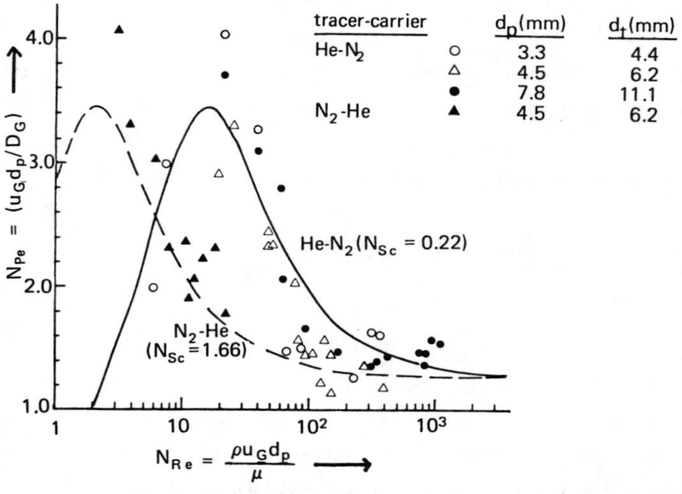

FIG. 3: AXIAL DISPERSION DATA COLLECTED ON THE SINGLE PELLET STRING

2. Diffusion-Cell Methods

Diffusion-cell methods are designed primarily to resolve the flow and diffusive phenomena of interest within the porous medium by eliminating the hydrodynamic "nuisance" factors of external mass transfer and inter-particle mixing, which complicate the packed bed approach. The earliest diffusion cells were steady state in character (14), but unsteady testing techniques have become increasingly popular in recent years.

Diffusion-cell techniques utilise a single particle or a small group of particles, either sealed into, or supported within, a custom-built cell. The concentration of the tracer gas is measured as a function of time at the cell entrance and exit (or sometimes at the exit only) following the imposition of a concentration disturbance upstream from the cell. The effective diffusivity D_p is then determined either by matching moments of a suitable mathematical model of the cell with observed moments, or by fitting an analytical solution of the model in the time domain.

The types of cell, the particle dimensions, methods of analysis employed, together with potential advantages and disadvantages, are summarised in Table 7. No cell is ideal in every respect. The most promising appear to be those developed by Dogu and Smith (19) and by Gibilaro and Waldram (20). The former utilises a single pellet sealed into a chamber. It offers the possibility of determining D_p from 1st system moments, which is a considerable advantage, and is extremely flexible. It is the only cell, for example, allowing both steady state or unsteady state experiments to be conducted and non-isobaric diffusion measurements to be taken. However, it has not, as yet, been applied to technical catalysts of relatively small size. The cell of Gibilaro and Waldram was specifically designed to house commercial catalyst pellets which, furthermore, do not need to be sealed into the chambers. Variability of diffusivities between individual pellets is averaged out to some extent by employing 5 inter-connected chambers, each containing a single particle. A potential drawback is the necessity of 2nd moments analysis on tailed distributions.

2.1 Model of the single pellet, double-faced diffusion cell

A "scaled-down" version of the diffusion cell of Dogu and Smith is considered, suitable for housing pellets of commercial size. In this section a mathematical analysis of the cell is presented. An experimental evaluation is given in Section 3.

A schematic diagram of the cell is shown in Fig. 4. The two flat faces of an encased cylindrical pellet, length L and cross-section A, of porosity β, are exposed to a carrier gas flow F, which passes through a small volume V over the flat faces. A transient concentration disturbance is imposed on one of the inlet flows and

TABLE 7: DIFFUSION CELL ARRANGEMENTS

Authors	Cell Arrangement	Particle Size /Shape Employed	Method of Analysis	Advantages / Disadvantages
Gorring (15), Yang (16)	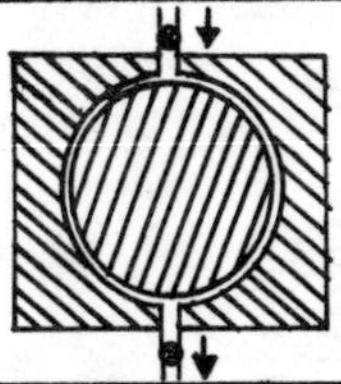	19 - 20.6 mm. spheres	time domain	Advantages: no sealing. Disadvantages: only a single pellet used. Suitable only when $D_p < 10^{-2}$ cm²/sec. Untested on commerical-size catalysts.
Gibilaro and Waldram (17)	single pellet, single faced 	cylinder 11 × 11 mms.	1st and 2nd moment matching	Disadvantages: sealing necessary. Only a single pellet used. 2nd moments subject to measurement error through tailing. Particle rather large.
Wakao (18), Dogu and Smith (19).	single pellet, double faced 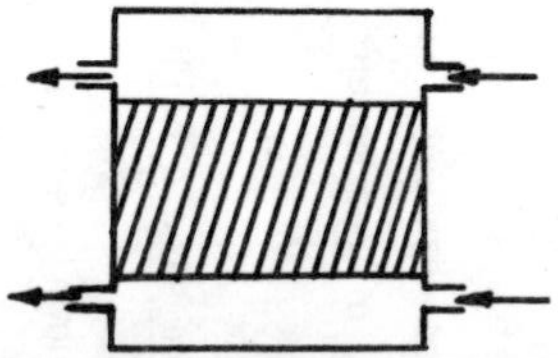	cylinders 115 ×27.6 mms diameter 24.4 ×13.5 mms. diameter	time domain 1st moment matching	Advantages: Only 1st moments needed. Greater flexibility. Disadvantages: only a single pellet employed. Untested on technical catalysts.
Gibilaro and Waldram (20)	5 CSTRs in series 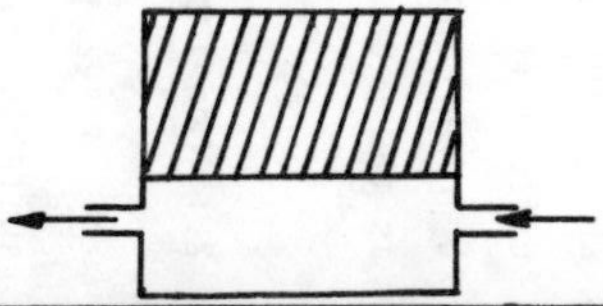	cylinders 6.27 ×6.74 mm dia. well mixed volumes = 102 mm³	1st and 2nd moment matching	Advantages: no sealing. Several pellets employed. Tested on technical catalysts. Disadvantages: severe "tailing".

detected in both outlet streams. The "no-bulk-flow" condition is achieved by controlling the flow to the face receiving the imposed transient so as to keep zero pressure difference between the faces.

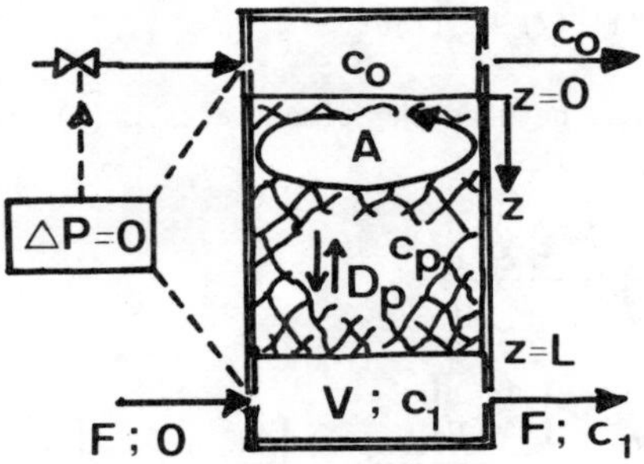

FIG. 4: SCHEMATIC OF THE DOGU/SMITH DIFFUSION CELL

A material balance over a differential slice of pellet leads to the equation

$$\left.\begin{aligned} &\beta \frac{\partial c_p}{\partial t} = D_p \frac{\partial^2 c_p}{\partial Z^2} \; ; \qquad c_p = 0, \quad t = 0 \\ &\text{with} \quad c_p = c_o, \quad Z = 0 \\ &\qquad\quad\; c_p = c_1, \quad Z = L \end{aligned}\right\} \tag{19}$$

A material balance over the lower chamber gives

$$V \frac{dc_1}{dt} = - Fc_1 - AD_p \left.\frac{\partial c_p}{\partial Z}\right|_{Z=L} \tag{20}$$

where it is assumed
- perfect mixing in both end volumes
- no mass transfer resistance at faces of pellet.

Eqns. (19) and (20) can be readily solved in the Laplace domain to give the relation

$$\tilde{E} = \frac{\tilde{c}_1}{\tilde{c}_o} = \frac{(AD_p/F.L)}{(1 + \frac{V.s}{F}) \frac{\sinh p}{p} + \frac{A.D_p}{F.L} \cosh p} \tag{21}$$

where $\quad p = \sqrt{\left(\frac{\beta \cdot s}{D_p}\right)} \cdot L$

It is not necessary formally to normalise this and call it a transfer function.

An estimate of D_p can be obtained by material balance

$$D_p = \frac{F.L}{A} \left(\frac{r_o}{1+r_o} \right) \tag{22}$$

where

$$r_o = \int_0^\infty c_1(t)dt / \int_0^\infty c_o(t)dt.$$

Alternatively, the difference in means between the time traces $c_1(t)$ and $c_o(t)$ may be used to provide a second estimate of D_p:

$$\Delta t_{(means)} = \frac{\int_0^\infty tc_1\, dt}{\int_0^\infty c_1 dt} - \frac{\int_0^\infty t\, c_o\, dt}{\int_0^\infty c_o\, dt}$$

$$= \frac{-\left[\frac{d}{ds}\tilde{c}_1\right]_{s\to o}}{\left[\tilde{c}_1\right]_{s\to o}} - \frac{-\left[\frac{d}{ds}\tilde{c}_o\right]_{s\to o}}{\left[\tilde{c}_o\right]_{s\to o}} = \left[\frac{\tilde{c}_1}{\tilde{c}_o}\frac{d}{ds}\left(\frac{\tilde{c}_o}{\tilde{c}_1}\right)\right]_{s\to o}$$

After a little algebra

$$\Delta t_{means} = \frac{\dfrac{(V + \frac{1}{2}\beta AL)}{F} + \dfrac{1}{6}\dfrac{\beta L^2}{D_p}}{(1 + \dfrac{AD_p}{F.L})} \tag{23}$$

Eqn. (23) can be used directly to determine D_p, or, instead, may be rearranged into the form

$$F.\Delta t_{means} = K_1.F + K_2.\Delta t_{means} + K_3 \tag{24}$$

where

$$K_1 = \frac{\beta L^2}{6D_p}, \quad K_2 = -\frac{A}{L}\cdot D_p, \quad K_3 = V + \frac{1}{2}\beta\, AL$$

Then, the data for different flow rates F may be analysed by least squares to determine the best value of D_p.

Apart from the attractions of this cell mentioned already in Table 7, one considerable advantage is that neither Eqns. (22) nor (23) relies on the form of the injected perturbation. The use of two detectors, instead of the single detector in the lower chamber outlet stream, as employed by Dogu and Smith (19), makes this attractive feature possible. It should be mentioned in passing that both Eqns. (22) and (23) provide estimates of D_p which are independent of "dead-endedness" of pores in the particle (21), a result which runs counter to the claim of Waldram and Dudukovic (22), who state that "the average time at which the tracer emerges having diffused through the pellet is dependent on any dead-endedness".

2.2 Some aspects of cell design

Optimal accuracy of D_p, as determined by material balance (Eqn. 22), requires that

$$\frac{AD_p}{FL} \sim 1 \tag{25}$$

This condition can only be approximately met for relatively large, coarsely porous cylindrical pellets, say 8×8 mm. with D_p ∿0.1 - 0.2 cm^2/sec (i.e. bulk diffusion). On the other hand reliable estimation of D_p from the difference of mean times (Eqn. 23) demands

$$\frac{\beta L^2}{6D_p} \gg \frac{V + \frac{1}{2}\beta AL}{F} \tag{26}$$

This condition can be easily satisfied for small cylinders (3×3 mm) in which Knudsen diffusion prevails ($D_p \sim 10^{-3} - 10^{-2}$ cm /sec), providing the end volumes V are kept small (e.g. 2×10^{-3} cm^3).

The choice of estimating equation and cell dimensions rests squarely on the mode of diffusion limiting molecular transport in the particle under test. It follows, therefore, that micro-meritic measurements are an essential pre-cursor to optimal cell design.

3. Experimental

An experimental evaluation of the packed bed and single pellet diffusion cell concludes this paper. We begin with the diffusion cell approach.

3.1 The single pellet diffusion cell

3.1.1 Preparation and working procedure

A "scaled-down" version of the single pellet cell of Dogu and Smith (19) was developed for direct evaluation of commercial catalysts. Details of the cell design and dimensions are given in Fig. 5.

The silica/alumina isomerisation catalyst employed in the cell was machined from its original spherical form into a cylinder - 3.18 mm diameter and between 3.3 and 4.26 mm. length - dried, and then sealed into a metal ring using "silicone" rubber. Great care was needed to ensure no rubber covered the end faces of the pellet. This proved to be an extremely tedious part of the preparation and restricted the working temperature of the cell to 50°C.

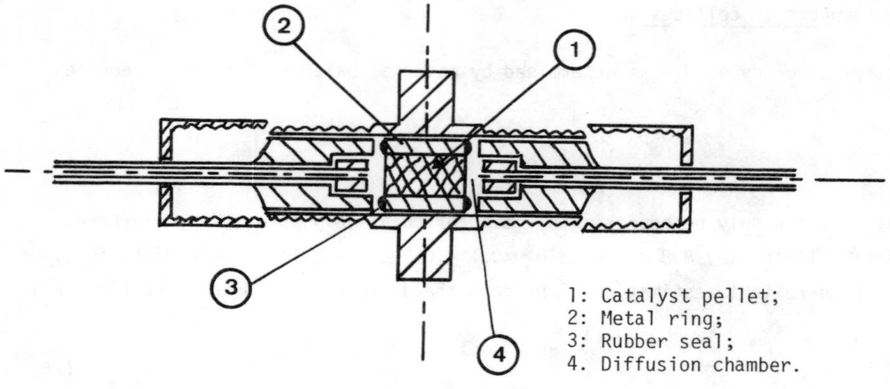

Cell dimensions and conditions (see Fig. 4 for description of symbols)

$V=2.38\times10^{-3}$ cm³, $A=7.94\times10^{-2}$ cm², $L=3.30$ to 4.26×10^{-1} cm, $\beta=0.50$, $F=(0.72$ to $2.44)\times10^{-1}$ cm³/sec. (at 50°C)

FIG. 5: THE DIFFUSION CELL - ABOUT TWICE ITS ACTUAL SIZE

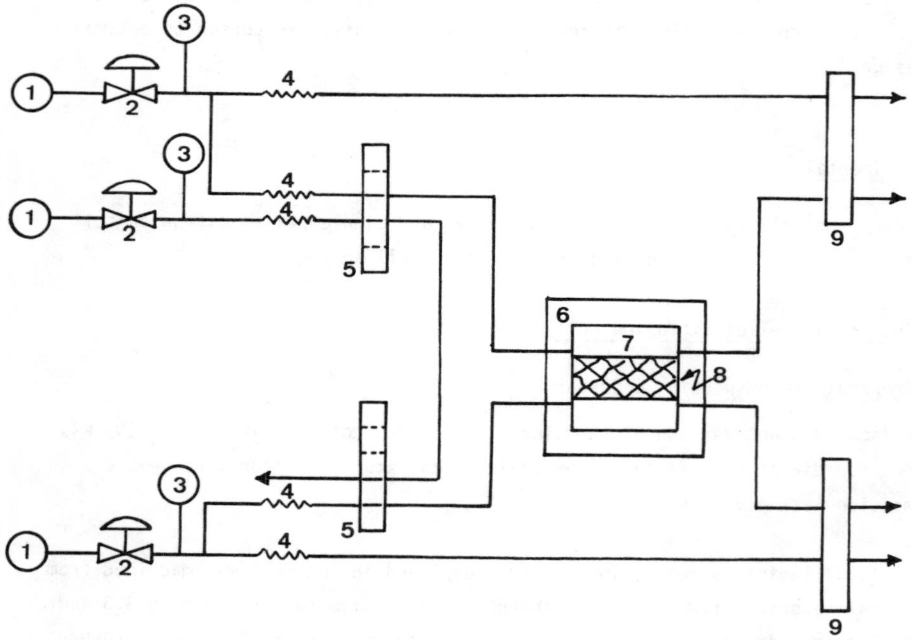

1: Gas cylinder; 2: Pressure regulator; 3: Pressure gauge; 4: Flow Restrictor; 5: 6-Port valve; 6: Oven; 7: Diffusion cell; 8: Catalyst pellet; 9: Detectors.

FIG. 6: SCHEMATIC DIAGRAM OF THE EXPERIMENTAL APPARATUS

The diffusion cell was screwed tight to ensure no leaks and then it was connected to the rest of the apparatus, as shown schematically in Fig. 6. This consisted of gas supply (helium and nitrogen cylinders), flow regulation (3 pressure gauges (Budenberg), 5 restrictors, 3 valves (Watts) and 1 soap bubble flowmeter), injection system (two 6-port injection valves (Pye) plus pneumatic control system), oven and temperature control (Taylor-Servomex), diffusion cell (Fig. 5) and detectors (2 micro-katharometers (Taylor-Servomex MK 158), control units and amplifiers), plotter (twin-pen Servoscribe).

The steps involved in an experiment were as follows:

(1) The oven thermostat was set at the desired operating temperature and switched on.

(2) The apparatus was left for 4 hours to reach the operating temperature.

(3) The nitrogen carrier was switched on and the flowrates through the two chambers of the cell equalised. Identical flows through identical geometries should ensure equality of pressures in the two chambers.

(4) The helium flow was turned on and the helium pressure set equal to the nitrogen pressure.

(5) The detectors and the twin pen recorder were switched on. The katharometers were allowed to warm up for 15 minutes before being balanced.

(6) The upper injection valve in Fig. 6 was switched to allow a pulse of He to pass through the cell. This preliminary pulse enabled the scales on the pen recorder to be set. The experiment was ready to begin.

(7) The paper was set in motion at 10 divisions per second, the upper valve switched and the traced obtained.

(8) The paper was stopped and the recorder scales reversed.

(9) The paper was again set in motion, the lower valve switched and a second set of traces recorded. The difference of mean times was averaged over the two injections:

$$\Delta t = (\Delta t_1 + \Delta t_2) / 2 \tag{27}$$

(10) The paper was stopped, the scales reversed and the switches returned to the normal position.

(11) Steps (1) - (10) were repeated for various flowrates and different pellets.

3.1.2 Results and Discussion

A typical cumulative pore-size distribution for the silica-alumina isomerisation catalyst, as measured by mercury porosimetry, is shown in Fig. 7. The mean pore radius of 34.9 Å puts the effective diffusion well into the Knudsen regime, guarantees that $A.D_p/F.L \ll 1$ in Eqn. (25) and $\beta L^2/6D_p \gg (V + \frac{1}{2}\beta AL)/F$ in Eqn. (26). The difference of mean times, given by Eqn. (23), is thus the preferred method of estimating D_p. Typical traces measured in the exit flows of the two chambers of the cell are shown in Fig. 8. Note the extreme tailing of the responses, particularly

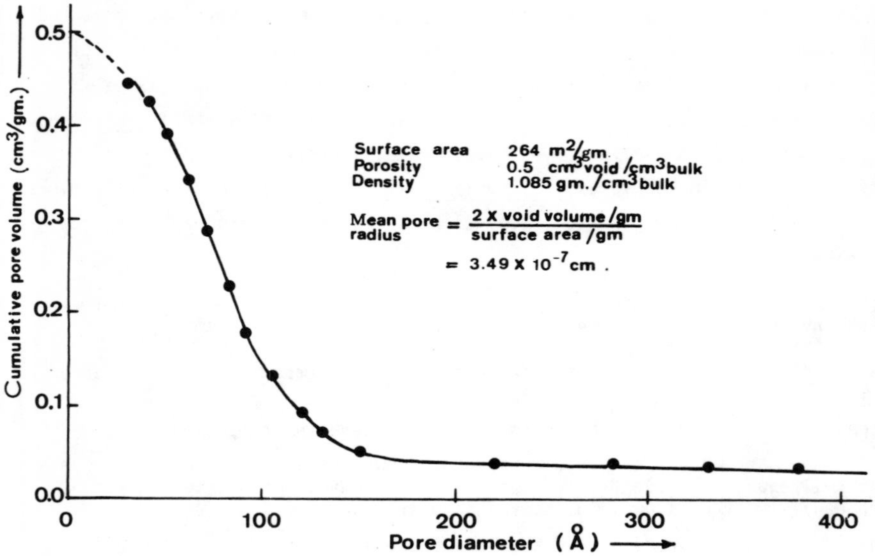

FIG. 7: CUMULATIVE PORE SIZE DISTRIBUTION FOR THE SiO_2/Al_2O_3 (Q17/3) CATALYST

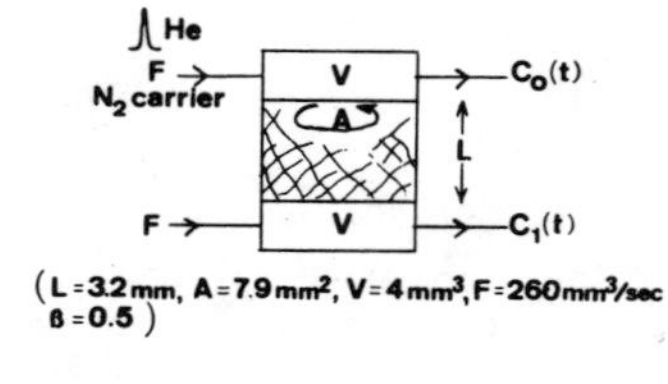

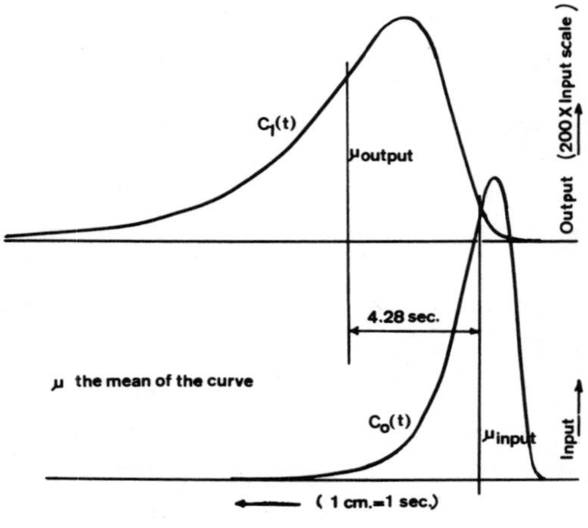

FIG. 8: TYPICAL TRACES MEASURED ON THE DIFFUSION CELL

that observed over the flat face remote from the injected pulse. Second moments of these traces would be virtually impossible to determine accurately.

Estimated effective diffusivities for one pellet are reported in Table 8 at various flow rates. There is little difference in the averaged estimates of D_p obtained from material balance or difference of mean times, though the latter is roughly five times more accurate. No correlation between D_p and the flow rate F was found, adding confidence to the results.

TABLE 8: ANALYSIS OF PELLET 1 AT DIFFERENT FLOW RATES

Flow Rate through the Chambers (50°C) (cm^3/sec)	Number of Runs	Effective Diffusivity, D_p (cm^2/sec)	
		Mass Balance: Eqn. (22)	Difference of mean Times: Eqns. (23), (27)
2.44×10^{-1}	2	3.84×10^{-3} 3.72 2.99 3.04	3.48×10^{-3} 3.49 3.51 3.46
2.09×10^{-1}	2	3.32×10^{-3} 3.39 2.81 2.74	3.51×10^{-3} 3.45 3.47 3.49
1.64×10^{-1}	2	4.66×10^{-3} 4.66 3.82 3.81	3.51×10^{-3} 3.55 3.54 3.52
1.19×10^{-1}	2	3.47×10^{-3} 3.81 4.10 3.98	3.46×10^{-3} 3.43 3.47 3.43
0.72×10^{-1}	2	3.49×10^{-3} 3.51 3.98 3.94	3.47×10^{-3} 3.50 3.46 3.50
Average diffusivity ±2×Standard Deviation		3.66×10^{-3} $\pm0.33\times10^{-3}$	3.48×10^{-3} $\pm0.07\times10^{-3}$

Altogether, five pellets, taken from the same batch of ex-plant regenerated catalyst, were examined, and their results are given in Table 9.

In Tables 8 and 9 a run consisted of the injection of a pulse on one side of the pellet and then again on the opposite face. From a single run, therefore, two estimates of D_p were obtained from Eqn. (22) and one estimate from Eqns. (23) and (27). A second run was carried out, upon resetting the flows, to give two further estimates by material balance and one further estimate by difference of mean times. By interchanging

TABLE 9: RESULTS OF THE ANALYSIS OF 5 PELLETS

Pellet Number	Number of Estimates	Average Effective Diffusivity (D_p), cm^2/sec.	
		Material Balance Eqn. (22)	Difference of Mean Times Eqns. (23), (27)
1	20	3.66×10^{-3}	3.48×10^{-3}
2	4	4.25×10^{-3}	4.01×10^{-3}
3	4	4.42×10^{-3}	4.27×10^{-3}
4	4	3.21×10^{-3}	3.34×10^{-3}
5	4	4.11×10^{-3}	3.95×10^{-3}
Weighted overall average from the 5 pellets		3.98×10^{-3}	3.81×10^{-3}

the means between the two replicate runs an additional two estimates of D_p can be found from Eqns. (23) and (27).

Pellet to pellet variations of effective diffusivity are considerably larger than the uncertainty limits associated with the measurements on a single particle. When using the diffusion cell technique it is recommended, therefore, that several pellets be examined in order to obtain a true measure of the mean effective diffusivity for use in reactor modelling.

The Knudsen diffusivity of helium in a straight round pore at 50°C ($r_p=3.49\times10^{-7}$ cms) is calculated from Eqn. (16) as $D_{SP}=3.043\times10^{-2}$ cm^2/sec. The tortuosity factor τ is obtained from

$$\tau = \beta \frac{D_{SP}}{D_p} = \frac{0.5 \times 3.043 \times 10^{-2}}{3.81 \times 10^{-3}} = 3.97 ,$$

where a weighted averaged D_p from the analysis of 5 pellets, using the more accurate difference of mean times estimator, is employed. Once τ has been determined, the effective diffusivities of much larger and reactive molecules, such as xylenes, can be estimated. Then, by modelling the interactions of diffusion and chemical reaction, the effect of increasing particle size on global rates of reaction can be assessed in an industrial reaction network, such as that of simultaneous xylenes isomerisation and disproportionation (23).

3.2 The packed bed

Pulse dispersion measurements were conducted over two single pellet string columns first packed with non-porous glass beads and then with porous spherical particles, using helium as the pulse gas and nitrogen as the carrier (Table 10).

TABLE 10: SCOPE OF PACKED BED EXPERIMENTS

	Bed 1	Bed 2	Bed 3	Bed 4
Length (L) cm	200	200	200	200
Diameter (d_t) cm	0.44	0.44	1.11	1.11
Packing Type	glass beads	porous SiO_2/Al_2O_3 (Q17/3)	glass beads	porous α-alumina (ALC182)
Diameter (d_p) cm	0.33	0.32	0.781	0.766
Porosity (β)	--	0.5	--	0.72
Bed Voidage (α)	0.59	0.585	0.632	0.617
U_G (cm/sec)	3 - 120	10 - 40	6 - 180	25 - 100
ΔP (cm H_2O)	1 - 120	3 - 25	1 - 60	2 - 25

The experimental set up is shown schematically in Fig. 1B. Helium pulses were detected upon entering and leaving the beds by means of Taylor-Servomex MK 158 microkatharometers, having a reported volume of 200 μlitres and time constant of 40 milliseconds. Connecting lines were of 1/16" tubing and the injection valve fitted with 1/8" connections. In each case shown in Table 10 the bed length to particle diameter ratio was sufficiently large that "end effects" could be safely neglected (1). Column porosities for non-porous glass beads were calculated from void volumes obtained by filling the packed and empty tubes with water and the average particle diameters were determined by measuring the volumetric displacement in water of a known number of randomly selected particles. For porous packings, on the other hand, the volume of packing in the tube (and thus the inter-particle voidage) was calculated from the weight of the particles and from the particle density, as measured by water pycnometry and checked by skeletal density and intra-particle porosity measurements. The average particle diameter was calculated from the estimated volume of a known number of particles packed into the column. The pressure drop across the columns was measured as a function of velocity in separate experiments. In the pulse dispersion experiments the pressure taps were disconnected and the water manometer removed. Maximum pressure drops measured over the porous packings were of the order of 2% of the total absolute pressure.

The carrier gas flow rates through the measurement side of the two micro-katharometers were always set equal by adjusting needle valves in the connecting lines. These flow rates lay in the range 0.7 to 5 cc/sec. At low column flow rates, the column pressure was raised in order to achieve an adequate flow of gas through the detectors by partially closing the valve in the flow line leaving the bottom of the column. On the larger column (d_t = 1.11 cm) the ratio of detector to column flows lay in the range 1 - 4%, whereas on the small column (d_t = 0.44 cm) the ratio was nearer 50%. Flow rates through the detectors and the column were measured at atmospheric pressure by a soap film meter. All runs were conducted at ambient temperature and a pressure 1.05 - 1.3 bar.

3.2.1 Results and Discussion

3.2.1.1 Diffusion in finely porous particles

The results of applying the experimental design criteria to finely porous particles (designated Q17/3) were set down in Table 4. For the single pellet string column these indicated an allowable working range of 6.5 - 49 cm/sec for the carrier gas velocity. To recap, the lower limit is set by significant axial dispersion intrusions and tends to be rather conservative. Usually, lower velocities can be tolerated. At this extreme the exit chromatograms tend to be near-Gaussian. The upper limit is set by the anti-tailing criterion (11), and operation near this limit minimises the effect of axial dispersion but tends to produce tailed chromatograms.

Experimental chromatograms are presented in Fig. 9 for carrier gas velocities within the designed range. These results exactly bear out the predictions of the design criteria. As a result, 5 different velocities were chosen, straddling the designed range, from which the pore diffusion coefficient D_p may be estimated. The experimental data are presented in Table 11.

Carrier gas velocities were estimated from the measured volumetric flow rate, corrected for the average column pressure, and from the difference of 1st moments, E_1, taking β=0.5 from independent measurement. The two independent estimates show good agreement.

When pore diffusion dominates axial dispersion, as is likely to be the case here, Eqn. (5) indicates a linear relationship between E_2^1 and E_1, i.e.

TABLE 11: EXPERIMENTAL DATA FOR THE FINELY POROUS CATALYST (Q17/3)

Run	Carrier Gas Velocity (U_G) Volumetric Flow (cm/sec)	1st Moments (cm/sec)	E_1 (sec)	E_2^1 (sec^2)
1	10.3	11.0	14.5	1.74
2	16.6	16.8	9.4	1.24
3	21.0	21.2	7.5	0.92
4	28.2	28.5	5.6	0.71
5	38.3	37.4	4.2	0.47

FIG. 9: TAILING OF THE EXIT PACKED BED TRACES

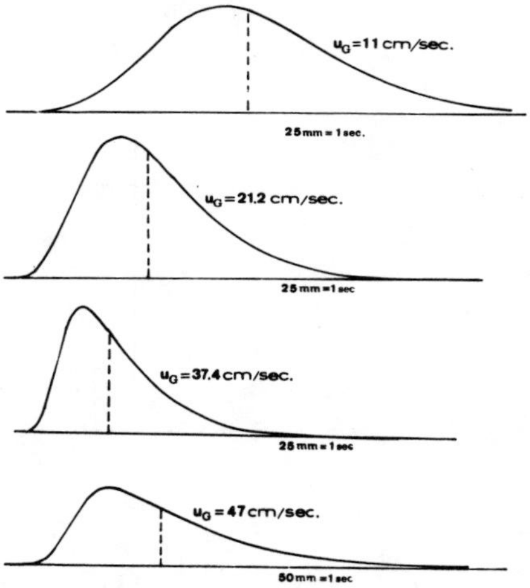

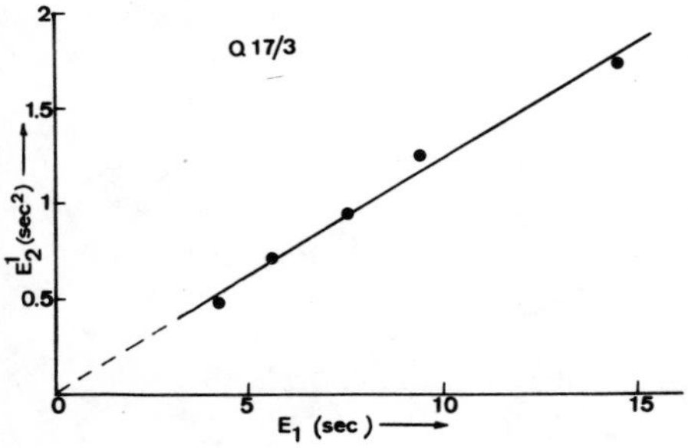

FIG. 10: PLOT OF E_2^1 VS. E_1 FOR THE SiO_2/Al_2O_3 CATALYST (Q17/3)

$$E_2^1 \simeq A.E_1 \qquad (28)$$

where $$A = \frac{2\beta^2(1-\alpha)R^2}{15\{\alpha + \beta(1-\alpha)\}D_p}$$

The data in Table 11, as plotted in Fig. 10, clearly support Eqn. (28). From the linear regression, 95% confidence limits on D_p give

$$D_p = (3.62 \pm 0.16)\times 10^{-3} \quad cm^2/sec.$$

A comparison of estimated pore diffusivities between the diffusion cell and packed bed techniques then follows in Table 12.

TABLE 12: COMPARISON OF PORE DIFFUSIVITIES BETWEEN THE DIFFUSION CELL AND THE PACKED BED

	Estimated Diffusivity $D_p\times 10^3$ (cm^2/sec.)
Single pellet diffusion cell (analysis of 5 pellets)	range 3.34 - 4.27
Packed bed (single pellet string)	(3.62 ± 0.16)

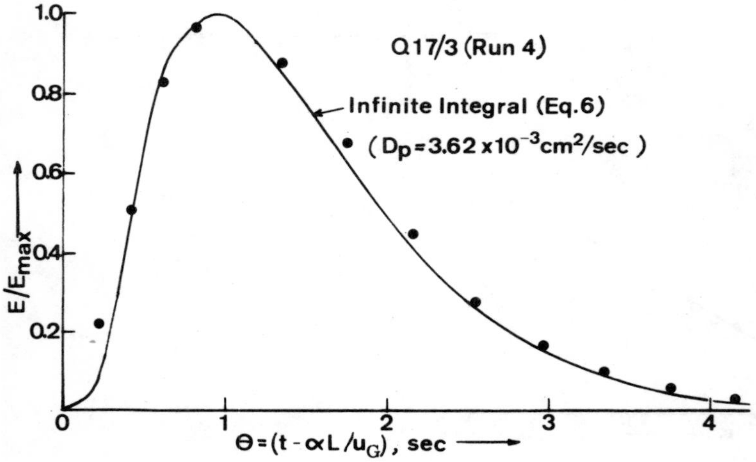

FIG. 11: COMPARISON OF MEASURED AND PREDICTED EXIT CHROMATOGRAMS FOR THE SiO_2/Al_2O_3 CATALYST (Q17/3)

The agreement reached between the two quite independent techniques is highly encouraging and lends confidence to the models and working procedures employed. The diffusion cell provides pore diffusion coefficients for individual particles and therefore shows a greater spread of estimated values than the packed bed, which provides an estimate of D_p averaged over several hundred particles. In calculating bounds on reactor performance individual particle estimates are more meaningful.

Further confidence in the packed bed model is provided by Fig. 11, in which the time-domain solution (Eqn. 6), appropriate to a sharp pulse input, is compared with selected points along the measured exit chromatogram.

3.2.1.2 Diffusion in coarsely porous particles

The situation regarding precise determination of pore diffusivities for coarsely porous particles is less satisfactory. This comes about as a result of axial dispersion always playing a significant, if not dominant, role in packed beds of coarsely porous particles. For the alumina catalyst support evaluated here, Table 5 indicates an allowable working range from ∿50 - 100 cm/sec. carrier gas velocity. Results extending somewhat beyond this range are summarised in Table 13.

TABLE 13: EXPERIMENTAL DATA FOR THE COARSELY POROUS CATALYST SUPPORT (ALC182)

Run	Carrier Gas Velocity (U_G) 1st Moments: (cm/sec)	E_1 (sec.)	E_2^1 (sec^2)
1	27.5	6.7	0.468
2	35	5.1	0.287
3	51.2	3.5	0.156
4	116	1.55	0.047
Bed repacked			
5	24.4	7.3	0.510
6	57.9	3.2	0.116
7	64.7	2.8	0.092

A particle porosity β=0.72 was estimated from 1st moment data collected at very low carrier gas velocities, such that the chromatograms were almost Gaussian. This estimate was subsequently confirmed independently.

In the case of coarsely porous particles, axial dispersion plays a significant role in broadening the input pulse and Eqn. (28) must be extended to the quadratic form

$$E_2^1 = A.E_1 + B.E_1^2 \tag{29}$$

where A is defined as in Eqn. (28) and

$$B = 4\left(\frac{R}{L}\right)\frac{1}{N_{Pe}} \tag{30}$$

The axial dispersion data presented in Fig. 3 show that N_{Pe} lies in the range 1 - 2 and is independent of N_{Re} when $N_{Re} > 10^2$, as is the case in all 7 runs given in Table 13. Thus B becomes constant, independent of E_1 in Eqn. (29). Two approaches would seem possible:

(i) Joint estimation of the constants A and B (and thus D_p and N_{Pe}) in Eqn. (29) by linear regression.

(ii) Estimation of the constant A (and thus D_p) with B held fixed from independent measurements over "identical" non-porous particles.

The results of the two methods of analysis are summarised below:

Joint parameter estimation

Minimum sum of squares 1.05×10^{-3}

		95% marginal confidence limits
N_{Pe}	0.992	0.757 - 1.227
D_p (cm²/sec)	0.279	0.079 - 0.478

Correlation coefficient $\rho_{N_{Pe}, D_p} = -0.964$

Independent parameter estimation

Minimum sum of squares 3.17×10^{-3}

$N_{Pe} = 1.40$ (limit as $N_{Re} \to \infty$ on non-porous glass beads (Fig. 3))

		95% confidence interval
D_p (cm²/sec)	0.150	0.127 - 0.174

The former procedure is preferred on statistical grounds and gives an excellent fit to the data in Fig. 12. However, the parameters are highly correlated. The latter procedure, on the other hand, does not give such a good fit to the data, but produces a more confident estimate of D_p.

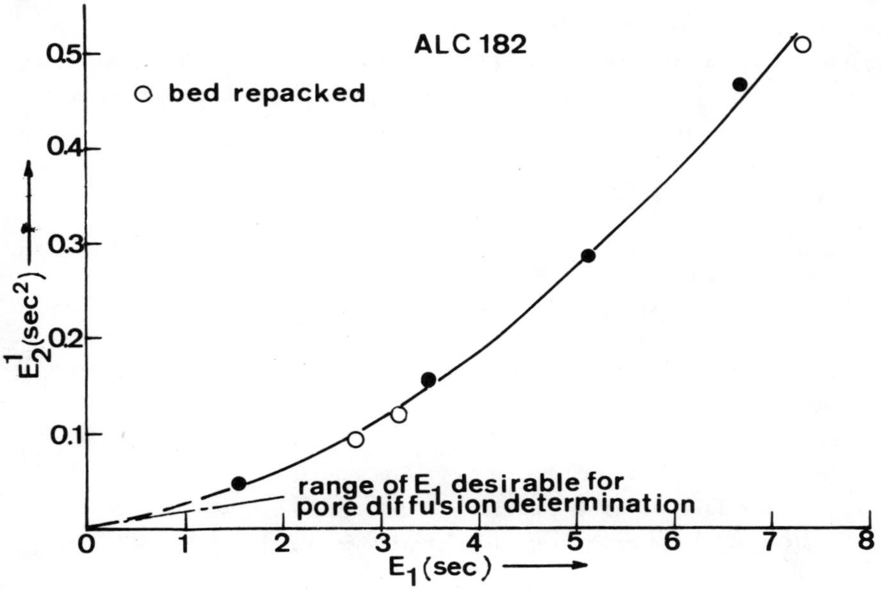

FIG. 12: PLOT OF E_2^1 VS. E_1 FOR THE ALUMINA SUPPORT (ALC 182)

It is clear from Fig. 12 that only a single data point can be included in the desired range of residence times (< 2 secs.) within which $AE_1 > BE_1^2$. Virtually this point alone contributes to the estimate of D_p, the other 6 points largely determining N_{Pe}. In order to overcome the high degree of correlation between D_p and N_{Pe}, more data points must be concentrated into the region $E_1 < 2$ sec. This would require substantially higher carrier gas velocities than 1 metre/sec., producing tailed chromatograms but, more importantly, leading to unacceptable column pressure drop and even to significant measurement lags.

On the other hand, it is by no means certain that the Peclet numbers for relatively rough porous supports and for glass beads are the same. Thus, independent measurement of N_{Pe} on glass beads may not lead to a reliable estimate of D_P.

It is concluded that the packed bed approach is best suited to the determination of effective diffusivities within finely porous particles. Comparison with the diffusion cell approach indicates quantitative results if care is taken in "designing" the experiments. The packed bed is probably adequate (though not as accurate as before) for studying diffusion within the transition region. Certain deficiencies in experimental design and data interpretation need to be resolved before the packed bed is suitable for studying diffusion within coarsely porous particles.

Nomenclature

		SI Units
A	cross-sectional area of cylindrical pellet sealed into diffusion cell	m^2
c_o, c_1	tracer concentrations in the upper and lower chambers of the diffusion cell	mol/m^3
c_G	inter-particle tracer concentration in packed bed	mol/m^3
c_P	intra-particle tracer concentration	mol/m^3
D_{AB}	binary gas diffusivity	m^2/sec
D_G	inter-particle axial dispersion coefficient	m^2/sec
D_P	intra-particle diffusion coefficient	m^2/sec
D_{SP}	Knudsen diffusion coefficient in a straight round pore	m^2/sec
d_p	equivalent sphere diameter (Eqn. 12)	m
$d_{p,mod}$	modified sphere diameter (Eqn. 13)	m
d_t	packed bed diameter	m
E	packed bed transfer function (Eqn. 3)	
E_1	differences between mean times of outlet and inlet traces	sec
E_2^1	differences between variances of outlet and inlet traces	sec^2
F	volumetric flow rate over faces of pellet in diffusion cell	m^3/sec
J_m	m'th zero of the Bessel function $J_0(x)$ (Table 2)	
k	shape factor in Eqn. (9). (Table 2)	
k_f	inter-particle mass transfer coefficient	m/sec
L	depth of packing between measurement points in packed bed. length of pellet sealed into diffusion cell	m
l	cylinder length (Table 2)	m
R	radius (half-thickness) of particle	m
r	radial co-ordinate of particle	m
s	Laplace transform variable	sec^{-1}
t	time	sec

U_G	superficial carrier gas velocity	m/sec
V	volume of well-mixed chambers in diffusion-cell	m^3
z	axial bed depth co-ordinate	} m
Z	axial co-ordinate in single pellet diffusion cell	

Greek Symbols

α	inter-particle voidage	m^3/m^3
β	intra-particle porosity	m^3/m^3
β'	constant in Eqn. (18)	---
γ	reciprocal tortuosity Eqn. (18)	---
$\Delta P/L$	pressure drop per unit bed depth	$kg/m^2sec.$
Δt_{means}	difference in mean times (Eqn. 23)	sec
λ	constant in Eqn. (18)	---
μ	carrier gas viscosity	kg/m.sec
ρ	carrier gas density	kg/m^3
τ	particle tortuosity	---

REFERENCES

1 D.S. Scott, Wey Lee and J. Papa, Chem. Eng. Sci 29 (1974), 2155.

2 P.N. Sarma and H.W. Haynes, Jr., A.C.S. Symposium Series 133 (1974), 205.

3 A.S. Anderssen and E.T. White, Chem. Eng. Sci. 26 (1971), 1203.

4 S.K. Gangwal, R.R. Hudgins, A.W. Bryson and P.L. Silveston, Can. Journ. Chem. Eng. 49 (1971), 113.

5 R.G. Rice, Chem. Eng. Sci. 37 (1982), 83.

6 H.W. Haynes, Jr., Chem. Eng. Sci. 30 (1975), 955.

7 G. Greco, G. Iorio, G. Tola and S.P. Waldram, Trans. Inst. Chem. Eng. 53 (1975), 55.

8 G. Iorio, G. Greco and S.P. Waldram, ibid 54 (1976), 199.

9 S. Ergun, Chem. Eng. Prog. 48 (1952), 89.

10 D.J. Gunn, Int. Journ. Heat and Mass Trans. 21 (1978), 467.

11 Tai-Sheng Chou, Chem. Eng. Sci. 34 (1979), 133

12 M.F. Edwards, J.F. Richardson, Chem. Eng. Sci. 23 (1968), 109.

13 J.C. Urban, A. Gomezplata, Can. Journ. Chem. Eng. 47 (1969), 353.

14 E. Wicke, R. Kallenbach, Zolloid Zeitschrift, 97 (1941), 135.

15 R.L. Gorring, A.J. de Rosset, Journal of Catalysis 3 (1964), 341.

16 R.T. Yang, Liu Rea-Tiing, M. Steinberg, I.E.C. Fundamentals 16 (1977), 486.

17 L.G. Gibilaro, S.P. Waldram, I.E.C. Fundamentals 12 (1973), 472.

18 N. Wakao, A.C.S. Symposium Series 133, (1974), 281.

19 G. Dogu, J.M. Smith, A.I.Ch.E.J. 21 (1975), 58.

20 L.G. Gibilaro, S.P. Waldram, Journ. Catalysis 67 (1981), 392.

21 L.G. Gibilaro, F. Gioa, G. Greco, Jr., Chem. Eng. Journal 1 (1970), 85.

22 S.P. Waldram, M.P. Dudukovic, Chem. Eng. Sci. 34 (1979), 1361.

23 N.H. Orr, D.L. Cresswell, D.E. Edwards, I.E.C. Proc. Des. Dev. (in press).

Stochastic Flow Reactor Modeling: A General Continuous Time Compartmental Model with Firstorder Reactions

L.T. Fan, J.R. Too, R. Nassar*

Department of Chemical Engineering, Kansas State University, Manhattan, KS 66506, U.S.A.

SUMMARY

A novel technique for modeling and simulating totally interconnected stirred tank networks is presented by using the theory of the Markov process (continuous time Markov chain). The present stochastic compartmental model is applicable to any steady state dispersive mixing process with linear first-order chemical reactions accompanied by flow of any material, gas, liquid or solid particles. The general model has been shown to reduce to a variety of specific compartmental models in a straightforward manner. The statistical basis of the residence time distribution theory for such a flow system is clarified. The technique is illustrated with two examples, and the results show a good fit with available experimental data.

INTRODUCTION

The compartmental model for flow systems is a generalization of a class of models, such as the completely mixed tanks-in-series model and the back-flow mixed tanks-in-series model. One of the common characteristics of these models is that the basic unit of the model is a completely mixed tank. Compartmental models have been widely

*Department of Statistics, Kansas State University.

employed in modeling a variety of flow systems, including flow chemical reactors and biological transport systems. The deterministic versions of such models have been extensively reviewed by Wen and Fan [1]. Stochastic versions of the models, predominantly those based on Markov chains, have also been employed to model flow systems containing n compartments (see, e.g., [2-6]).

Stochastic approaches have been widely employed in dealing with the kinetics of chemical reactions in batch reactors (see, e.g., [7,8]). They have also been utilized to analyze and model the phenomena of residence time distributions in flow chemical reactors (see, e.g., [9-12]). It is, therefore, natural that a unified stochastic approach be developed for the analysis and modeling of a flow system in which chemical reactions and dispersive mixing occur simultaneously. Furthermore, a stochastic model can provide not only mean values of the parameters characterizing the system, e.g., mean concentration-time histories, but also their fluctuations.

The process of simultaneous chemical reactions and flow in a system with n compartments is essentially continuous in time and discrete in state which represents the position of a molecule in the flow system and is characterized by the compartment in which the molecules exist. Hence, it is advantageous to analyze or model the process as a Markov process (continuous time Markov chain) rather than a Markov chain. In this work, a relatively novel technique for solving totally interconnected stirred tank networks is presented by using the theory of the Markov process. Results include the distribution of numbers of molecules of a given type in any compartment as well as the residence time distribution of the molecules in the system. It will be shown that the present general model will reduce to a variety of specific compartmental models.

GENERAL COMPARTMENTAL MODEL

Suppose that a linear first-order chemical reaction

$$A \xrightarrow{\text{first-order}} \text{products}$$

occurs in a flow system consisting of n well mixed compartments totally interconnected as shown in Figure 1. The volumes of the com-

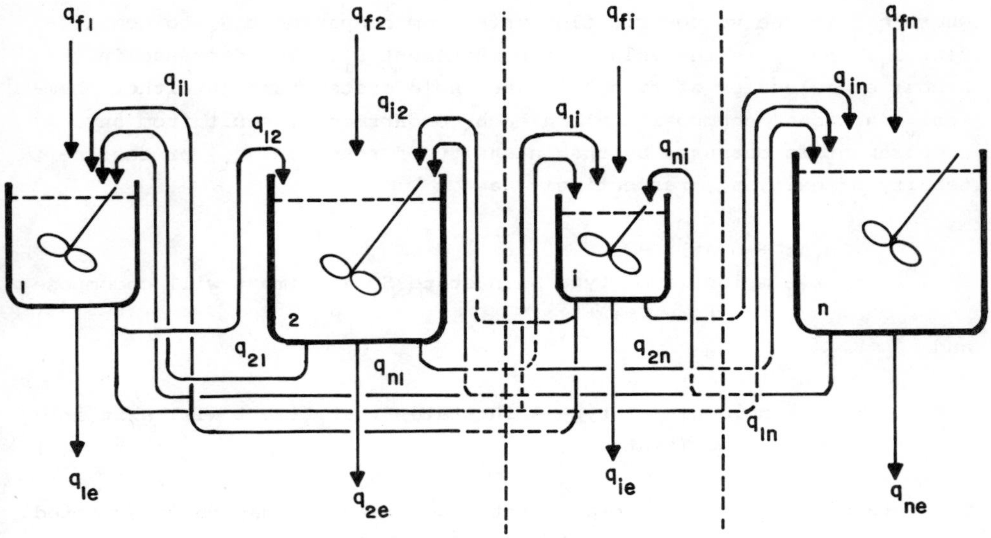

Figure 1. A schematic diagram of the general compartmental model.

partments are not necessarily identical. Let S_i ($i = 1, 2, \ldots, n$) denote the compartments in this system. A molecule of type A originally in compartment S_i may continuously transfer to and from any of the n compartments, may decompose in any of the compartments or may exit from the system. In parlance of stochastic processes, compartment S_1, S_2 ..., S_n may be considered as transient states, and both reaction and exit can be viewed as leading to the absorbing (or death) states; collectively, these processes are analogous to the so-called general migration process (see, e.g., [13]).

The transition of a molecule of type A from one compartment (or state) to another is assumed to be independent of transitions made by other molecules. Let ν_{ij} denote the intensity of transition defined as follows:

$$\begin{aligned}&\nu_{ij}\Delta t + o(\Delta t)\\&= \Pr[\text{a molecule of type A in state } S_i \text{ at time } t \text{ will be in}\\&\qquad \text{state } S_j \text{ at time } (t+\Delta t),\ i \neq j]\end{aligned} \tag{1}$$

For a well mixed compartment, ν_{ij} can be identified to be (see, e.g., [5,14])

$$\nu_{ij} = \frac{q_{ij}}{V_i} \tag{2}$$

where q_{ij} is the volumetric flow rate from compartment S_i to compartment S_j, and V_i is the volume of compartment S_i. The decrease in the number of molecules of type A in the whole system through either chemical reaction (decomposition) in each compartment or exit from any compartment is measured by the intensity of reaction, η_i, or the intensity of exit, μ_i, respectively, as

$$\eta_i \Delta t + o(\Delta t) = \Pr[\text{a molecule of type A in state } S_i \text{ at time t will decompose at time } (t+\Delta t)] \quad (3)$$

and

$$\mu_i \Delta t + o(\Delta t) = \Pr[\text{a molecule of type A in state } S_i \text{ at time t will exit at time } (t+\Delta t)] \quad (4)$$

The rate constant for a linear first-order reaction may be interpreted as the probability that one molecule of type A undergoes chemical decomposition during a unit time interval, i.e., the intensity of reaction is related to the rate constant (see, e.g., [12]). If we assume that the temperature of each compartment remains constant, η_i is then independent of time. The intensity of exit, μ_i, can be expressed as

$$\mu_i = \frac{q_{ie}}{V_i} \quad (5)$$

where q_{ie} is the volumetric rate of out-flow from compartments S_i. From Equations (1), (3) and (4), we have

$$1 - [\sum_{j=1}^{n} \nu_{ij} \Delta t + \eta_i \Delta t + \mu_i \Delta t] + o(\Delta t) = \Pr[\text{a molecule of type A in state } S_i \text{ at time t will remain in it at time } (t+\Delta t)] \quad (6)$$

If this probability is denoted by $1 + \nu_{ii} \Delta t + o(\Delta t)$, we have

$$\nu_{ii} = -[\sum_{\substack{j=1 \\ j\neq i}}^{n} \nu_{ij} + \eta_i + \mu_i], \; i = 1, 2, \ldots, n \quad (7)$$

Letting

$p_{ij}(t)$ = transition probability that a molecule of type A in state S_i at time 0 will be in state S_j at time t; $i, j = 1, 2, \ldots, n$, it can be shown that the transition probabilities, $\{p_{ij}(t)\}$, satisfy the following Kolmogorov forward differential equations (see, e.g., [13, 16])

$$\frac{d}{dt} p_{ij}(t) = \sum_{k=1}^{n} p_{ik}(t)\nu_{kj}, \quad i, j = 1, 2, \ldots, n \tag{8}$$

with the initial condition

$$p_{ij}(0) = \begin{cases} 1, & i = j \\ 0, & i \neq j \end{cases} \tag{9}$$

In matrix notation, Equations (8) and (9) can be written, respectively, as

$$\frac{d}{dt} \underline{P}(t) = \underline{P}(t)\underline{U} \tag{8a}$$

and

$$\underline{P}(0) = \underline{I} = \text{identity matrix} \tag{9a}$$

where

$$\underline{P}(t) = \begin{bmatrix} p_{11}(t) & p_{12}(t) & \cdots & p_{1n}(t) \\ p_{21}(t) & p_{22}(t) & \cdots & p_{2n}(t) \\ \vdots & \vdots & \ddots & \vdots \\ p_{n1}(t) & p_{n2}(t) & \cdots & p_{nn}(t) \end{bmatrix} \tag{10}$$

and

$$\underline{U} = \begin{bmatrix} \nu_{11} & \nu_{12} & \cdots & \nu_{1n} \\ \nu_{21} & \nu_{22} & \cdots & \nu_{2n} \\ \vdots & \vdots & \ddots & \vdots \\ \nu_{n1} & \nu_{n2} & \cdots & \nu_{nn} \end{bmatrix} \tag{11}$$

We assume that the eigenvalues, $\rho_1, \rho_2, \ldots, \rho_n$, of the matrix $\underline{U}$ defined by its characteristic equation

$$|\rho\underline{I} - \underline{U}| = 0 \tag{12}$$

are real and distinct. The characteristic matrix, $\underline{B}(k)$, is

$$\underline{B}(k) = \rho_k\underline{I} - \underline{U}, \quad k = 1, 2, \ldots, n \tag{13}$$

A non-zero column vector $\underline{Q}_k(\ell)$, defined as

$$\underline{Q}_k(\ell) = \begin{bmatrix} B_{\ell 1}(k) \\ B_{\ell 2}(k) \\ \cdot \\ \cdot \\ \cdot \\ B_{\ell n}(k) \end{bmatrix} \tag{14}$$

then is the eigenvector of $\underline{U}$ corresponding to the eigenvalue ρ_k; it is the ℓ-th column of the adjoint matrix (or matrix of cofactor) of $\underline{B}(k)$. The solution to Equation (8a) is given as

$$\underline{P}(t) = \underline{Q}(\ell)\underline{E}(t)\underline{Q}^{-1}(\ell) \tag{15}$$

where

$$\underline{Q}(\ell) = \begin{bmatrix} B_{\ell 1}(1) & B_{\ell 1}(2) & \cdots & B_{\ell 1}(n) \\ B_{\ell 2}(1) & B_{\ell 2}(2) & \cdots & B_{\ell 2}(n) \\ \vdots & \vdots & \ddots & \vdots \\ B_{\ell n}(1) & B_{\ell n}(2) & \cdots & B_{\ell n}(n) \end{bmatrix}$$

and

$$\underline{E}(t) = \begin{bmatrix} e^{\rho_1 t} & 0 & \cdots & 0 \\ 0 & e^{\rho_2 t} & \cdots & 0 \\ \vdots & \vdots & \ddots & \vdots \\ 0 & 0 & \cdots & e^{\rho_n t} \end{bmatrix}$$

By expanding Equation (15), we obtain

$$p_{ij}(t) = \sum_{k=1}^{n} B_{\ell i}(k) \frac{Q_{jk}(\ell)}{|\underline{Q}(\ell)|} e^{\rho_k t}, \quad i, j = 1, 2, \ldots, n \tag{16}$$

where $Q_{jk}(\ell)$ is the cofactor of the element $B_{\ell j}(k)$ of the matrix $\underline{Q}(\ell)$ and $|\underline{Q}(\ell)|$ is the determinant of $\underline{Q}(\ell)$. All eigenvalues of the matrix $\underline{U}$, by virtue of Equation (6), are known to be negative.

If the matrix $\underline{U}$ has multiple eigenvalues, ρ_1, ρ_2, ..., ρ_a, with respective multiplicities n_1, n_2, ..., n_a, such that

$$n_1 + n_2 + \dots + n_a = n,$$

then the solution of Kolmogorov differential equations in Equation (8a) subject to the initial condition, Equation (9a), is given by [13]

$$\underline{P}(t) = \underline{Q}(\ell)\ \mathrm{diag}\ [\underline{E}_1(t)\ \underline{E}_2(t)\ \dots\ \underline{E}_a(t)]\underline{Q}^{-1}(\ell) \tag{17}$$

where

$$\underline{E}_k(t) = \begin{bmatrix} e^{\rho_k t} & \frac{t}{1!} e^{\rho_k t} & \dots & \frac{t^{n_k-1}}{(n_k-1)!} e^{\rho_k t} \\ 0 & e^{\rho_k t} & \dots & \frac{t^{n_k-2}}{(n_k-2)!} e^{\rho_k t} \\ \vdots & \vdots & \ddots & \vdots \\ 0 & 0 & \dots & e^{\rho_k t} \end{bmatrix}$$

$$\underline{Q}(\ell) = [\underline{Q}_1^{(0)}(\ell)\ \dots\ \underline{Q}_1^{(n_1-1)}(\ell)\ \dots\ \underline{Q}_a^{(0)}(\ell)\ \dots\ \underline{Q}_a^{(n_a-1)}(\ell)]$$

and

$$\underline{Q}_k^{(j)}(\ell) = \frac{1}{j!} \frac{d^j}{d\rho_k^j} \begin{bmatrix} B_{\ell 1}(k) \\ B_{\ell 2}(k) \\ \vdots \\ B_{\ell n}(k) \end{bmatrix}, \quad \begin{matrix} j = 1, 2, \dots, (n_k-1) \\ k = 1, 2, \dots, a \end{matrix}$$

Let $r_i(t)$ be the probability that a molecule of type A in state S_i at time 0 will decompose or exit by time t. Then, we see that

$$r_i(t) = \int_0^t \sum_{j=1}^{n} p_{ij}(\tau)\ (\eta_j + \mu_j)\ d\tau, \quad i = 1, 2, \dots, n \tag{18}$$

A molecule of type A, which is in state S_i originally or at $t = 0$, will either be in state S_j ($j = 1, 2, \dots, n$), decompose or exit from the system at time t. Since the probabilities of these three events will sum up to one, we can write

$$\sum_{j=1}^{n} p_{ij}(t) + r_i(t) = 1 \tag{19}$$

Note that $r_i(t)$ is the probability for the last two events as we can see from Equation (18).

Now, let $X_i(t)$ be the random variable representing the number of molecules of type A in compartment S_i at time t. We denote the corresponding numbers of molecules of type A in compartments by the vector

$$\underline{X}(t) = [X_1(t)\ X_2(t)\ \ldots\ X_n(t)]$$

Random vector $\underline{X}(t)$ is composed of two vectors $\underline{Y}(t)$ and $\underline{Z}(t)$, that is,

$$\underline{X}(t) = \underline{Y}(t) + \underline{Z}(t) \tag{20}$$

Each of the components of $\underline{Y}(t)$,

$$\underline{Y}(t) = [Y_1(t)\ Y_2(t)\ \ldots\ Y_n(t)]$$

is the number of survivors of the inventory molecules of type A, which were in the system originally (t = 0), in the respective compartment at time t; each of the components of Z(t),

$$\underline{Z}(t) = [Z_1(t)\ Z_2(t)\ \ldots\ Z_n(t)]$$

is the number of molecules of type A among those which have entered the system during the time interval (0,t) and have survived in the respective compartment at time t.

Let $m_i(0)$ denote the number of molecules of type A in compartment or state S_i at time 0. Each of the $m_i(0)$ molecules will be in one of the n compartments or will disappear due to decomposition or exit from the system at time t. Hence,

$$m_i(0) = \sum_{j=1}^{n} Y_{ij}(t) + D_i(t) \tag{21}$$

where

$Y_{ij}(t)$ = random variable representing the number of molecules of type A in state S_j at time t, which were in state S_i at time 0,

$D_i(t)$ = random variable representing the number of molecules of type A, which were in state S_i at time 0, disappearing by time t due to decomposition or exit from the system.

For a given $m_i(0)$, we have a multinomial distribution according to

Equation (19), i.e.,

$$\Pr[Y_{i1}(t) = y_{i1}, Y_{i2}(t) = y_{i2}, \ldots, Y_{in}(t) = y_{in}]$$

$$= \frac{m_i(0)!}{\prod_{j=1}^{n} y_{ij}![\, m_i(0) - \sum_{j=1}^{n} y_{ij}]!} \prod_{j=1}^{n} [p_{ij}(t)]^{y_{ij}}$$

$$\cdot\ [r_i(t)]^{\{m_i(0) - \sum_{j=1}^{n} y_{ij}\}} \qquad (22)$$

Here, y_{ij} is the number of molecules of type A in state S_j at time t, which were initially in state S_i at time 0. The value $[m_i(0) - \sum_{j=1}^{n} y_{ij}]$ is the number of those which decomposed or exited during the time interval (0,t). It is easy to see that

$$Y_j(t) = \sum_{i=1}^{n} Y_{ij}(t)$$

Then, by assuming that transitions among molecules of type A are independent of each other, it can be seen that the joint probability of $\{Y_1(t), Y_2(t), \ldots, Y_n(t)\}$ is

$$\Pr[Y_1(t) = y_1, Y_2(t) = y_2, \ldots, Y_n(t) = y_n]$$

$$= \sum \prod_{i=1}^{n} \frac{m_i(0)!}{\prod_{j=1}^{n} y_{ij}!\ [m_i(0) - \sum_{j=1}^{n} y_{ij}]!} \prod_{j=1}^{n} [p_{ij}(t)]^{y_{ij}}$$

$$\cdot\ [r_i(t)]^{\{m_i(0) - \sum_{j=1}^{n} y_{ij}\}} \qquad (23)$$

where the summation is taken over all mutually exclusive sets, $\{y_{ij};\ i, j = 1, 2, \ldots, n\}$, such that

$$\sum_{i=1}^{n} y_{ij} = y_j$$

The expected number and the variance of $Y_j(t)$ as well as the covariance between $Y_i(t)$ and $Y_j(t)$ can be obtained by using familiar formulae of the multinomial distribution as (see, e.g., [13,17])

$$E[Y_j(t)] = \sum_{i=1}^{n} m_i(0) p_{ij}(t) \qquad (24)$$

$$\mathrm{Var}[Y_j(t)] = \sum_{i=1}^{n} m_i(0)\ p_{ij}(t)\ [1 - p_{ij}(t)] \qquad (25)$$

and

$$\mathrm{Cov}[Y_i(t),\ Y_j(t)] = -\sum_{k=1}^{n} m_k(0)\ p_{ki}(t)\ p_{kj}(t),\ i \neq j \tag{26}$$

Suppose that, at any time τ, molecules of type A flow into each compartment at rate of $\zeta_i(\tau)$ ($i = 1, 2, \ldots, n$) molecules per unit time. Thus, $\zeta_i(\tau)$ may be expressed as

$$\zeta_i(\tau) = q_{fi}\ C_{fi}(\tau)\ N \tag{27}$$

where

q_{fi} = volumetric flow rate of the feed stream to compartment S_i,
C_{fi} = molar concentration of A in q_{fi},
N = Avogadro's number

As soon as a freshly fed molecule enters a compartment, it may begin to transfer from one compartment to another, may exit from the system or may decompose. Therefore, vector $\underline{Z}(t)$ is the outcome of sequences of events of input, transitions among the compartments, and survival from decomposition and exit. Here, we assume that all molecules in the system behave stochastically and independently of one another. It has been shown (see, e.g., [13]) that the distribution of $\underline{Z}(t)$ is of the multiple Poisson form with parameters $\{\lambda_i(t);\ i = 1, 2, \ldots, n\}$.

The parameter, $\lambda_i(t)$, which is the expected value of $Z_i(t)$, can be determined by considering a sequence of events. The number of molecules of type A that enter compartment S_i during some time interval $(\tau, \tau+d\tau)$, $0 \leq \tau \leq t$, is $\zeta_i(\tau)d\tau$. Therefore, the number of molecules of type A in compartment S_j at time t, which have arisen from $\zeta_i(\tau)d\tau$ molecules, is

$$\zeta_i(\tau)d\tau\ p_{ij}(t - \tau)$$

For distinct values of $i = 1, 2, \ldots, n$, and for distinct values of τ, $0 \leq \tau \leq t$, the corresponding sequences are mutually independent. Hence, we have

$$\lambda_j(t) = E[Z_j(t)]$$

$$= \int_0^t \sum_{i=1}^{n} \zeta_i(\tau)\ p_{ij}(t - \tau)d\tau \tag{28}$$

When $\zeta_i(\tau) = \zeta_i$ is independent of time, we obtain

$$\lambda_j(t) = \sum_{i=1}^{n} \zeta_i \int_0^t p_{ij}(t - \tau)d\tau \qquad (29)$$

The expected value and variance of $Z_j(t)$ are identical and equal to the parameter $\lambda_j(t)$, i.e. (see, e.g., [17]),

$$E[Z_j(t)] = Var[Z_j(t)] = \lambda_j(t) \qquad (30)$$

According to Equations (20), (24) and (28), the expected value of $X_j(t)$ is

$$E[X_j(t)]$$

$$= E[Y_j(t)] + E[Z_j(t)]$$

$$= \sum_{i=1}^{n} m_i(0)p_{ij}(t) + \int_0^t \sum_{i=1}^{n} \zeta_i(\tau)p_{ij}(t - \tau)d\tau \qquad (31)$$

Since $\underline{Y}(t)$ and $\underline{Z}(t)$ are obviously independent vectors in the present model, the variance of $X_j(t)$ can be obtained from Equations (20), (25) and (30)

$$Var[X_j(t)]$$

$$= Var[Y_j(t)] + Var[Z_j(t)]$$

$$= \sum_{i=1}^{n} m_i(0)p_{ij}(t)[1 - p_{ij}(t)] + \int_0^t \sum_{i=1}^{n} \zeta_i(\tau)p_{ij}(t - \tau)d\tau \qquad (32)$$

Since the concentration of A in compartment S_j at time t, $C_j(t)$, is given by

$$C_j(t) = \frac{X_j(t)}{NV_j} \qquad (33)$$

the expected value and the variance of $C_j(t)$ can be obtained accordingly.

Compartments-in-Series Model

The compartments-in-series model is one of the most frequently used sub-classes of the general compartmental model discussed previously. Here, a special case of the model containing n completely mixed compartments of equal size arranged in series is considered. Molecules of type A enter the system only through the first compartment and leave it through the last compartment.

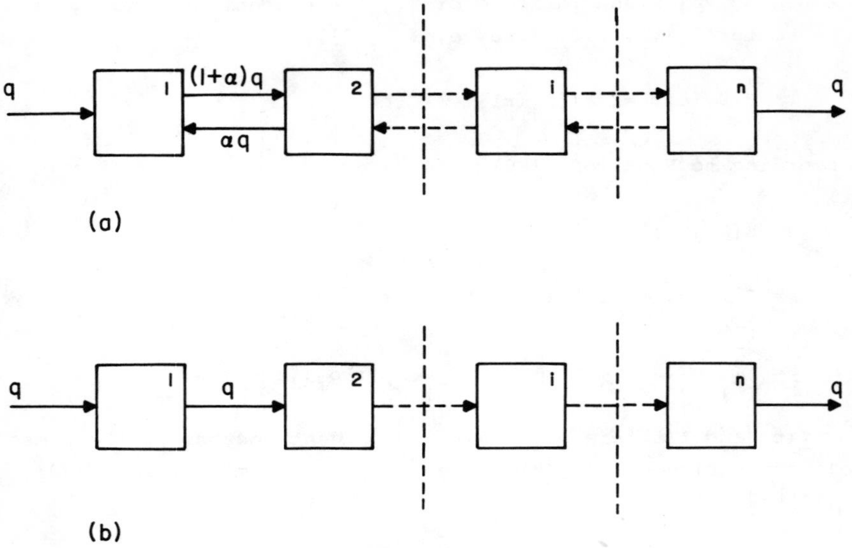

Figure 2. Compartments-in-series model,
(a) with back-flow and, (b) without back flow.

Let us first examine the case with back-flow shown in Figure 2a. The system corresponds to the following conditions in the general model:

$$q_{fi} = \begin{cases} q, & i = 1 \\ 0, & \text{otherwise} \end{cases}$$

$$q_{ie} = \begin{cases} q, & i = n \\ 0, & \text{otherwise} \end{cases}$$

$$\zeta_i = 0, \text{ for } i \neq 1$$

$$\mu_i = 0, \text{ for } i \neq n$$

The intensity matrix $\underline{U}$ in Equation (11) becomes a tridiagonal matrix as

$$\underline{U} = \begin{bmatrix} \nu_{11} & \nu_{12} & & & & \\ \nu_{21} & \nu_{22} & \nu_{23} & & 0 & \\ & \cdot & \cdot & \cdot & & \\ & & \cdot & \cdot & \cdot & \\ & & & \nu_{n-1,n-2} & \nu_{n-1,n-1} & \nu_{n-1,n} \\ & 0 & & & \nu_{n,n-1} & \nu_{nn} \end{bmatrix} \tag{34}$$

where

$$\nu_{i,i+1} = \frac{(1+\alpha)q}{V_i}, \qquad i = 1, 2, \ldots, (n-1)$$

$$\nu_{i+1,i} = \frac{\alpha q}{V_i}, \qquad i = 1, 2, \ldots, (n-1)$$

α = fraction of flow undergoing back mixing between the compartments.

For the compartments-in-series without back-flow model shown in Figure 2b, α is zero, and thus its intensity matrix, $\underline{U}$, may be written as

$$\underline{U} = \begin{bmatrix} \nu_{11} & \nu_{12} & & & \\ & \nu_{22} & \nu_{23} & & 0 \\ & & \cdot & \cdot & \\ & & & \cdot & \cdot \\ & 0 & & \nu_{n-1,n-1} & \nu_{n-1,n} \\ & & & & \nu_{nn} \end{bmatrix} \tag{35}$$

which is a bidiagonal matrix. Furthermore, we have

$$\nu_{i,i+1} = \frac{q}{V_i} = \frac{1}{\bar{t}_i}, \qquad i = 1, 2, \ldots, (n-1)$$

where $\bar{t}_i$ is the mean residence time of molecules of type A in an individual compartment.

By means of the same procedure given previously, we obtain the transition probabilities $\{p_{ij}(t);\ i, j = 1, 2, \ldots, n\}$ for the case of compartments-in-series. Since the molecules only enter through the first compartment, the expected value and the variance of $X_i(t)$ for this case are reduced, respectively, to

$$E[X_i(t)] = \sum_{i=1}^{n} m_i(0)p_{ij}(t) + \int_0^t \zeta_1(\tau)p_{1j}(t-\tau)d\tau \tag{36}$$

and

$$\mathrm{Var}[X_i(t)] = \sum_{i=1}^{n} m_i(0)p_{ij}(t)[1 - p_{ij}(t)] + \int_0^t \zeta_1(\tau)p_{1j}(t - \tau)d\tau \quad (37)$$

Besides the compartment-in-series model, numerous specific models, such as the multi-loop circulation model (see, e.g., [2,18]) and the progression model (see, e.g., [1]), have been widely employed to model flow systems and reactors. It can be shown that the present general model reduces to such models in a straightforward manner as in the case of the compartments-in-series models. This will be illustrated by means of examples.

RESIDENCE TIME DISTRIBUTION

The residence time refers to the time spent by a molecule in a flow system when no chemical reaction occurs. Let us consider a molecule entering compartment S_i at time $t = 0$. At $t > 0$, the molecule may remain in the same compartment, may transfer into another compartment or may exit from the flow system. Here, the residence or life time of a molecule is defined to be the total time spent by the molecule in the system prior to its exit from the system. First, we shall determine the mean of the life time distribution of molecules in the system.

Let

$$I_{ij}(\tau) = \begin{cases} 1, & \text{if a molecule is in compartment } S_j \text{ at time } \tau, \\ & \text{given that it was initially in compartment } S_i \\ 0, & \text{otherwise} \end{cases}$$

Also let $a_{ij}(t)$ denote the time spent by the molecule in compartment S_j in the time interval $(0,t)$ given that it was in compartment S_i at $t = 0$. It can be seen that

$$a_{ij}(t) = \int_0^t I_{ij}(\tau)d\tau, \quad i, j = 1, 2, \ldots, n \quad (38)$$

The expected duration of stay in compartment S_j in the interval $(0,t)$ is

$$E[a_{ij}(t)] = \int_0^t E[I_{ij}(\tau)]d\tau$$

$$= \int_0^t \{1 \cdot p_{ij}(\tau) + 0 \cdot [1 - p_{ij}(\tau)]\}d\tau$$

$$= \int_0^t p_{ij}(\tau)d\tau \qquad (39)$$

The second moment of the duration of stay in compartment S_j in the same interval $(0,t)$ is

$$E[\{a_{ij}(t)\}^2] = E[(\int_0^t I_{ij}(\tau)d\tau)^2]$$

$$= \int_0^t \int_0^t E[I_{ij}(\tau)I_{ij}(s)]dsd\tau \qquad (40)$$

Notice that $E[I_{ij}(\tau)I_{ij}(s)]$ is the probability that the molecule is in compartment S_j both at time τ and at time s starting from compartment S_i at $t = 0$. Thus, we have

$$E[I_{ij}(\tau)I_{ij}(s)] = p_{ij}(\min(\tau,s))p_{jj}(|\tau-s|) \qquad (41)$$

Because of the symmetry of $p_{ij}(\tau)$, we have, from Equations (40) and (41),

$$E[\{a_{ij}(t)\}^2] = 2 \int_0^t ds \int_0^s p_{ij}(\tau)p_{jj}(s-\tau)d\tau \qquad (42)$$

The variance of duration of stay in compartment S_j, given that the molecule was initially in compartment S_i, is then

$$\mathrm{Var}[a_{ij}(t)] = E[\{a_{ij}(t)\}^2] - \{E[a_{ij}(t)]\}^2$$

$$= 2 \int_0^t ds \int_0^s p_{ij}(\tau)p_{jj}(s-\tau)d\tau - [\int_0^t p_{ij}(\tau)d\tau]^2 \qquad (43)$$

The expected life time of a molecule in the system starting from compartment S_i is then

$$E[\sum_{j=1}^n a_{ij}(t)] = \sum_{j=1}^n E[a_{ij}(t)]$$

$$= \sum_{j=1}^n \int_0^t p_{ij}(\tau)d\tau \qquad (44)$$

The life time or residence time distribution of molecules in the system under the steady state condition is derived below.

Let the random variable T_i denote the life time or life span of a molecule entering into compartment S_i initially. Then,

$$Pr[T_i > t] = \sum_{j=1}^{n} p_{ij}(t) \tag{45}$$

Hence, the cumulative life time distribution, $F_i(t)$, is

$$\begin{aligned} F_i(t) &= Pr[T_i \leq t] \\ &= 1 - \sum_{j=1}^{n} p_{ij}(t), \; t \geq 0 \end{aligned} \tag{46}$$

$F_i(t)$ is the probability that a molecule, which was orginally in comparment S_i, will exit from the flow system by age t. The probability density function of T_i is the derivative of $F_i(t)$, i.e.,

$$\begin{aligned} f_i(t) &= \frac{dF_i(t)}{dt} \\ &= - \sum_{j=1}^{n} p'_{ij}(t) \end{aligned} \tag{47}$$

From this expression, the expected life time of the molecule is obtained as

$$\begin{aligned} E[T_i] &= \int_0^{\infty} t f_i(t) dt \\ &= \sum_{j=1}^{n} \int_0^{\infty} p_{ij}(t) dt \end{aligned} \tag{48}$$

Note that Equation (44) reduces to this expression as $t \to \infty$, as expected. The variance of the life time distribution is

$$\begin{aligned} &Var[T_i] \\ &= E[T_i^2] - \{E[T_i]\}^2 \\ &= \int_0^{\infty} t^2 f_i(t) dt - [\int_0^{\infty} t f_i(t) dt]^2 \\ &= 2 \sum_{j=1}^{n} \int_0^{\infty} t p_{ij}(t) dt - [\sum_{j=1}^{n} \int_0^{\infty} p_{ij}(t) dt]^2 \end{aligned} \tag{49}$$

The input rate of molecules into compartment S_i, $\zeta_i(\tau)$, is independent of time for the steady state, i.e.,

$$\zeta_i(\tau) = \zeta_i$$

Since molecules may enter the system through any of the compartments, the residence time distribution of molecules may be expressed as a weighted average of $f_i(t)$ $(i = 1,2,\ldots,n)$; the weight for $f_i(t)$ is the ratio between the fixed input rate of molecules into compartment S_i and the overall input rate into the system. Thus,

$$f(t) = \frac{1}{\zeta} \sum_{i=1}^{n} \zeta_i f_i(t) \tag{50}$$

where

$$\zeta = \sum_{i=1}^{n} \zeta_i$$

EXAMPLES

Two examples given here demonstrate the use of the present stochastic model. A compartments-in-series model without back-flow is considered in the first example. The expressions of the residence time distribution and the mean concentration of reactant leaving the system are formulated. In the second example, we show that the general model reduces to a multi-loop circulation model in a straightforward manner.

Example 1. The Compartments-in-Series Model without Back-Flow

First, let us consider a flow system containing n compartments of equal size in series without back-flow. The residence time distribution of molecules in this flow system can be derived as follows:

The intensity matrix, $\underline{U}$, for this model without chemical reaction is, from Equation (35),

$$\underline{U} = \begin{bmatrix} -\nu & \nu & & & & 0 \\ & -\nu & \nu & & & \\ & & \cdot & \cdot & & \\ & & & \cdot & \cdot & \\ & 0 & & & \cdot & \cdot \\ & & & & -\nu & \nu \\ & & & & & -\nu \end{bmatrix} \tag{51}$$

Here, ν is the reciprocal of the mean residence time of molecules in each compartment, i.e.,

$$\nu = \frac{1}{\bar{t}_i} = \frac{q}{V_i} = \frac{nq}{V} = \frac{n}{\bar{t}} \tag{52}$$

The eigenvalue of this matrix is $-\nu$ with multiplicity n. From Equation (17), the transition probability matrix, $\underline{P}(t)$, can be expressed as

$$\underline{P}(t) = \underline{Q}(n)\ \underline{E}_1(t)\ \underline{Q}^{-1}(n) \tag{53}$$

where

$$\underline{Q}(n) = \begin{bmatrix} \nu^{n-1} & & & & 0 \\ & \nu^{n-2} & & & \\ & & \cdot & & \\ & & & \cdot & \\ 0 & & & & 1 \end{bmatrix}$$

and

$$\underline{E}_1(t) = \begin{bmatrix} e^{-\nu t} & te^{-\nu t} & \cdots & \frac{t^{n-1}}{(n-1)!}e^{-\nu t} \\ & e^{-\nu t} & \cdots & \frac{t^{n-2}}{(n-2)!}e^{-\nu t} \\ & & \ddots & \vdots \\ 0 & & & e^{-\nu t} \end{bmatrix}$$

By expanding Equation (53), we obtain

$$p_{1j}(t) = \frac{e^{-\nu t}(\nu t)^{j-1}}{(j-1)!}, \qquad j = 1, 2, \ldots, n \tag{54}$$

According to Equation (46), the cumulative distribution of the residence time is then written as

$$F(t) = 1 - \sum_{j=1}^{n} p_{1j}(t)$$

$$= 1 - \sum_{j=1}^{n} \frac{(\nu t)^{j-1}e^{-\nu t}}{(j-1)!} \tag{55}$$

It has been shown that (see, e.g., [17,19])

$$F(t) = 1 - \sum_{j=1}^{n} \frac{(\nu t)^{j-1} e^{-\nu t}}{(j-1)!}$$

$$= \int_0^t \frac{\nu^n x^{n-1} e^{-\nu x}}{\Gamma(n)} dx, \qquad t > 0 \tag{56}$$

Accordingly, the probability density function of the residence time is

$$f(t) = \frac{d}{dt} F(t)$$

$$= \frac{\nu(\nu t)^{n-1} e^{-\nu t}}{\Gamma(n)}, \quad t > 0, \tag{57}$$

that is, the residence or life times of molecules in the flow system, T, are distributed in the form of a gamma function with parameters n and ν. The mean and variance of this distribution are, respectively (see, e.g., [17]),

$$E[T] = \frac{n}{\nu} = \bar{t} \tag{58}$$

and

$$\mathrm{Var}[T] = \frac{n}{\nu^2} = \frac{\bar{t}^2}{n} \tag{59}$$

Furthermore, we define a dimensionless variable which measures time in units of the mean residence time of the whole system, $\bar{t}$. This is the so-called reduced time, i.e.,

$$\theta = \frac{t}{\bar{t}}$$

Then from Equation (52), we have

$$\nu t = n\theta \tag{60}$$

and Equation (57) may be rewritten as

$$f(\theta) = \frac{n}{\Gamma(n)} (n\theta)^{n-1} e^{-n\theta}, \qquad \theta > 0 \tag{61}$$

which is in agreement with the known result obtained from the deterministic approach (see, e.g., [20]).

For a compartments-in-series model without back-flow, the residence time of a molecule in this flow system, T, may be expressed as

$$T = \sum_{i=1}^{n} T(i)$$

where T(i) is the duration of stay of the molecule in compartment S_i. Once the molecule enters compartment S_i, it sojourns in this compartment for a random length of time (duration of stay), which has an exponential density function according to the pure death process (see, e.g., [13,16]). Thus, T(i) has the density as

$$f_{T(i)}(t) = \nu e^{-\nu t}, \quad i = 1, 2, \ldots, n \tag{62}$$

It has been shown that the sum of independent identically distributed exponential random variables is gamma-distributed (see, e.g., [17,19]). Thus, the residence time, T, has a gamma distribution with parameters n and ν, which is Equation (57).

For the compartments-in-series model, molecules enter the flow system only through compartment S_1 and exit from compartment S_n. The probability that a molecule will exit from the system during the time interval (t, t+dt), given that it entered the system at t = 0, is

$$p_{1n}(t)\mu_n(dt)$$

The residence time distribution function of molecules through a flow system is defined in such a way that f(t)dt is the fraction of molecules in the exit stream with age between t and t+dt. Therefore, we have

$$f(t) = p_{1n}(t)\mu_n = p_{1n}(t)\nu \tag{63}$$

Substitution of $p_{1n}(t)$, Equation (54), into this equation yields Equation (57).

If a first-order chemical reaction is involved, the intensity matrix, $\underline{U}$, may be written as [see Equation (35)],

$$\underline{U} = \begin{bmatrix} -(\nu+\eta) & \nu & & & & \\ & -(\nu+\eta) & \nu & & 0 & \\ & & \cdot & \cdot & & \\ & & & \cdot & \cdot & \\ & 0 & & & -(\nu+\eta) & \nu \\ & & & & & -(\nu+\eta) \end{bmatrix} \tag{64}$$

where η is the rate constant. The eigenvalue of this matrix is $-(\nu+\eta)$ with multiplicity n. The transition probabilities can be obtained from Equation (17) as

$$p_{1j}(t) = \frac{e^{-(\nu+\eta)t}(\nu t)^{j-1}}{(j-1)!}, \quad j = 1, 2, \ldots, n \tag{65}$$

The mean concentration of A in compartment S_n at time t, $\bar{C}_n(t)$, may be expressed as

$$\bar{C}_n(t) = \frac{E[X_n(t)]}{NV_n} \tag{66}$$

where $E[X_n(t)]$ is obtained from Equation (36). The mean concentration of A leaving the system unreacted, $\bar{C}(t)$, equal to $\bar{C}_n(t)$. By letting $t \to \infty$, we obtain $\bar{C}(\infty)$ for the steady state condition, i.e.,

$$\begin{aligned} \bar{C}(\infty) &= \lim_{t\to\infty} \bar{C}(t) \\ &= \frac{1}{NV_n} \lim_{t\to\infty} E[X_n(t)] \end{aligned} \tag{67}$$

Substituting Equations (36) and (65) into Equation (67), we finally obtain

$$\frac{\bar{C}(\infty)}{C_{f1}} = \frac{1}{(1 + \eta \frac{\bar{t}}{n})^n} \tag{68}$$

which is the known result (see, e.g., [20]).

Example 2. The Residence Time Distribution of a Multi-loop Circulation Model

Gibilaro <u>et al</u>. [2] used the Markov chain to simulate numerically the residence time distribution of multi-loop circulation model shown in Figure 3. In their experiments, impulse response tests were performed on a flow system containing 6 well mixed compartments of equal size. The total volume of the compartments is 100 liters, and the mean residence time of this system is 500 sec., i.e.,

$$\frac{V}{q} = 500 \text{ sec}$$

The tracer material (Nigrosine dye solution) was injected into the inlet line as a square pulse of 5 sec duration; for practical purposes, this can be considered as an impulse. The feed dip pipe directed flow into compartments S_1 and S_3. The output from a photocell detector on the glass outlet line from compartment S_5 was connected to a digital voltmeter and a data logger. During each run, this output was read at 1 sec intervals and recorded. Typical results are shown in Figures 4a and 4b. The abscissa of each figure plots the reduced time, θ, and the ordinate plots the normalized concentration, C/C_0, in the out-flow stream. In other words, these two figures show the residence time distribution, $f(\theta)$, for different values of $\frac{V}{q}$.

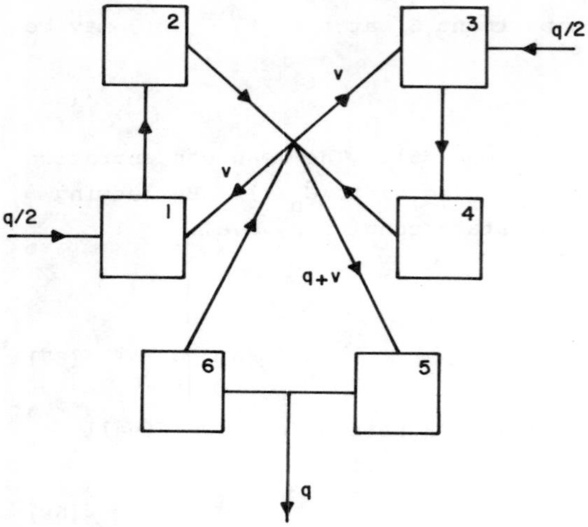

Figure 3.
Three loop circulation systems with inflow divided equally between upper loops [2].

For this flow system, the intensity matrix, U, in Equation (11) is easily formulated. For instance, the elements of the second row of U are

$$\nu_{21} = \nu_{23} = \frac{v}{(3v + q)} \frac{(v + \frac{q}{2})}{V_2}$$

$$\nu_{24} = \nu_{26} = 0$$

$$\nu_{25} = \frac{(v + q)}{(3v + q)} \frac{(v + \frac{q}{2})}{V_2}$$

and

$$\nu_{22} = -(\nu_{21} + \nu_{23} + \nu_{25})$$

Following the procedure given previously, we obtain the transition probabilities $\{p_{ij}(t);\ i, j = 1, 2, \ldots, 6\}$. The probability that a tracer molecule exits from the system during the time interval $(t, t+dt)$ is

$$\frac{1}{2}\,[p_{15}(t) + p_{35}(t)]\mu_5\, dt$$

Since tracer molecules only entered the system through compartments S_1 and S_2 and exited from compartment S_5, the probability density function of the residence time is, according to Equation (50),

$$f(t) = \frac{1}{2}\,[p_{15}(t) + p_{35}(t)]\mu_5$$

$$= \frac{1}{2}\,[p_{15}(t) + p_{35}(t)]\,\frac{q}{V_5}$$

or

$$f(\theta) = \bar{t}\, f(t)$$

Good agreement between the response data and the present model are observed in Figures 4a and 4b.

DISCUSSION

So far, only the irreversible first-order chemical reaction has been considered in the general compartmental model. In general, any linear first-order reactions can be modeled in a manner similar to the case of the irreversible first-order reaction. For example, if a consecutive unimolecular reaction

$$A \underset{k_{21}}{\overset{k_{12}}{\rightleftharpoons}} B \underset{k_{32}}{\overset{k_{23}}{\rightleftharpoons}} C$$

occurs in a flow system containing two compartments, instead of a (2x2) transition matrix as suggested by Equation (11), we may write matrix $\underline{U}$ as

$$\underline{U} = \begin{array}{c} \\ S_{1A} \\ S_{1B} \\ S_{1C} \\ S_{2A} \\ S_{2B} \\ S_{2C} \end{array} \begin{array}{c} \begin{array}{cccccc} S_{1A} & S_{1B} & S_{1C} & S_{2A} & S_{2B} & S_{2C} \end{array} \\ \left[\begin{array}{ccc|ccc} \nu_{1A} & k_{12} & 0 & \nu_{12} & 0 & 0 \\ k_{21} & \nu_{1B} & k_{23} & 0 & \nu_{12} & 0 \\ 0 & k_{32} & \nu_{1C} & 0 & 0 & \nu_{12} \\ \hline \nu_{21} & 0 & 0 & \nu_{2A} & k_{12} & 0 \\ 0 & \nu_{21} & 0 & k_{21} & \nu_{2B} & k_{23} \\ 0 & 0 & \nu_{21} & 0 & k_{32} & \nu_{2C} \end{array}\right] \end{array}$$

where S_{iA} $(i = 1, 2)$ denotes a molecule of type A in compartment S_i. The diagonal elements of this matrix need to be modified accordingly. For example, ν_{1B} is

$$\nu_{1B} = -\,(k_{21} + k_{23} + \nu_{12} + \mu_1)$$

Then, the same procedure presented previously can be used to obtain the transition probabilities.

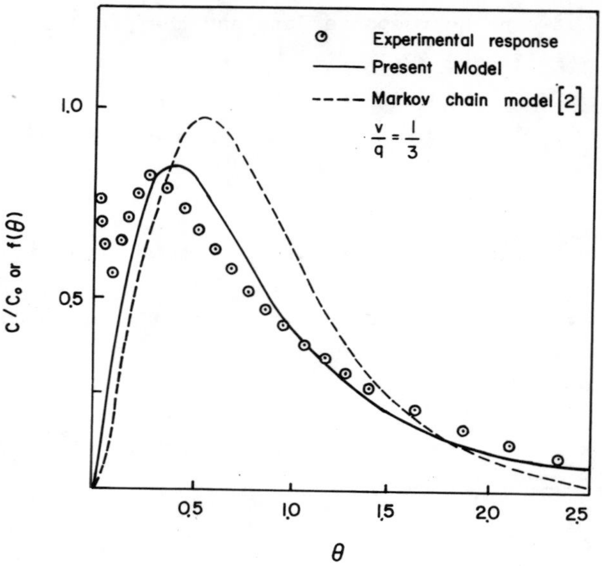

Figure 4a. Comparison between the experimental response and the present model for v/q = 1/3.

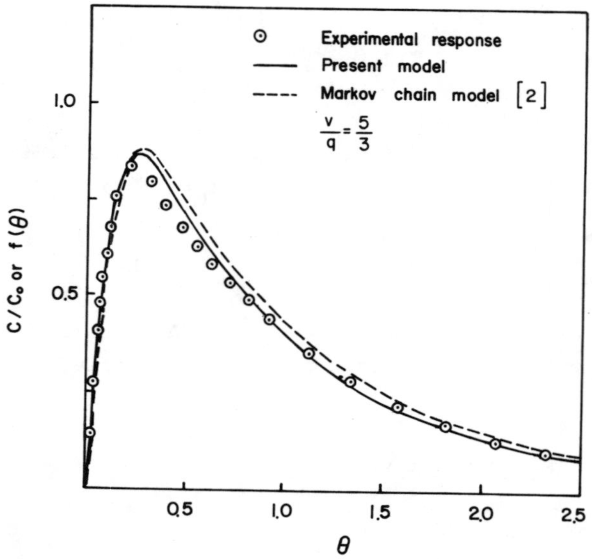

Figure 4b. Comparison between the experimental response and the present model for v/q = 5/3.

In the discrete time Markov chain model employed by Gibilaro et al. [2] and Chang and Fitzgerald [5], an assumption is made that transitions occur instantaneously at each instant of the discretized time. Therefore, the smaller the Δt (time interval between two transitions), the closer the approximation of the discrete time model to the continuous time process. The accuracy of the present model does not depend on Δt since it is time continuous. Figures 4a and 4b show that, as expected, the present model gives rise to a slightly better fit than the model based on the discrete time Markov chain.

CONCLUSIONS

This work presents a systematic method for stochastically modeling a flow system with first-order chemical reactions. The method is applicable to a flow system satisfying the conditions that the flow rates of all streams passing through the system remain constant, but the concentration of the reactant in each feed stream may be made as a function of time. The reacting stream can be composed of any materials, gas, liquid or solid particles. The present model leads to the representation of such a system by a set of first-order, linear, ordinary differential equations with constant coefficients which are the intensities of transition, reaction and exit. The transition probability of a molecule from one compartment to another in the system is derived as a function of these intensities. The joint distribution of the numbers of molecules in various compartments is formulated. In the absence of chemical reactions, the residence time distribution of molecules in the flow system is recovered.

By means of examples, we have shown that the results obtained from the present stochastic model are in agreement with the known deterministic result based on the mass balance. The advantage of the present stochastic model is its simplicity and generality. Furthermore, the model can provide not only the mean concentration of the reactant in each compartment, but also its fluctuations or higher moments. The general model can be reduced in a straightforward manner to specific models, such as the compartments-in-series model, the progression model and the multi-loop circulation model.

NOTATION

$a_{ij}(t)$	= time spent by a molecule in compartment S_j in the time interval (0,t) given that it was in compartment S_i at t = 0
$\underline{B}(k)$	= characteristic matrix of $\underline{U}$ corresponding to eigenvalue ρ_k
$C_{fi}(t)$	= molar concentration of A in the feed stream q_{fi}
$C_i(t)$	= molar concentration of A in compartment S_i at time t
$D_i(t)$	= random variable representing the number of molecules of type A, which were in state S_i at time 0, disappearing by time t
$E[X_i(t)]$	= expected value of $X_i(t)$
$F_i(t)$	= cumulative distribution function of T_i
$f(t)$	= probability density function of the residence time
$f_i(t)$	= probability density function of T_i
$I_{ij}(\tau)$	= indicator function
$m_i(0)$	= number of molecules of type A in compartment S_i at time 0
N	= Avogadro's number
n	= number of compartments
$p_{ij}(t)$	= transition probability that a molecule of type A in state S_i at time 0 will be in state S_j at time t
$\underline{Q}_k(\ell)$	= eigenvector of matrix $\underline{U}$ corresponding to ρ_k
q_{fi}	= volumetric flow rate of feed stream to compartment S_i
q_{ie}	= volumetric rate of out-flow from compartment S_i
q_{ij}	= volumetric flow rate from compartment S_i to compartment S_j
$r_i(t)$	= probability that a molecule of type A in state S_i at time 0 will decompose or exit by time t
S_i	= compartment or state of the flow system
T_i	= random variable denoting the life span of a molecule which entered compartment S_i at time 0
$\bar{t}$	= mean residence time of molecules in the flow system
$\bar{t}_i$	= mean residence time of molecules in compartment S_i
$\underline{U}$	= intensity matrix
V_i	= volume of compartment S_i
$Var[X_i(t)]$	= variance of $X_i(t)$
$X_i(t)$	= random variable representing the number of molecules of type A in compartment S_i at time t
$Y_i(t)$	= random variable representing the number of survivors of the inventory molecules of type A in compartment S_i at time t

$Y_{ij}(t)$ = random variable representing the number of molecules of type A in state S_j at time t, which were in state S_i at time 0

$Z_i(t)$ = random variable representing the number of molecules of type A in compartment S_i at time t, which have arisen from the molecules entering the system during (0,t)

Greek Letters

α = fraction of flow undergoing back mixing between the compartments

$\zeta_i(\tau)$ = flow rate, in terms of number, of molecules of type A into compartment S_i

η_i = intensity of reaction

$\lambda_i(t)$ = parameter of the Poisson distribution

$\mu_i(t)$ = intensity of exit

ν_{ij} = intensity of transition from compartment S_i to compartment S_j

ρ_i = eigenvalue of matrix $\underline{U}$

REFERENCES

1. C. Y. Wen and L. T. Fan, Models for Flow Systems and Chemical Reactors, Marcel Dekker, New York, 1975.
2. L. G. Gibilaro, H. W. Kropholler and D. J. Spikins, Chem. Eng. Sci. 22 (1967) 517.
3. B. A. Buffham, L. G. Gibilaro and H. W. Kropholler, Chem. Eng. Sci. 24 (1969) 7.
4. F. W. Chang, Discrete Modeling of Flow Systems, Ph.D. Thesis, Oregon State University, 1976.
5. F. W. Chang and T. J. Fitzgerald, AIChE J. 23 (1977) 558.
6. F. W. Chang, J. of Chinese Inst. of Chem. Engrs. 9 (1978) 165.
7. A. G. Fredrickson, Chem. Eng. Sci. 21 (1966) 687.
8. D. A. McQuarrie, J. Appl. Prob. 4 (1967) 413.
9. F. J. Krambeck, R. Shinnar and S. Katz, Ind. Eng. Chem. Fundamentals 6 (1967) 277.
10. R. Nassar, L. T. Fan, J. R. Too and L. S. Fan, Chem. Eng. Sci. 36 (1981) 1307.
11. R. Nassar, J. R. Too and L. T. Fan, J. Appl. Polym. Sci. 26 (1981) 3745.

12. R. Nassar, J. R. Too, C. H. Ahn and L. T. Fan, submitted to AIChE J. for publication, 1982.
13. C. L. Chiang, An Introduction to Stochastic Processes and Their Applications, Krieger, New York, 1980.
14. L. T. Fan, L. S. Fan and R. Nassar, Chem. Eng. Sci. 34 (1979) 1172.
15. K. Ishida, Bull, Chem. Soc. Japan 33 (1960) 1030.
16. N. T. J. Bailey, The Elements of Stochastic Processes, Wiley, New York, 1964.
17. A. M. Mood, F. A. Graybill and D. C. Boes, Introduction to the Theory of Statistics, McGraw-Hill, New York, 1974.
18. J. G. van de Vusse, Chem. Eng. Sci. 17 (1962) 507.
19. R. V. Hogg and A. T. Craig, Introduction to Mathematical Statistics, Macmillan, Toronto, Canada, 1970.
20. G. F. Froment and K. B. Bischoff, Chemical Reactor Analysis and Design, Wiley, New York, 1979.

Fixed Bed Reactors, Flow and Chemical Reaction

V. Hlavacek

Department of Chemical Engineering
State University of New York at Buffalo
Buffalo, New York 14260

SUMMARY

The subject of transport and flow models describing packed bed behavior is a troubling one. One of the roots of the associated complications is represented by the fact that frequently the governing parameters are estimated from measurements performed in absence of a chemical reaction. Taking advantage of these measurements we decided either for the dispersion or for the cell model. There is no gross (i.e. long distance) mass backmixing in the bed, the depth of penetration of the longitudinal back diffusion is only a fraction of the pellet diameter and it diminishes rapidly with the increasing flow rate. The addition of the second derivative term to describe the dispersion effect creates a difficulty since this model predicts backmixing. A physically acceptable model for mass transfer must satisfy four requirements: (1) it must be a conservative system, (2) it must not allow back mixing, (3) it must predict a finite speed of signal propagation, (4) it must produce the correct asymptotic form.

The cell model with delay can satisfy these requirements. There exist experimental material that supports the cell model description. The situation for the axial heat dispersion is different. The back mixing model for heat is capable of reasonable describing such effect as creeping profiles, character of kinetic and diffusion regimes, prediction of ignition temperature, etc.

Based on these arguments, a reasonable description of a packed bed is the classical stirred tank array for axial mass transfer and a cell model with back mixing for axial heat transfer. Models of this complexity offer the possibility of explaining all known phenomena of multiplicity in a packed bed.

INTRODUCTION.

Owing to the recent experimental observations and increasing computational capability of current computers physical description of reaction processes occurring in fixed bed are much better understood than a decade ago. Models of great complexity have been proposed and compared with experimental data so that it is possible to simulate steady state and transient behavior of catalytic reactors and calculate qualitatively reliable results. The description of temperature and concentration fields which are triggered by a catalytic heterogeneous reaction may be expressed in terms of continuous or descrete models. A packed bed is an assembly of randomly arranged particles that are bathed by the reactant fluid which flows in a random manner around the pellets. The heterogeneous system consisting of the solid particles and reacting gas may be treated as though it were homogeneous and a hypothetical anisotropic continuum considered. It is supposed that the gross temperature and concentration profiles are smooth functions of the axial coordinate. On the other hand, each catalyst pellet along with the neighboring empty volumes may be considered as a small reactor. This description is sometimes referred to as a cell model. In models of this type the heterogeneous system is approximated by a sequence of cells which are connected in the direction of fluid flow. Data obtained from dispersion experiments have been used to predict the parameters of particular models. Unfortunately, the parameters are estimated from measurements performed in absence of a chemical reaction. A good agreement between experimental observations and fitted models does not necessarily mean that the model can be safely used for calculation of concentration and temperature fields in a packed bed and that all qualitative properties of reacting gas-solid systems can be predicted. Recent theoretical and experimental observations revealed that many models may strongly differ if an exothermic or autocatalytic reaction occurs in the system. These reactions may give rise to ignition and extinction phenomena, multiplicity pattern, creeping profiles and other wave phenomena. As a rule, the particular models are extremely sensitive in predicting these effects. Qualitative capability of forecasting particular situation is a very powerful tool and may be used to assess their physical reliability.

The goal of the paper is to make an attempt to evaluate different models of a packed bed based on their qualitative properties and to compare their behavior with accessible experimental data.

2. Models of the Fixed Bed.

In Table I. various models of packed bed are reported incorporating axial heat and mass dispersion and gas-to-pellet diffusion. Models A-D are based on the quasi-continuum approach while models E-H takes advantage of the cell description.

The model A, the simplest one takes into consideration only the convection mechanism of heat and mass transfer. It is sometimes referred to as a piston-flow model. There are no gas-to-particle transport resistances and the effect of dispersion processes is omitted. This description is frequently used for calculation of industrial packed bed adiabatic reactors for the nonadiabatic case the model is extended by considering radial transport of heat and mass. The model may work satisfactory for long packed bed reactors and high linear velocity in the packing. The piston flow description is usually capable of assessing the shapes of gross external fields of concentration and temperature as long as a unique steady state exists. The high parametric sensitivity of the model indicates the possibility of existence of multiple steady states [4]. The ignition point is usually very well described by the piston flow model [3] in terms of high parametric sensitivity. Absence of any feedback mechanism in the model precludes prediction of multiplicity pattern. This model cannot be recommended for transient calculations, the upstream moving profiles cannot be predicted.

The model B includes the dispersion effects. Frequently this model is called the dispersion model. While the piston flow model is formulated as an initial value problem, the dispersion model is represented by a boundary value problem. Evidently proper boundary conditions must be assigned. It is a general consensus that the Danckwerts boundary conditions are the most reliable. For a nonadiabatic tube packed with an inert aftersection, they must be modified. [5]. The model is capable of describing a rich spectrum of experimental observation. For adiabatic tubular exothermic systems, ignition-extinction effects can be predicted. For nonadiabatic reacting systems, three stable steady states have been calculated [6] and experimentally observed [3]. A vain attempt to locate experimentally three stable steady states in a bed packed by $Pt/A\ell_2O_3$ catalyst can be explained by an inappropriate use of Danckwerts boundary conditions at the reactor exit [6]. Modified Danckwerts boundary conditions give rise only to two stable steady states. The dispersion model can also explain experimental observations on creeping profiles, both situations of upstream and downstream moving fronts can be numerically simulated [9]. The dispersion model, however, failed to predict multiple propagating fronts [7] and experiments performed in an isothermal tubular reactor by Hegedus et al. [8].

The model C omits longitudinal heat conductivity and mass dispersion, gas-to-particle heat and mass transfer is considered. This description is represented by an initial value problem, the right-hand sides of the differential equations must be evaluated from the nonlinear algebraical equations. For an exothermic reaction, the nonlinear right-hand sides may possess multiplicity and discontinuous jumps of temperature and concentration can result. A detailed analysis of this model has been performed by Votruba et. al. [10]. They have shown that for certain values of parameters a number of steady states is possible. However, standard experimental start-up procedures would result only in two stable steady states. Puszynski [6] in his experimental study used heated wire placed at different axial positions to check the final asymptotic states. The rich spectrum of theoretically possible steady states was never observed experimentally. Apparently this model is able to simulate the observations made by Hegedus et. al. [8]. For the transient properties of this description, the conclusion drawn for model A are valid.

The two-phase model including axial heat conduction and mass dispersion belongs to the most complicated models. Computational results have shown that in a certain range of Damkohler numbers an infinite number of profiles may exist. A detailed analysis indicated that the majority of these solutions is unstable (saddle points) and hence only two steady states are possible [11]. Recently Vortmeyer [12] proposed a very clever method of reduction of the two phase model; assuming that the second derivatives of the temperature profiles in the gas phase and solid phase are the same two phase model can be reduced to a one-phase description. In the reduced model the coefficient of "effective thermal conductivity" containes the gas-to-solid heat transfer. This observation reveals that many transient heat transfer measurements in the packed bed may be disguised by solid-to-gas transfer. Vortmeyer analysis and our own results prove that this model is qualitatively equivalent to the model B.

The empty volume between the catalyst pellets can be considered as a perfectly mixed reactor. For an isothermal system, steady state conditions and first order reaction, the mixing cell model is a good approximation of dispersion phenomena occurring in a packed bed, for an infinite number of mixers the piston-flow description results. Various finite-stage models have been published. The four most important are discussed below-cell model, cell model with axial mixing, two-phase cell model and two phase cell model with axial mixing.

The mixing cell description (model E) may give rise for complex kinetics or non-isothermal conditions to a number of stable steady states [13]. For isothermal conditions or adiabatic conditions, we can easily display the solution of transport equations in a graphical way. The rich spectrum of possible multiple steady states has been observed experimentally by Hegedus et. al. Apparently, this paper provided a crucial prove of mass transport mechanism in packed bed. The Hiby's experiments [14] have shown that there is no gross (i.e. long distance) back mixing in the bed. Wicke [15] also indicated that the depth of penetration of the longitudinal back diffusion is only a fraction of the pellet diameter even at low Reynolds numbers and it diminishes rapidly with increasing flow rate. The addition of the second derivative term to describe the dispersion effects creates difficulty since the model predicts backmixing. Based on these experiments, we can conjecture that the mixing cell model is a physical sound description of a true mechanism of axial mass transfer.

When one considers interaction between neighboring stages, a mixing-cell model with axial backflow can be developed. Of course, to include a realistic description of heat transfer, this is a more realistic description. A systematic analysis of a cell model, using different mechanism for axial heat and mass transfer was performed by Sinkule et al. [16]. They indicated that realistic physical values for axial heat and mass transfer result in qualitative agreement with the one-phase dispersion model. For an adiabatic reactor only two-stable steady states exist. Recently, Deckwer used the backflow cell model to simulate a homogeneous reaction-oxidation of sodium thiosulfate by hydrogen peroxide. The measured and calculated steady-state and transient temperature profiles are in a good agreement. In addition, he made a comparison of regions of multiplicity calculated from the dispersion and backflow cell model and concluded that the agreement is satisfactory.

3. Dispersion Model or Cell Model?

Recently Sunaresan, Amundson and Aris [18], have shown that a physically acceptable model for mass transfer must satisfy four requirements: (1) it must be a conservative system; (2) it must not allow back mixing; (3) it must predict a finite speed of signal propagation; (4) it must produce the correct asymptotic form.

They have shown that the cell model with delay can satisfy all these requirements.

A very important paper which supports the cell model concept is that of Hegedus et. al. [8]. These authors observed experimentally a large number of steady states. In a tubular isothermal reactor in these experiments the reaction kinetics along with mass transfer inside the catalyst may produce an S-shaped curve and leads to multiple steady states in a single reactor. As a result, in an array of stirred tanks a number of steady states may exist. However, using this reaction rate expression in a classical dispersion model only two steady states would result. This is also a strong support for the Wicke's suggestion that the depth of the longitudinal back mass diffusion is of the magnitude of one pellet diameter.

The situation for the axial heat dispersion is different. Using the one-phase backflow cell model we can show that already a weak thermal back interaction eliminates the complex multiplicity pattern [16], and that only two stable steady states survive. This observation is in agreement with the fact that for adiabatic conditions only two stable steady-state profiles were observed. The backmixing model for heat is capable of reasonable describing such effects as creeping profiles, multiplicity, types of ignition-extinction loop, etc.

Based on these arguments, it is likely that for a physically sound description of a packed bed reactors the classical stirred tank array for axial mass transfer and cell model with backmixing ought to be used. Models of this complexity offer the possibility of explaining all known experimental phenomena of multiplicity in packed beds.

TABLE I. Transport Models Describing Heat and Mass Transfer in Packed Catalytic Reactors

	Specification	Mass Balance	Heat Balance
A.	piston flow model	$-v \frac{dc_i}{dl} + R(c_i,T) = 0$	$-v\rho c_p \frac{dT}{dl} + (-\Delta H)R(c_i,T) = 0$
B.	dispersion model	$D_e \frac{d^2c_i}{dl^2} - v \frac{dc_i}{dl} + R(c_i,T) = 0$	$k_e \frac{d^2T}{dl^2} - v\rho c_p \frac{dT}{dl} + (-\Delta H)R(c_i,T) = 0$
C.	piston flow model with external transfer	$-u \frac{dc_i}{dl} + k_c a(c_i - c_{is}) = 0$ $k_c a(c_i - c_{is}) - R(c_{is},T_s) = 0$	$-u\rho c_p \frac{dT}{dl} + \alpha\, a(T_s - T) = 0$ $\alpha a(T_s - T) - (-\Delta H)R(c_{is},T_s) = 0$
D.	dispersion model with external transfer	$D_e \frac{d^2c_i}{dl^2} - u \frac{dc_i}{dl} + k_c a\,(c_i - c_{is}) = 0$ $k_c a(c_i - c_{is}) - R(c_{is}, T_s) = 0$	$k_e \frac{d^2T}{dl^2} - u\rho c_p \frac{dT}{dl} + \alpha a(T_s - T) = 0$ $\alpha a(T_s - T) - (-\Delta H)R(c_{is},T_s) = 0$
E.	cell model	$vS(c_i^k - c_i^{k-1}) + V\,R\,(c_i^k, T^k) = 0$	$v\rho c_p S(T^k - T^{k-1}) + V(-\Delta H)R(c_i^k,T^k) = 0$
F.	cell model with axial mixing	$S[v(c^k - c_i^{k-1}) - q(c_i^{k+1} - c_i^k)] + VR(c_i^k,T^k) = 0$	$\rho c_p\, S[v(T^k - T^{k-1}) - q(T^{k+1} - T^k)]$ $+V(-\Delta H)R(c_i^k, T^k) = 0$
G.	two-phase cell model	$uS(c_i^k - c_i^{k-1}) + Vk_c a(c_i^k - c_i^{k-1}) = 0$ $k_c a(c_i^k - c_{is}^k) - R(c_{is}, T_s^k) = 0$	$u\rho c_p S(T^k - T^{k-1}) + \alpha a V(T_s^k - T^k) = 0$ $\alpha a(T_s^k - T^k) - (-\Delta H)R(c_{is}^k,T^k) = 0$
H.	two-phase cell model with axial mixing	$S[u(c_i^k - c_i^{k-1}) - q(c_i^{k+1} - c_i^k)] +$ $+ Vk_c a(c_i^k - c_{is}^{k-1}) = 0$ $k_c a(c_i^k - c_{is}^k) - R(c_{is}^k, T_s^k) = 0$	$\rho c_p S[u(T^k - T^{k-1}) - q(T^{k+1} - T^k)] +$ $+ V\alpha a(T_s^k - T^k) = 0$ $\alpha a(T_s^k - T^k) - (-\Delta H)R(c_{is}^k,T_s^k) = 0$

NOMENCLATURE

a external surface of catalyst

A pre-exponential factor

c_i, c_{is} concentration of component i in gas phase, on catalyst surface

c_p specific heat

D_e effective diffusivity

E activation energy

$(-\Delta H)$ heat of reaction

k, K rate and equilibrium constants

k_c mass transfer coefficient

k_e effective axial thermal conductivity

l axial coordinate

L length of catalytic bed

q backflow velocity

S cross sectional area

T, T_s, T_o temperature of gas, solid phase, inlet gas.

u mean interstitial velocity

v gas velocity based on empty tube

V volume of mixer in cascade

Y outlet conversion

α heat transfer coefficient

ρ gas density

REFERENCES

(1.) Hlavacek V. and Votruba J.; Steady State Operation of Fixed Bed Reactors and Monolithic Structures, in Chemical Reactor Theory. A Review (Eds. L. Lapidus and N. R. Amundson) Prentice Hall (1977).

(2.) Hlavacek V. and van Rompay P.: Chem. Eng. Sci. 36, (1981) 1587.

(3.) Hlavacek V. and Votruba J.: Experimental Study of Multiple Steady States in Adiabatic Catalytic Systems, Advances in Chemistry Series 133, (American Chem. Society 1974) p. 545.

(4.) Puszynski J; Snita D; Hlavacek V. and Hofmann H.:Chem. Eng. Sci. 36, (1981) 1605.

(5.) Hlavacek V., Holodniok M., Sinkule J., Kubicek M., Chem. Eng. Commun. 3, (1979), 451.

(6.) Puszynski J.: Ph.D. Thesis, Inst. of Chem. Technology Prague, (1980).

(7.) Puszynski J. and Hlavacek V.: Chem. Eng. Sci. 35, (1980) 1769.

(8.) Hegedus L. L., Oh S. E. and Baron K.: AICHE Jour. 23, (1977) 632.

(9.) Puszynski J. and Hlavacek V.: Chem. Eng. Sci. in press.

(10.) Votruba J., Kubicek M. and Hlavacek V.: Chem. Eng. Sci. 29, (1974) 2333.

(11.) Hlavacek V. and Holodniok M.: in preparation.

(12.) Vortmeyer D. and Schaefer R. J.: Chem. Eng. Sci. 29, (1974) 485.

(13.) Sinkule J., Hlavacek V., Votruba J. and Tvrdik, I.: Chem. Eng. Sci. 29, (1974), 689.

(14.) Hiby J. W.: Interaction between Fluids and Particles, p. 312, Inst. Chem. Engrs. London, England (1953).

(15.) Wicke E.: Adv. Chem. Ser. 148, p. 75, Am. Chem. Soc., Washington, D.C. (1975).

(16.) Sinkule J., Hlavacek V., and Votruba J.: Chem. Eng. Sci. 31, (1976) 31.

(17.) Deckwer W. D.: Chem. Eng. Jour. 8, (1974) 135.

(18.) Sundaresan S., Amundson N. R. and Aris R.: AICHE Jour. 26 (1980) 529.

A Spectral-Theoretic View of Axial Dispersion Models

S. J. Parulekar, D. Ramkrishna

School of Chemical Engineering, Purdue University, West Lafayette, Indiana 47907, U.S.A.

SUMMARY

Axial dispersion models are a useful implement for the analysis of many continuous flow systems because of their capacity to amend the predictions of the plug flow model without loss of the latter's unidimensional simplicity. For tubes of finite length, an issue of debate has been the appropriateness of the boundary conditions (generally attributed to Danckwerts). Paradoxically most arguments in defense of the boundary conditions in the steady state imply their impropriety for transient analysis. The present work views the situation of chemical reaction (or separation) with linear rates in an axially dispersed tube flow as occurring in a finite section (such as in a bed of catalyst particles) sandwiched between two (mathematically) semi-infinite flow sections without reaction. The formulation submits to an elegant spectral-theoretic analysis displaying a mixture of discrete and continuous spectra as dispersion coefficients are varied in the reaction and appended sections. The practical utility of such spectra is demonstrated to be in the analysis of axial dispersion problems free from the use of the Danckwerts boundary conditions and in the identification of dispersion parameters from experimental data on residence time distributions.

1. INTRODUCTION

The axial dispersion model has been a popular feature of chemical engineering analysis. It has been used in a diverse variety of dispersion problems, **in analysis** of tubular chemical reactors, and in numerous applications of continuous separation processes. Its main attractiveness is its power to fruitfully amend the predictions of the plug flow model while still retaining the latter's unidimensional simplicity. A further factor that evinced interest in axial dispersion models is the early work of *Taylor* [1] that established the reducibility of important two dimensional situations of convective-diffusion of a solute in a solvent stream to one dimensional convective-dispersion problems. Of particular interest to the present paper is the problem of a solute undergoing a first order chemical reaction while being axially dispersed in a solvent stream in plug flow through a tube. Further, the tube is assumed to be of finite length, a constraint that has presented the treatment of axial dispersion models with a perplexing problem in regard to the appropriate boundary conditions. The basic difficulty in the formulation of the boundary conditions lies in the dependence of events at the boundary on those that prevail beyond, which are frequently unknown or difficult to model without substantial loss of simplicity. The most attractive solution to this problem thus far has been the use of boundary conditions generally attributed to *Danckwerts*[2] although more recently *Aris*[3] has traced their origin further back to a paper by *Langmuir*[4]. Since the publication of Danckwerts however, there has been considerable discussion of his boundary conditions in the literature [5-7], mostly with a view to assess the conditions of their validity. The bulk of these attempts consist in appending a semi-infinite upstream section at the inlet to the tube and a semi-infinite downstream section to the outlet. Dispersion (but no reaction) is presumed to persist in the appended sections with dispersion coefficients that may or may not be identical to that in the reaction section. The "practical" lengths of the appended sections are however dependent on the magnitudes of the dispersion coefficients in these sections, virtually vanishing when negligible dispersion occurs. Much of the discussion has been confined to steady state problems for which, paradoxically enough, the actual situation in the appended section is quite immaterial to what transpires in the reaction section as long as the Danckwerts boundary conditions are implied. There is little that has been said of the *transient* situation for which the foregoing arguments in essence imply the invalidity of the Danckwerts boundary conditions, except of course when there is no dispersion in the appended sections.

Transient analyses of axially dispersed systems have generally employed the Danckwerts boundary conditions[2,7,8]. Arguments in support have depended on, for example, not permitting the solute to disperse out of the medium (such as a porous bed) at the entrance where it is introduced while at the other end a zero axial grandient prevents the occurrence of an interior maximum or minimum in solute concentration. If the dispersing medium such as a porous bed is preceded by an inlet section, there is perhaps not much reason to forbid a dispersive escape *out* at the entrance. Likewise, the zero gradient boundary condition at the exit is not *necessary* to prevent interior concentration extrema. Furthermore, in reactive systems in particular, there is no reason why dispersion in the outlet section should not give rise to an interior extremum. Inspite of the foregoing objections, the Danckwerts boundary conditions have been valuable for transient analysis in that their implications, although not essential, are in all likelihood nearly satisfied. The main advantage of the boundary conditions is that it retains the "finite domain" nature of the boundary value problem.

The discomfiture that pervades the residual uncertainty behind the appropriateness of the Danckwerts boundary conditions has been most candidly expressed by *Amundson*[8]; he observes that "...the imposition of the zero gradient boundary condition at s=1 (reactor outlet) leaves one with an uncomfortable feeling for it seems to be artificial in the sense of its physical realization...but the fact remains that there seems to be no boundary condition which is any more reasonable at the outlet..." Indeed Amundson's concern is expressed pointedly at the exit boundary condition. In addressing the transient problem with the Danckwerts boundary conditions, one need only specify the initial state in the reactor section since the situation 'outside' of this section is irrelevant to the analysis. It should therefore be evident that any departures of predictions on the foregoing basis from actual behavior should depend on the initial condition in the 'inlet' and 'outlet' sections.

Amundson[8] points out that the major difficulty in appending semi-infinite inlet or outlet sections for transient analysis lies in the numerical solution to which one is constrained in dealing with nonlinear reactor problems. While this is certainly true in dealing with nonlinearities, *linear* problems present some interesting possibilities that have not been explored in the past. Our objective in this paper is to draw on the spectral theory of linear operators to produce new integral transforms to deal with axial dispersion models accounting for semi-infinite inlet and outlet sections where the dispersion coefficient may or may not be the same as that in the reactor section.

Basically our strategy is as follows. The finite length tubular reactor is viewed as one of infinite length with semi-infinite inlet and outlet sections. Reaction is presumed to occur in the entire tube with a rate 'constant' which varies with axial position in a discontinuous manner; it remains constant within the reactor section and *vanishes* outside it, i.e., in the inlet and outlet sections. Thus a *single* equation is obtained in the reactant (or product) concentration which is subject to the following constraints. The concentration and the flux must be continuous everywhere and especially at the entrance and exit planes. Further, the concentration must be bounded at ∞ and must assume asymptotically the feed concentration at $-\infty$. We have thus an equation, which holds in the infinite interval $(-\infty, \infty)$ to be solved satisfying the additional stipulations just mentioned.

Linear differential boundary value problems on an infinite interval may be solved by the method of Fourier transforms only when constant coefficients are involved. In the present case, although the rate constant is a constant coefficient in the reaction section, its vanishing in the inlet and outlet sections essentially yields a situation with non-constant coefficient in the infinite domain. Thus the Fourier transform cannot be used to solve the present problem. We construct in this work new integral transforms that can be used to obtain solutions to the transient axial dispersion problem. The construction of these transforms requires the spectral theory of second order differential operators and the reader unfamiliar with this area may regard our end result as a substitute for the Fourier transform. Thus functions defined on the infinite interval (such as the concentration distribution) may be *transformed* to corresponding functions in the transform variable. Similarly, the transforms can be *inverted* to recover the original functions. The strategy of solution will consist in transforming the differential equation in concentration, solving for the transform and subsequently inverting it to obtain the concentration distribution.

In the following sections, we will present the equations for the transient axial dispersion problem with chemical reaction within a finite domain, in a particular form suitable for the application of our transform; we will then present the transform, its inversion formula and some of its important properties. The details of the evolution of the transform are covered in other works by us. It turns out that the integral transforms have strikingly varying properties depending on the Peclet numbers in the reactor and appended sections and the Damkohler number. These properties are discussed in a separate section on the integral transforms. Once the transforms are available, the solution of the transient problem is virtually instantaneous. Finally, we include numerical calculations of transient behavior of axially dispersed systems using the above transforms and compare the results with those obtained using the Danckwerts boundary conditions.

2. FORMULATION OF EQUATIONS

The reactor is assumed to stretch along the axial coordinate z with the reaction section of half-length L between z=-L and z=L. The first order reaction

$$A \xrightarrow{k} \text{Products}$$

occurs in the reaction section. The feed stream is presumed to enter with concentration C_f of the reactant at $z=-\infty$. The dispersion coefficients in the inlet section ($-\infty < z < -L$), the reaction section ($-L \leq z \leq L$) and the outlet section ($L < z < \infty$) are denoted D_-, D and D_+ respectively. The dispersion coefficient in each section is assumed to be constant. In the reaction section, the concentration C satisfies the differential equation

$$D \frac{\partial^2 C}{\partial z^2} - v \frac{\partial C}{\partial z} - kC = \frac{\partial C}{\partial t} \quad , \quad -L < z < L \quad , \quad t > 0 \tag{1}$$

In the inlet section we have

$$D_- \frac{\partial^2 C}{\partial z^2} - v \frac{\partial C}{\partial z} = \frac{\partial C}{\partial t} \quad , \quad -\infty < z < -L \quad , \quad t > 0 \tag{2}$$

while in the outlet section C satisfies

$$D_+ \frac{\partial^2 C}{\partial z^2} - v \frac{\partial C}{\partial z} = \frac{\partial C}{\partial t} \quad , \quad L < z < \infty \quad , \quad t > 0 \tag{3}$$

The entrance condition is expressed by

$$\lim_{z \to -\infty} C(z,t) = C_f \tag{4}$$

At $z=\infty$, the concentration C must be bounded. Furthermore, we must have continuity of concentration and flux everywhere and in particular at the entrance and exit planes. Thus

$$\lim_{z \to L+0} - D_+ \frac{\partial C}{\partial z} = \lim_{z \to L-0} - D \frac{\partial C}{\partial z} \tag{5a}$$

$$\lim_{z \to -L-0} - D_- \frac{\partial C}{\partial z} = \lim_{z \to -L+0} - D \frac{\partial C}{\partial z} \tag{5b}$$

The crux of our approach is to reformulate the above equations into a form that fits the mold of the spectral theory of second order differential operators. To accomplish this, it is convenient to switch to the following dimensionless quantities.

$$Pe \equiv \frac{Lv}{D}, \quad Pe_- \equiv \frac{Lv}{D_-}, \quad Pe_+ \equiv \frac{Lv}{D_+}, \quad Pe_o \equiv \min\{Pe_-, Pe_+\}, \quad Da \equiv \frac{kL^2}{D}$$

The foregoing dimensionless parameters arise on defining the dimensionless variables

$$\chi \equiv \frac{C_f - C}{C_f}, \quad \tau \equiv \frac{Dt}{L^2}\frac{Pe_o}{Pe}$$

$$x \equiv \begin{cases} \dfrac{Pe_-}{Pe}\dfrac{z}{L} - \left(1 - \dfrac{Pe_-}{Pe}\right) & -\infty < z < -L \\[2ex] \dfrac{z}{L} & -L < z < L \\[2ex] \dfrac{Pe_+}{Pe}\dfrac{z}{L} + \left(1 - \dfrac{Pe_+}{Pe}\right) & L < z < \infty \end{cases} \tag{6}$$

The dimensionless axial coordinate (6) converts the continuity conditions (5a) and (5b) on the flux to continuity of the dimensionless axial *derivative* of the dimensionless concentration χ at $x = \pm 1$. The boundary value problem may now be cast in the succinct form

$$\frac{1}{r(x)}\left[- \frac{\partial^2 \chi}{\partial x^2} + Pe \frac{\partial \chi}{\partial x} - \{H(x+1) - H(x-1)\}\, Da(1-\chi)\right] = - \frac{\partial \chi}{\partial \tau} \tag{7}$$

where H(x) is the Heaviside step function defined by

$$H(x) = \begin{cases} 0 & x < 0 \\ 1 & x \geq 0 \end{cases} \tag{8}$$

Further the function r(x) is given by

$$r(x) = [1 - H(x+1)]\frac{Pe_o}{Pe_-} + [H(x+1) - H(x-1)]\frac{Pe_o}{Pe} + H(x-1)\frac{Pe_o}{Pe_+} \tag{9}$$

when the dispersion coefficients D, D_+ and D_- are equal then we clearly have r(x)=1. The boundary condition at $x=-\infty$ given by (4) becomes

$$\lim_{x \to -\infty} \chi(x,\tau) = 0 \tag{10}$$

At $x=\infty$ we demand that

$$\lim_{x \to \infty} \chi(x,\tau) < \infty \tag{11}$$

The initial condition for χ may be written as

$$\chi(x,0) = F(x) \quad , \quad -\infty < x < \infty \tag{12}$$

Note in particular that it is necessary to state the initial concentration distribution not only within the reactor but also outside it. This issue is an important one in the analysis presented in this work and we shall have more to say on it at a later stage.

The differential equation (7), together with continuity requirements on χ and $\frac{\partial\chi}{\partial x}$ everywhere in $(-\infty,\infty)$, boundary condition (10), boundedness condition (11), and initial condition (12) represents the complete statement of the mathematical problem.

Some limiting cases are of interest. One could accommodate, for example, the case of zero dispersion in one of the appended sections. If $D_-=0$, then $Pe_-=\infty$ and the Danckwerts boundary condition will hold at x=-1. In this case the inlet section becomes unnecessary and we have a semi-infinite domain for the mathematical problem. Similarly, if we let $D_+=0$, we have $Pe_+=\infty$ and the outlet section may be eliminated with the zero gradient boundary condition at x=1; again we have a semi-infinite domain. If $D_+=D_-=0$, then we have the usual finite domain problem with the Danckwerts boundary conditions as normally stipulated at the ends.

There are two other limiting cases that are very useful. These occur when either D_+ or D_- become infinitely large which corresponds to the situation of 'perfect' mixing in the appended sections. Since the appended volumes considered above are infinite, a value of $D_-=\infty$ would imply that $\chi=0$ at x=-1 for all times τ and only a minor change in analysis is called for. On the other hand, if $D_+=\infty$ we have the physically unrealistic situation of χ taking on a fixed value at all times at the reactor outlet x=1. Thus the limits of infinite dispersion coefficients in either of the appended sections of *infinite* volume are somewhat uninteresting. But a situation that indeed is interesting arises when the appended section is of finite (but open) volume in which the fluid is well-stirred before emerging from it. This occurs when the reactor is fed from (or discharges into) a continuous well-stirred tank. Situations of this kind have been dealt with by *Ramkrishna and Amundson*[9]. However, Ramkrishna and Amundson assume the Danckwerts boundary condition at the end where the stirred tank is not present. This assumption is relaxed in this work by the procedure of appending semi-infinite sections. We now identify the relevant equations.

Stirred Tank Before or After Tubular Reactor

Equation (1), which holds for the reaction section, remains the same for this situation. For the case where the stirred tank precedes the reactor, we assume a semi-infinite outlet section with a dispersion coefficient D_+. Thus Equations (3) and (5a) also hold here while at z=-L a mass balance in the stirred tank yields

$$v\, C_f = \lim_{z \to -L+0} \left[v\, C - D \frac{\partial C}{\partial z} + \frac{V_-}{A} \frac{\partial C}{\partial t} \right] \qquad (13)$$

where V_- is the volume of the stirred tank in which no chemical reaction is assumed to take place. A is the reactor cross-section. When V_- vanishes, condition (13) is the same as the Danckwerts boundary condition at the entrance.

When the tubular reactor discharges into the stirred tank of volume V_+, Equations (1), (2), (4) and (5b) hold while at the reactor outlet we must have

$$\lim_{z \to L-0} \left[\frac{V_+}{A} \frac{\partial C}{\partial t} + D \frac{\partial C}{\partial z} \right] = 0 \qquad (14)$$

when V_+ is allowed to vanish the zero gradient boundary condition is recovered.

In switching to dimensionless variables, we only refer to those that need some alteration for the two cases under study, viz., the case where the stirred tank precedes the reactor which we refer to as *Case 1* and that where the reactor discharges into a stirred tank referred to as *Case 2*.

For *Case 1*, the independent variables are non-dimensionalized as

$$x = \begin{cases} \dfrac{z}{L} & -L \le z \le L \\ \dfrac{Pe_+}{Pe}\left(\dfrac{z}{L} - 1\right) + 1 & L \le z < \infty \end{cases} \qquad (15)$$

$$\tau = \frac{t\, v\, Pe_+}{L\, Pe^2} \qquad (16)$$

The dimensionless parameters which must be restated or added are

$$r_+(x) = \begin{cases} Pe_+/Pe & -1 < x < 1 \\ 1 & 1 < x < \infty \end{cases} \tag{17}$$

$$g_- \equiv \frac{V_- Pe_+}{AL\ Pe}$$

Thus the dimensionless boundary-initial value problem may be stated as

$$\frac{1}{r_+(x)} \left[- \frac{\partial^2 \chi}{\partial x^2} + Pe \frac{\partial \chi}{\partial x} - Da\ Y(x)\ (1-\chi)\right] = - \frac{\partial \chi}{\partial \tau}, \quad -1 < x < \infty, \quad \tau > 0 \tag{18}$$

where we have introduced the abbreviation

$$Y(x) = H(x+1) - H(x-1) \tag{19}$$

The dimensionless version of the boundary condition at the reactor inlet is given by

$$\frac{1}{g_-}\left[\frac{\partial \chi}{\partial x} - Pe\ \chi\right] = \frac{\partial \chi}{\partial \tau}, \quad x = -1, \quad \tau > 0 \tag{20}$$

In addition χ and $\frac{\partial \chi}{\partial x}$ are continuous in $[-1,\infty]$. Condition (11) must also hold. The initial condition must not only include the reactor and the outlet sections but also the stirred tank (see for example *Ramkrishna and Amundson*[9]). Thus

$$\chi(x,0) = F(x) \qquad -1 < x < \infty \tag{21}$$

$$\chi(-1,0) = F_1 \tag{22}$$

where F_1 is the initial dimensionless concentration in the tank.

For *Case 2* which puts the stirred tank after the reactor the dimensionless variables are

$$x = \begin{cases} \frac{Pe_-}{Pe}\left(\frac{z}{L} + 1\right) - 1 & -\infty < z \leq -L \\ \frac{z}{L} & -L \leq z \leq L \end{cases} \tag{23}$$

$$\tau = \frac{t\ v\ Pe_-}{L\ Pe^2} \tag{24}$$

while the parameters which must be added or changed are

$$r_-(x) = \begin{cases} 1 & -\infty < x < -1 \\ Pe_-/Pe & -1 < x < 1 \end{cases} \tag{25}$$

$$g_+ = \frac{V_+ \, Pe_-}{AL \, Pe}$$

The dimensionless boundary-initial value problem becomes

$$\frac{1}{r_-(x)} \left[- \frac{\partial^2 \chi}{\partial x^2} + Pe \frac{\partial \chi}{\partial x} - Da \; Y(x) \; (1-\chi)\right] = - \frac{\partial \chi}{\partial \tau} \quad , \quad -\infty < x < 1 \quad , \quad \tau > 0 \qquad (26)$$

At the reactor outlet we must have

$$\frac{1}{g_+} \frac{\partial \chi}{\partial x} = - \frac{\partial \chi}{\partial \tau} \quad , \quad x = 1, \; \tau > 0 \qquad (27)$$

The entrance condition (10) applies in addition. Further χ and $\frac{\partial \chi}{\partial x}$ must be continuous in $(-\infty,1]$. The initial condition may be stated as

$$\chi(x, 0) = F(x) \qquad -\infty < x < 1 \qquad (28)$$

$$\chi(1, 0) = F_1 \qquad (29)$$

which again states the concentration in the tank in addition to the concentration distribution in the inlet and reactor sections.

We have thus identified the dimensionless reactor equations for all the situations of interest to us. Some minor modifications are possible (and in some cases relevant) which introduce no special difficulties of a mathematical nature. Consequently, they will not be dealt with here. As mentioned earlier, the form of the dimensionless equations has been inspired by the applicability of the spectral theory of singular second order differential operators. It should be clear that the use of standard techniques such as the method of infinite Fourier (or Laplace) transforms is not possible because of the non-constant nature of the coefficients in the differential equations (7), (18), or (26) either due to variation in the dispersion coefficients or reaction rate 'constants'. Standard transforms such as Fourier or Laplace transforms are in fact spectral representations of certain differential operators on infinite domains and can be used only in a restricted variety of problems. The approach in this work is to construct integral transforms using the machinery of the spectral theory of self-adjoint differential operators (see for example *Jorgens*[10] or *Titchmarsh*[11]). It will turn out that the resulting transforms (together with their inversion formulae) will naturally solve the steady and unsteady state problems in axially dispersed systems. Further, they may also be used for solving other multi-dimensional dispersion problems. In the next section we present the integral transforms for the different situations considered herein.

3. INTEGRAL TRANSFORMS

As pointed out earlier, the integral transforms here arise from spectral representations of certain self-adjoint operators associated with the boundary value problems. We present in the Appendix some theorems which establish the existance of suitable spectral representations of the operators concerned. The actual construction of the transforms and their inversion formulae is somewhat tedious and the reader is referred to *Parulekar*[12] for such details. We present here only the final results. However, before we present them, we shall describe the associated differential operators. Let us first observe that in defining a differential operator one must specify the formal differential expression along with the subspace of functions on which it acts. Accordingly we first take up the operator for the situation in which the reactor is appended with semi-infinite inlet and outlet sections where dispersion occurs without reaction. In view of the limiting cases of zero dispersion in either of the appended sections the operators are defined with minor differences in these cases. In order to distinguish between the various cases we use different symbols for the differential operators. The family of differential operators encountered here are most appropriately described as the *axial dispersion operators*.

For the most general situation of finite non-zero dispersion in the appended sections we let

$$A \equiv \frac{1}{r(x)}\left[-\frac{d^2}{dx^2} + Pe\,\frac{d}{dx} + Y(x)\,Da\right], \quad -\infty < x < \infty \tag{30}$$

where r(x) is given by (9). The differential expression A is constrained to act on a subspace D(A), called the domain of A, defined by

$$D(A) = \{u(x): \lim_{x \to \pm\infty} u(x)\, e^{-Pe\, x} = 0, \quad u \text{ and } u' \text{ continuous in } (-\infty,\infty)\} \tag{31}$$

For certain technical reasons, we have constrained the behavior of the function u at infinity different from conditions (10) and (11). Condition (10) is automatically implied and although (11) is physically reasonable and hence the solution will actually reflect it. From a mathematical viewpoint even a suitably controlled growth rate can be tolerated. This is reflected in the domain D(A) in Equation (31). The operator $\tilde{A} = \{A, D(A)\}$ comprises both A and its domain D(A). In Section 4, we represent the boundary-initial value problem of interest succinctly in terms of the operator $\tilde{A}$.

When $D_- = 0$ we let

$$A_+ = \frac{1}{r_+(x)}\left[-\frac{d^2}{dx^2} + Pe\,\frac{d}{dx} + Y(x)\,Da\right] \quad -1 < x < \infty \tag{32}$$

where $r_+(x)$ is given by (17). The domain $D(A_+)$ is given by

$$D(A_+) = \{u(x):\ u'(-1) = Pe\ u(-1),\ \lim_{x \to \infty} u(x)e^{-Pe\ x} = 0,\ u \text{ and } u' \text{ continuous in } [-1,\infty)\} \tag{33}$$

where the reader must particularly notice the homogeneous Danckwerts boundary condition at x=-1. The operator $\underset{\sim}{A}_+ = \{A_+, D(A_+)\}$ may be used in defining the boundary-initial value problem for this case.

For the situation of $D_+=0$ we define

$$A_- = \frac{1}{r_-(x)} [- \frac{d^2}{dx^2} + Pe \frac{d}{dx} + Y(x)\ Da],\ -\infty < x < 1 \tag{34}$$

where $r_-(x)$ is defined by (25). The domain $D(A_-)$ is given by

$$D(A_-) = \{u(x):\ \lim_{x \to -\infty} u(x)e^{-Pe\ x} = 0,\ u'(1) = 0,\ u \text{ and } u' \text{ continuous in } (-\infty,1]\} \tag{35}$$

so that $\underset{\sim}{A}_- = \{A_-, D(A_-)\}$. Note here the zero gradient boundary condition satisfied by functions belonging to $D(A_-)$. As in the other cases the operator $\underset{\sim}{A}_-$ can be used to concisely represent the axial dispersion problem for this case.

In the limiting cases which arise by appending before or after the reactor continuous well-stirred tanks, we define, following *Ramkrishna and Amundson*,[9] the matrix differential expression for *Case 1*.

$$A^s_+ = \begin{bmatrix} \frac{1}{r_+(x)} [- \frac{d^2}{dx^2} + Pe \frac{d}{dx} + Da\ Y(x)] & 0 \\ - \frac{1}{g_-} [\frac{d}{dx} - Pe]_{x=-1} & 0 \end{bmatrix} \tag{36}$$

which acts on vectors $\begin{bmatrix} u(x) \\ u_1 \end{bmatrix}$. More specifically, the domain of A^s_+ is given by

$$D(A^s_+) = \{\begin{bmatrix} u(x) \\ u_1 \end{bmatrix}:\ u(-1) = u_1,\ \lim_{x \to \infty} u(x)e^{-Pe\ x} = 0,\ u \text{ and } u' \text{ continuous in } [-1,\infty)\} \tag{37}$$

so that $\underset{\sim}{A}^s_+ = \{A^s_+, D(A^s_+)\}$.

For *Case 2* we define the matrix differential expression

$$A^s_- \quad \begin{bmatrix} \frac{1}{r_-(x)} [- \frac{d^2}{dx^2} + Pe \frac{d}{dx} + Da\ Y(x)] & 0 \\ \frac{1}{g_+} \frac{d}{dx}\Big|_{x=1} & 0 \end{bmatrix} \tag{38}$$

which operates on vectors $\begin{bmatrix} u(x) \\ u_1 \end{bmatrix}$ belonging to the domain below.

$$D(A^s_-) = \{\begin{bmatrix} u(x) \\ u_1 \end{bmatrix} : \; u(1) = u_1, \; \lim_{x \to -\infty} u(x)e^{-Pe\,x} = 0, \text{ u and u' continuous in } (-\infty,1]\} \tag{39}$$

Thus $\underset{\sim}{A}^s_- = \left\{A^s_-, \, D(A^s_-)\right\}$ represents the differential operator of interest.

It is proved in the Appendix that the operators $\underset{\sim}{A}$, $\underset{\sim}{A}_+$, $\underset{\sim}{A}_-$, $\underset{\sim}{A}^s_+$, $\underset{\sim}{A}^s_-$, are self-adjoint when suitable inner products are used.

Integral transforms

The reader will be familiar with finite Fourier transforms which arise in the solution of heat conduction or mass diffusion problems in bounded slabs, cylinders, etc. Here the transform of a function is the result of integrating it over the interval of interest with the jth eigenfunction (corresponding to the jth eigenvalue) of the heat conduction or diffusion operator. The inversion formula recovers the function from its transform by *summing* the product of the transform and the corresponding eigenfunction over *all* (normalized) eigenfunctions. Similarly in dealing with heat conduction or mass diffusion in infinite slabs, cylinders, etc., one encounters infinite Fourier transforms where the transform of a function again involves integrating it over the infinite interval with any eigenfunction. There occurs in this case a *continuous spectrum* of *real* eigenvalues and eigenfunctions and the inversion of the transform requires *integrating* (instead of summing) its product with the corresponding eigenfunction over *all* eigenfunctions. This is the essence of all transforms and their inversions. When discrete eigenvalues are involved the inversion is accomplished by summing and when a continuous spectrum of eigenvalues occurs the inversion requires integrating.

Now in the operators of interest here, it turns out that there may occur both discrete (or proper) eigenvalues and continuous (at times called improper) eigenvalues. Thus the inversion of the transform would require *summing* over the discrete range of eigenvalues *and integrating* over the continuous range of eigenvalues. The continuous spectrum is always present here but whether or not discrete eigenvalues occur depends on the relative values of the parameters involved. We present the different situations with respect to the character of the spectrum for the different operators in tabular form listing the number of discrete eigenvalues. In view of certain differences between the set of operators $\underset{\sim}{A}$, $\underset{\sim}{A}_+$ and $\underset{\sim}{A}_-$, and the set of operators $\underset{\sim}{A}^s_+$ and $\underset{\sim}{A}^s_-$, we will deal with the two sets separately in presenting their associated integral transforms.

In what follows, we let $\underset{\sim}{L}$ be any of the operators $\underset{\sim}{A}$, $\underset{\sim}{A}_+$ and $\underset{\sim}{A}_-$. We assume that there are N eigenvalues, the jth eigenvalue λ_j being associated with the normalized eigenfunction $u_j(x)\,e^{\frac{1}{2}Pex}$ where $u_j(x)$ will be spelled out for each of the above operators in Appendix II. In addition there is a continuous spectrum which consists of all real numbers $\lambda > \frac{Pe^2}{4}$, represented by $\lambda = \omega^2 + \frac{Pe^2}{4}$ where ω can take on any real value. The eigenfunction (sometimes referred to as the improper eigenfunction) corresponding to the parameter ω is represented $u(x,\omega)$. In our calculations, considerations based on algebra have either led to a complex form for $u_j(x)$ and $u(x,\omega)$ for some operators or real form for others. In order to encompass both forms within a single format the integral transform will be defined featuring the *complex conjugate* of the eigenfunction (with the understanding that a real form will have itself for its conjugate) while the inversion formula will feature the eigenfunction.

The transform applies to any function f(x) such that

$$\int_a^b w(x)\ |f(x)|^2\ e^{-Pe\ x}\ dx < \infty \tag{40}$$

where the limits a and b depend on the operator in the set $\underset{\sim}{A}$, $\underset{\sim}{A}_+$ and $\underset{\sim}{A}_-$. These limits are presented in Table 3.1 below which also shows the *weight* function $w(x)$ to be used in (40)-(42). Condition (40) is indeed satisfied by functions of practical interest here. Since the transform must be defined with respect to eigenfunctions corresponding to both discrete and continuous eigenvalues we write

$$\bar{f}(\omega) = \int_a^b w(x)\ u^*(x,\omega)\ e^{-\frac{1}{2}Pe\ x}\ f(x)\ dx\ ,\ -\infty < \omega < \infty \tag{41}$$

for the transform with respect to eigenfunctions corresponding to continuous eigenvalues and

$$\bar{f}_j = \int_a^b w(x)\ u_j^*(x)\ e^{-\frac{1}{2}Pe\ x}\ f(x)\ dx\ ,\ j = 1,2,\ldots,N \tag{42}$$

for the transform with respect to the eigenfunction corresponding to the discrete eigenvalues. Table 3·2 shows how one arrives at N, the number of discrete eigenvalues (the situation of a vacuous discrete spectrum being represented by N=0) for the operators $\underset{\sim}{A}$, $\underset{\sim}{A}_+$ and $\underset{\sim}{A}_-$. The actual characteristic equation which must be solved to obtain the eigenvalues is included in Appendix II (II·1·1).

The inversion formula for recovering f(x) from the transforms (41) and (42) is given by

$$f(x) = \sum_{j=1}^{N} \bar{f}_j\ u_j(x)\ e^{\frac{1}{2}Pe\ x} + \int_0^\infty \bar{f}(\omega)\ u(x,\omega)\ e^{\frac{1}{2}Pe\ x}\ d\omega \tag{43}$$

Formulae (42) and (43) represent the entire machinery for solving the problems of interest here. *Ramkrishna and Parulekar*[13] first presented the analysis for the case of *equal* dispersion coefficients ($D_-=D_+=D$) for which no discrete spectrum exists. The resulting transform was referred to as the 'R-transform'. The work reported here is essentially the extended exploitation of the R-transform method which has been the result of Parulekar's doctoral effort.[12]

TABLE 3.1

$\underset{\sim}{L}$	w(x)	a	b
$\underset{\sim}{A}$	r(x)	$-\infty$	∞
$\underset{\sim}{A}_+$	$r_+(x)$	-1	∞
$\underset{\sim}{A}_-$	$r_-(x)$	$-\infty$	1

TABLE 3.2

m > 0		$m \leq 0$
C1 > 0	$C1 \leq 0$	
N = M	N = M-1	N = 0

$$m \equiv \frac{Pe^2}{4}\left(\frac{Pe_o}{Pe} - 1\right) - Da \qquad M \equiv \text{smallest integer} \geq \frac{2}{\pi}\sqrt{m} \quad (m > 0)$$

$$C1 = 2\sqrt{m} - (M-1)\pi - \tan^{-1}\left[\sqrt{\frac{Pe^2}{4m}}\left\{1 - \frac{Pe_o}{\max(Pe_-, Pe_+)}\right\}\right]$$

The transforms defined in (41) and (42) have their most crucial property in the following. Whenever $\underset{\sim}{f} \equiv \{f(x): a < x < b\} \in D(\underset{\sim}{L})$.

$$\overline{\underset{\sim}{L}\underset{\sim}{f}}(\omega) = \left(\omega^2 + \frac{Pe^2}{4}\right)\overline{f}(\omega) \tag{44}$$

$$\overline{\underset{\sim}{L}\underset{\sim}{f}}_j = \lambda_j \overline{f}_j \tag{45}$$

The properties (44) and (45) are the ones that help solve the transient axial dispersion problem. This will be demonstrated in the next section. Next we take up the operators $\underset{\sim}{A}^s{}_+$ and $\underset{\sim}{A}^s{}_-$ and the transforms generated by them.

In dealing with the operators $\underset{\sim}{A}^s{}_+$ and $\underset{\sim}{A}^s{}_-$ one must consider functions (see *Ramkrishna and Amundson*[9]) of the type

$$\underset{\sim}{f} \equiv \begin{bmatrix} f(x) \\ f_1 \end{bmatrix}$$

(The reader is advised to refer to our 'Notation' in regard to the use of vector symbols) where f(x) satisfies (40). We represent the transform of $\underset{\sim}{f}$ with respect to eigenfunctions corresponding to the continuous spectrum by $\underset{\sim}{f}(\omega)$ and write

$$\overline{f}(\omega) = \int_a^b w(x)\, u^*(x,\omega)\, e^{-\frac{1}{2} Pe\, x} f(x)\, dx + g\, f_1\, u^*(c,\omega)\, e^{-\frac{1}{2} Pe\, c} \tag{46}$$

$$-\infty < \omega < \infty$$

where w(x), g, a, b and c are specified in Table 3.3 below for the operators $\underset{\sim}{A}^s{}_+$ and $\underset{\sim}{A}^s{}_-$. Representing the transform of $\underset{\sim}{f}$ with respect to the eigenfunction corresponding to the jth eigenvalue λ_j we have

$$\bar{f}_j = \int_a^b w(x)\, u_j^*(x)\, e^{-\frac{1}{2} Pe\, x} f(x)\, dx + g\, f_1\, u_j^*(c)\, e^{-\frac{1}{2} Pe\, c} \qquad (47)$$

Table 3.4 shows how one arrives at N the number of eigenvalues for $\underset{\sim}{A}^s_+$ and $\underset{\sim}{A}^s_-$. Appendix II (II•2.1) gives the characteristic equations for the calculation of the eignevalues. The eigenfunctions corresponding to discrete and continuous eigenvalues are also identified in Appendix II (II.2).

TABLE 3.3

L	w(x)	g	a	b	c
A^s_+	$r_+(x)$	g_-	-1	∞	-1
A^s_-	$r_-(x)$	g_+	$-\infty$	1	1

TABLE 3.4

<table>
<tr><td rowspan="7"></td><td colspan="2" rowspan="4">S2≥0</td><td colspan="12">S1>0</td><td colspan="3" rowspan="3">S1≤0</td></tr>
<tr><td colspan="12">S2<0</td></tr>
<tr><td colspan="2" rowspan="3">S3≤0</td><td colspan="10">S3>0</td></tr>
<tr><td colspan="5">C2>0</td><td colspan="5">C2≤0</td><td rowspan="4">S2≥0</td><td colspan="2" rowspan="3">S2<0</td></tr>
<tr><td rowspan="3">C1>0</td><td rowspan="3">C1≤0</td><td colspan="3">C3>0</td><td colspan="2">C3≤0</td><td colspan="3">C3>0</td><td colspan="2">C3≤0</td></tr>
<tr><td rowspan="2">C2>0</td><td rowspan="2">C2≤0</td><td colspan="2">C4=0</td><td rowspan="2">C4≠0</td><td rowspan="2">C5=2</td><td rowspan="2">C5≠2</td><td colspan="2">C4=0</td><td rowspan="2">C4≠0</td><td rowspan="2">C5=2</td><td rowspan="2">C5≠2</td></tr>
<tr><td>C6=0</td><td>C6≠0</td><td>C6=0</td><td>C6≠0</td><td>C7>0</td><td>C7≤0</td></tr>
<tr><td>N=</td><td>M</td><td>M-1</td><td>M+1</td><td>M</td><td>M+1</td><td>M</td><td>M+1</td><td>M</td><td>M+1</td><td>M</td><td>M-1</td><td>M</td><td>M-1</td><td>M</td><td>0</td><td>1</td><td>0</td></tr>
</table>

(i) $Pe_o = Pe_+$ and $g = g_-$ if $Pe_- = 0$

(ii) $Pe_o = Pe_-$ and $g = g_+$ if $Pe_+ = 0$

$$S1 = \frac{Pe^2}{4}\left(\frac{Pe_o}{Pe} - 1\right) - Da$$

$$S2 = \frac{Pe}{2} - g\,\frac{Pe^2}{4}$$

$$S3 = \frac{g\ Pe}{Pe_o}\left(Da + \frac{Pe^2}{4}\right) - \frac{Pe}{2}$$

$$S4 = \sqrt{\frac{Pe^2}{4} - \frac{(g\ Pe-1)}{g^2}}$$

M = smallest integer greater than or equal to

$$\frac{2}{\pi}\sqrt{S1} \qquad (S1 > 0)$$

$$C1 = 2\sqrt{S1} - \pi(M-1) - \tan^{-1}\left(\frac{S2}{\sqrt{S1}}\right)$$

$$C2 = \sqrt{S1} - \frac{\pi}{2} M + \frac{1}{2}\tan^{-1}\left(-\frac{S2}{\sqrt{S1}}\right)$$

$$C3 = S3 - \sqrt{\frac{Pe}{Pe_o}}\sqrt{S1}$$

$$C4 = \frac{Da}{\left(\frac{Pe_o}{Pe} - 1\right)} - \frac{g\ Pe-1}{g^2}$$

$$C5 = \frac{1}{S3} - \left(\frac{Pe}{Pe_o}\right)^{-\frac{1}{2}} (S1)^{-\frac{1}{2}}$$

$$C6 = \tanh(2\ S4) - \frac{[2\ g\ S4 + 1]}{[1-2\frac{Pe_o}{Pe} - 2\ g\ S4]}$$

$$C7 = -\frac{S2}{\sqrt{-S1}} - \tanh(2\sqrt{-S1}) \qquad (S1 \leq 0)$$

The inversion formula for $\underset{\sim}{f}$ is given by

$$\underset{\sim}{f} \equiv \begin{bmatrix} f(x) \\ f_1 \end{bmatrix} = \sum_{j=1}^{N} \bar{f}_j \begin{bmatrix} u_j(x)\ e^{\frac{1}{2} Pe\ x} \\ u_j(c)\ e^{\frac{1}{2} Pe\ c} \end{bmatrix} + \int_0^{\infty} \begin{bmatrix} u(z,\omega)\ e^{\frac{1}{2} Pe\ x} \\ u(c,\omega)\ e^{\frac{1}{2} Pe\ c} \end{bmatrix} \bar{f}(\omega)\ d\omega \qquad (48)$$

As before the crucial property of the transform which solves the axial dispersion problem is contained in formulae (44) and (45) except in this case $\underset{\sim}{L}$ must be interpreted as $\underset{\sim}{A}^S_+$ or $\underset{\sim}{A}^S_-$ and $\underset{\sim}{f}$ as $\begin{bmatrix} f(x) \\ f_1 \end{bmatrix}$.

Before we close this section we note that operators $\underset{\sim}{A}_+$ and $\underset{\sim}{A}_-$ may be generated from $\underset{\sim}{A}$ by letting $D_-=0$ or $D_+=0$ respectively. $\underset{\sim}{A}_+$ and $\underset{\sim}{A}_-$ may also be generated from $\underset{\sim}{A}^S_+$ by letting $g_+=0$ and from $\underset{\sim}{A}^S_-$ by letting $g_-=0$ respectively. The reader will notice that these properties are reflected in all information concerning the spectra of the different operators; this harmony is a very valuable source of verification of our derivations and calculations. It is interesting to note that as D_+ and D_- become smaller, the eigenvalues in the discrete spectrum of $\underset{\sim}{A}$ proliferate to a countably infinite population at the limit $D_+=D_-=0$. This is as it should be since in this case we arrive at the Danckwerts boundary conditions at both ends. We caution however, that such limiting procedures be not considered carelessly because of the intimate manner in which the limiting quantities appear in the dimensionless equations.

4. SOLUTION OF THE TRANSIENT PROBLEM

Since much of the spade work for the solution of the boundary-initial value problem has already been completed in the preceding two sections we are now in a position to provide a unified discussion of *all* the transient problems. Thus we represent the transient problem by means of the operator equation

$$\underset{\sim}{L}\,\underset{\sim}{\chi}(\tau) - \underset{\sim}{S}(\tau) = -\frac{d}{d\tau}\,\underset{\sim}{\chi}(\tau) \qquad (49)$$

where $\underset{\sim}{\chi}(\tau) \equiv \{\chi(x,\tau): \ a < x < b$ is a vectorial notation of the function. In dealing with $\underset{\sim}{A}^s_+$ or $\underset{\sim}{A}^s_-$, we have $\underset{\sim}{\chi}(\tau) \equiv \begin{bmatrix}\chi(x,\tau\\ \chi(c,\tau\end{bmatrix}$. Similarly $\underset{\sim}{S}(\tau) \equiv \{S(x,\tau)\}$ is a vectorially represented known inhomogeneous term which, besides including the term $\frac{-\mathrm{Da}\ Y(x)}{r(x)}$ (see for example Equation (18) or (26)), can also account for a possible "source rate" of solute as when material may be introduced within the system by an injection device of one kind or another. Equation (49) must be solved subject to the initial condition

$$\underset{\sim}{\chi}(0) = \underset{\sim}{F} \qquad (50)$$

Note that the boundary conditions are already contained in the definition of the operator and require no special mention in this notational scheme. The solution of the transient problem proceeds by taking the integral transform of (48) and (50) with respect to eigenfunctions corresponding to both continuous and discrete eigenvalues and using formulae (44) and (45). Thus we have

$$(\omega^2 + \frac{Pe^2}{4})\,\overline{\chi}(\omega,\tau) - \overline{S}(\omega,\tau) = -\frac{d}{d\tau}\,\overline{\chi}(\omega,\tau) \qquad (51)$$

$$\lambda_j\,\overline{\chi}_j(\tau) - \overline{S}_j(\tau) = -\frac{d\overline{\chi}_j(\tau)}{d\tau} \qquad (52)$$

where $\overline{\chi}(\omega,\tau)$ is the transform corresponding to the continuous spectrum and $\overline{\chi}_j(\tau)$ is the transform corresponding to the discrete spectrum. Equations (51) and (52) must be solved subject to the initial conditions

$$\overline{\chi}(\omega,0) = \overline{F}(\omega) \quad , \quad \overline{\chi}_j(0) = \overline{F}_j \qquad (53)$$

The resulting solutions are readily found to be

$$\overline{\chi}(\omega,\tau) = \overline{F}(\omega)\ \exp\left[-(\omega^2 + \frac{Pe^2}{4})\tau\right] + \int_0^\tau \overline{S}(\omega,\tau')\ \exp\left[-(\omega^2 + \frac{Pe^2}{4})(\tau-\tau')\right] d\tau' \qquad (54)$$

$$\overline{\chi}_j(\tau) = \overline{F}_j\ e^{-\lambda_j\tau} + \int_0^\tau \overline{S}_j(\tau')\ e^{-\lambda_j(\tau-\tau\ )}\ d\tau' \qquad (55)$$

The solution $\chi(x,\tau)$ is then directly obtained from formula (43) if $\underset{\sim}{L}$ is one of $\underset{\sim}{A}$, $\underset{\sim}{A}_+$ and $\underset{\sim}{A}_-$ or from (48) if $\underset{\sim}{L}$ is one of $\underset{\sim}{A}^s_+$ and $\underset{\sim}{A}^s_-$.

Because of the complicated nature of the eigenfunctions it is unreasonable to expect an analytical evaluation of the integrals which appear in the foregoing solutions. *Parulekar*[12] (see also *Ramkrishna and Parulekar*[13]) has performed the inversion numerically. The evaluation involves insignificant computation time. For example a typical transient solution such as that presented in the next section took at most 2 minutes on a CDC 6600 computer.

Radial and Axial Diffusion

We now show that it is possible to use the integral tramsforms above to solve dispersion problems in which the solute may diffuse axially and transversely. For example, consider the situation in which a solute, capable of undergoing a first order chemical reaction, is introduced at a rate $\dot{Q}(t)$ through an injector tube of radius R_o concentrically located within the tubular reactor in which the flow velocity v is uniform. The solute diffuses axially and radially in an axi-symmetric situation. It is readily shown that the boundary value problem may be represented by

$$-\frac{\gamma^2}{\rho}\frac{\partial}{\partial\rho}\left[\rho\frac{\partial}{\partial\rho}\underset{\sim}{\chi}(\rho,\tau)\right] + \underset{\sim}{A}\,\underset{\sim}{\chi}(\rho,\tau) - \underset{\sim}{S}(\rho,\tau) = -\frac{\partial}{\partial\tau}\underset{\sim}{\chi}(\rho,\tau) \tag{56}$$

where $\underset{\sim}{\chi}(\rho,\tau) \equiv \{\chi(x,\rho,\tau): \ -\infty < x < \infty\}$ is a dimensionless concentration defined by

$$\chi(x,\rho,\tau) \equiv \frac{c(z,r,t)\ \pi R^2 v}{\dot{Q}_{max}} \tag{57}$$

which is different from the definition considered earlier because we do not assume here that the solute enters at $-\infty$. In (56) $\underset{\sim}{A}$ is the axial dispersion operator encountered in Section 2 and $\underset{\sim}{S}(\rho,\tau) \equiv \{S(x,\rho,\tau)\}$ is a source term given by

$$S(x,\rho,\tau) = h(\tau)\ Pe\ \sigma(\rho)\ \delta(x - x_o) \tag{58}$$

In (56) through (58) we have let

$$\rho \equiv \frac{r}{R}\,,\quad \gamma^2 \equiv \frac{L^2}{R^2}\frac{D_r}{D}\,,\quad h(\tau) \equiv \frac{\dot{Q}(t)}{\dot{Q}_{max}}\,,\quad \sigma(\rho) \equiv \begin{cases} R_o^2/R^2 & r \le R_o \\ 0 & R_o < r < 1 \end{cases}$$

where D_r is the radial transport coefficient, $\dot{Q}_{max}$ is the maximum injection rate and δ is the Diract delta function. The solution of (56) subject to the initial condition

$$\chi(x,\rho,o) = F(x,\rho) \tag{59}$$

is obtained by taking the integral transform of Equation (56)

$$-\frac{\gamma^2}{\rho}\frac{\partial}{\partial\rho}\left[\rho\frac{\partial}{\partial\rho}\overline{\chi}(\omega,\rho,\tau\right] + \left(\omega^2 + \frac{Pe^2}{4}\right)\overline{\chi}(\omega,\rho,\tau) - \overline{S}(\omega,\rho,\tau) = -\frac{\partial}{\partial\tau}\overline{\chi}(\omega,\rho,\tau) \tag{60}$$

Similarly an equation is obtained for transform for the discrete spectrum. Since our calculations were done for the case $Pe_-=Pe_+=Pe$ no discrete spectrum exists for this case. The boundary conditions with respect to the axial coordinate were already contained in the definition of $\underset{\sim}{A}$. With respect to ρ we have

$$\frac{\partial\chi}{\partial\rho} = 0 \quad \text{at } \rho = 0.1 \tag{61}$$

which must hold for the transform $\overline{\chi}$. Further the transform of (59) yields

$$\overline{\chi}(\omega,\rho,0) = \overline{F}(\omega,\rho) \tag{62}$$

The solution of (60) subject to (61) and (62) is readily obtained in terms of the eigenfunctions of the radial diffusion operator. Once this is obtained the inversion formula (43) yields the solution $\chi(\rho,x,\tau)$. Since this is well known methodology we wish not to burden space with it. The results of our computations are presented in the next section.

5. APPLICATIONS

The solution via our integral transforms described in the previous section was set to numbers in a variety of cases. First, the Peclet numbers in the three sections were assumed to be the same. For this situation no discrete spectrum exists. In the second, the dispersion coefficients in the appended sections are assumed to be equal but different from that in the reaction section. In the third the dispersion coefficients in all the three sections are assumed to be different. In all cases the transient predictions are compared with those based on Danckwerts boundary conditions at both ends.

Figure 5.1 below shows the results of calculations obtained with all the Peclet numbers equal. The initial condition shows χ to be zero corresponding to the situation of the reactor and the appended sections being filled with the reactant. For small values of τ, the condition of zero gradient at x=1 is clearly far from true. The outlet value of χ is considerably lower than that predicted with Danckwerts boundary condition. The reason for this is obvious, for the effect of the high initial concentration just outside the reactor is to increase the concentration of the reactant and lower the value of χ at the reactor exit. Indeed eventually this effect of the downstream section disappears, of course thanks to convection, so that the reactor section will head towards a steady state well before the outlet section has reached a steady state. The outlet section will never truly reach a steady state in that it is a semi-infinite region in which sufficiently far away the effect of the initial condition will persist. The profiles near the entrance to the reactor seem in agreement with that obtained with Danckwerts boundary condition. This is because the initial condition has been chosen so as to fill the inlet section with the fresh feed. On the other hand if the semi-infinite inlet section has been maintained at some other initial condition one could indeed have found transients drastically different from those predicted with Danckwerts boundary conditions. The semi-infinite inlet and outlet sections have *infinite* capacity and initial conditions could be selected to produce a virtually everlasting effect on transient operation. The question of course then arises as to the practical significance of such transients in view of the fact that real reactors afterall must be of finite size and do not have infinite appended sections. To answer this let us first consider what the advantages of semi-infinite appended sections might be. First, it does not shift the problem of finding boundary conditions to that for the dispersion problem in the

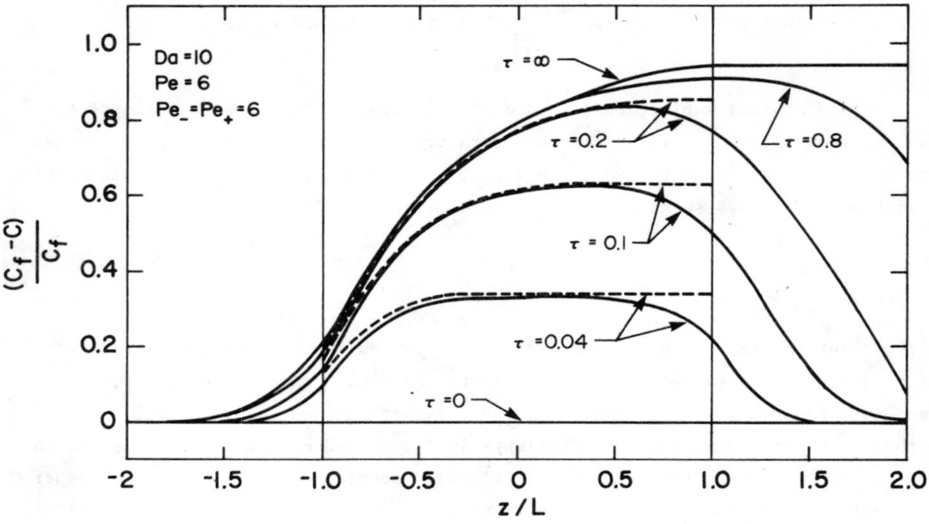

Figure 5.1

Transient reactor profiles for equal Peclet numbers. Dashed curves computed with Danckwerts boundary conditions.

appended sections. (If finite appended sections were used one is again faced with the problem of finding boundary conditions for the appended sections). Infinite appended sections require only finiteness at infinity. Events within the reactor influence reciprocally those outside the reactor but as long as the influence of the appended section on the reactor behavior arises from a fraction that does not exceed the actual extension of the reactor the idea of the semi-infinite appended section is a good one. The implication is that one is not at liberty to pick initial conditions indiscriminately in the appended sections. In this connection there is more latitude with conditions in the outlet section where the influence of the downstream section is 'washed out' by convective motion. On the other hand, the inlet section must be viewed with more care. A safe guidline is of course to maintain the initial concentration to be that of the feed beyond the actual entrance region in the direction of negative infinity.

Figure 5.2 shows the result of calculations for the case of equal dispersion coefficients in the appended section but different from that in the reactor. The initial condition is the same as that in Figure 5.1. The breaks in the derivatives (since it is the flux that is continuous) of the concentration at the inlet and outlet are indeed noticable. Again the deviation from the zero gradient boundary condition becomes more pronounced when dispersion in the appended section is higher. A similar situation also occurs at the entrance.

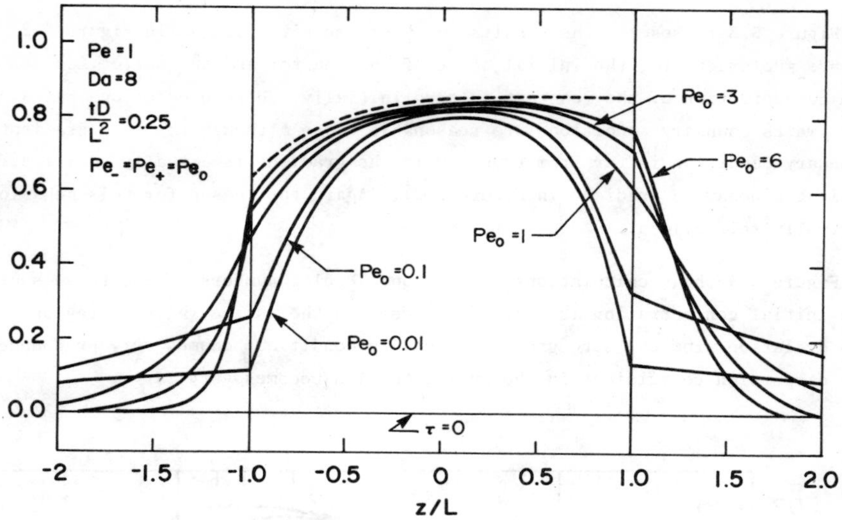

Figure 5.2

Transient reactor profiles. $Pe_- = Pe_+ \neq Pe$. Effect of $Pe_{\pm}$ at fixed time. Dashed curve computed with Danckwerts boundary conditions.

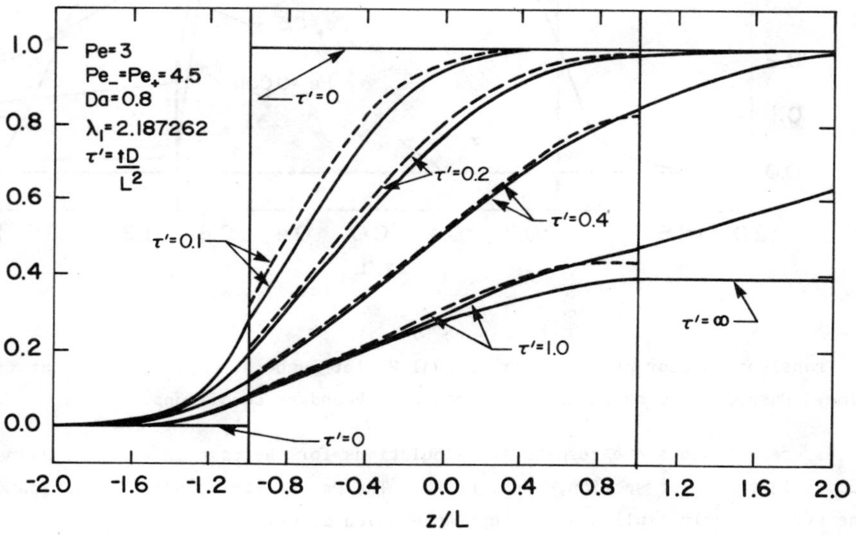

Figure 5.3

Transient reactor profiles at various times for the case $Pe_- = Pe_+ \neq Pe$. Dashed curves computed with Danckwerts boundary conditions.

Figure 5.3 represents the results for the same situation as in Figure 5.2, i.e., $Pe_+=Pe_-\neq Pe$ except for the initial state of the reactor and the outlet section where the concentration of the reactant is zero initially. Here predictions based on the Danckwerts boundary conditions are reasonable close although the zero gradient boundary condition is far from true. Here the gradient is actually positive (as against a negative gradient in Figure 5.2). Again the reason for this behavior is virtually self-evident.

Figure 5.4 shows calculations with unequal Peclet numbers in the three sections. The initial concentration is that of the feed in the entire infinite region. Again the deviation from the zero gradient boundary condition becomes very pronounced when the dispersion coefficient in the outlet section becomes very large.

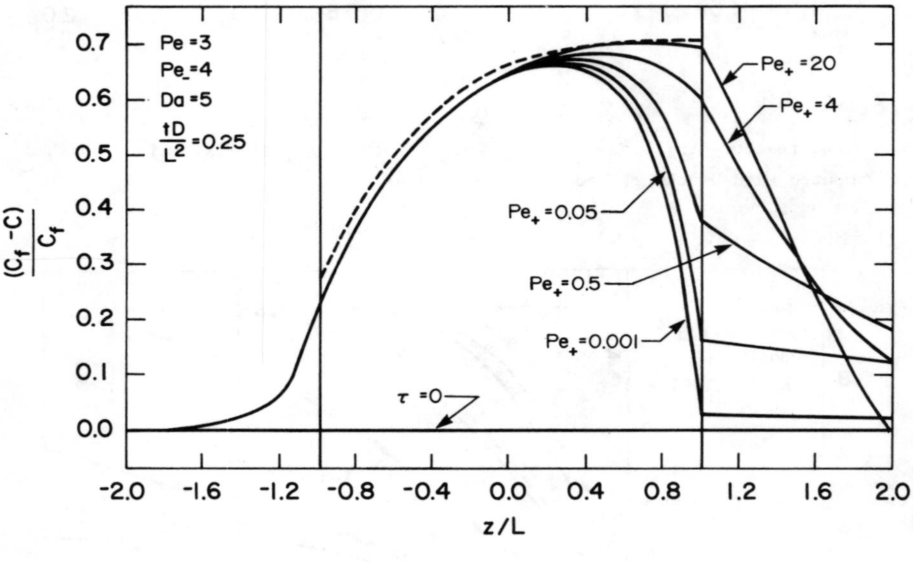

Figure 5.4

Transient reactor profiles for unequal Peclet numbers. Effect of Pe_+ at fixed time. Dashed curve computed with Danckwerts boundary conditions.

Figure 5.5 shows the results of calculations for the case in which no dispersion occurs in the inlet section, i.e., $Pe_-=\infty$. The Danckwerts boundary condition is therefore exactly implied at the entrance which is well borne out by the calculations. The initial concentration of the reactant has been so chosen that there is no reactant in the outlet section. Thus the zero gradient boundary condition is badly negated for short times. The situation at steady state of course agrees with that predicted using the Danckwerts boundary conditions.

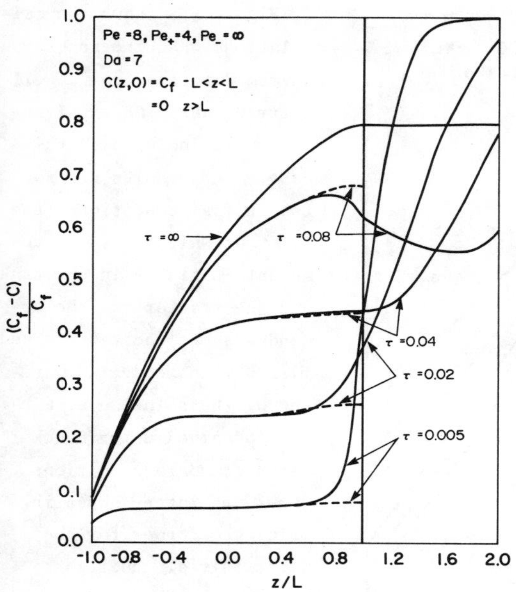

Figure 5.5

Transient reactor profiles with $Pe_-=\infty$ Dashed curves computed with Danckwerts boundary conditions.

The solutions displayed so far do not reflect the character of the spectrum of the operator in regard to whether or not there are discrete eigenvalues. For example, calculations in Figures 5.1, 5.2, 5.4 and 5.5 involved no discrete eigenvalues, while those in Figure 5.3 featured a small number of discrete eigenvalues. A plot of the concentration at some fixed point against time can show an exponential decay when discrete eigenvalues are present. This can be used to great advantage in the identification of parameters from experimental data. We shall take this up presently.

Even in the absence of chemical reaction we are not aware of transient calculations in dispersion problems such as in a packed bed with semi-infinite appended sections where the solute dispersion coefficients are non-zero and different from that in the packed section. *Brenner*[7] used the Danckwerts boundary conditions in the calculations. The formulations in this work for the reactor can readily accommodate the pure dispersion problem by setting Da=0. Particularly interesting is the fact that a discrete spectrum appears when the Peclet numbers in the appended sections increase. Figure 5.6 shows the results for different Peclet numbers in the appended sections. Brenner's solution which corresponds to infinite Peclet numbers outside the packed section is plotted alongside for comparison. By experimentally measuring concentrations at three different locations such as those shown in Figure 5.7, it is shown how the smallest eigenvalue can help in the estimation of the three Peclet numbers in the dispersion of a solute. The experimental data in this case were created by computation with assumed Peclet numbers. Table 5.1 shows the favorable comparison of the estimated Peclet numbers with those assumed in the calculations.

TABLE 5.1

	Assumed	Estimated
Pe_-	12.5	12.29
Pe	3.2	3.17
Pe_+	8.4	8.54

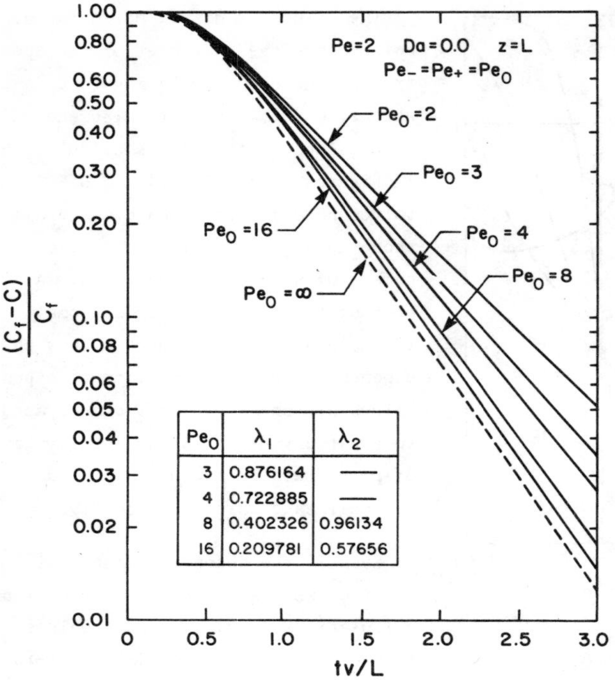

Figure 5.6

Outlet concentration of tracer at different times for $Pe_-=Pe_+$. Dashed curve computed with Danckwerts boundary conditions.

Figure 5.8 shows the calculations when the reactor is fed directly from a well-stirred tank. Chemical reaction is included in this case. The results are for two initial conditions, the first of which shows no reactant initially in the tank and the reactor and the second assumes the tank to be filled with feed. Comparison of the solution with that obtained using Danckwerts boundary conditions shows the latter appearing below the former for the first initial condition while for the second the situation is exactly reversed reflecting obviously the inertial effect of the tank volume.

Finally, calculations for the case where the solute diffuses axially and transversely (considered in Section 4) are shown in Figure 5.9 for different values of the parameter γ and for $R_o=0$. The nature of the evolving radial concentration profiles is readily explained.

6. CONCLUSIONS

We have presented a natural approach to the solution of problems dealing with axially dispersed systems which overcomes the difficulties inherent in the use of Danckwerts boundary conditions. Although the restriction to linear rates is essential for calculations, linearization methods, for example, for the purposes of stability criteria have been obtained by *Parulekar*[12] for tubular reactors without the use of Danckwerts boundary conditions. The spectra of the operators which we have presented are also important in characterizing the dynamic response of tubular reactors especially in regard to control. It would be interesting for example to consider the control problem by manipulating concentrations in stirred tanks before or after the reactor. Again the dynamic response of the reactor would be governed by the spectral behavior of the operators concerned.

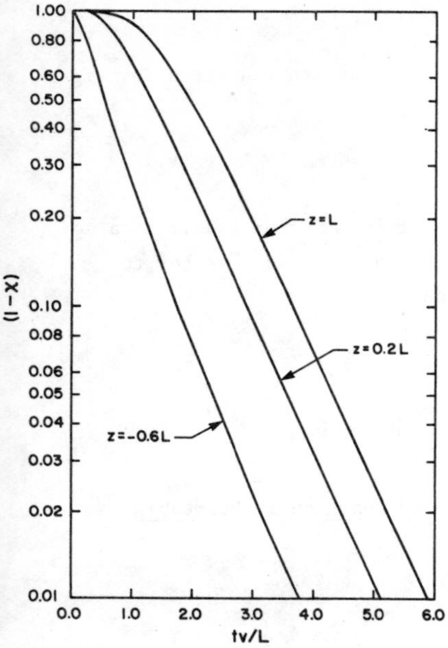

Figure 5.7

Transients at fixed reactor locations for parameter estimation.

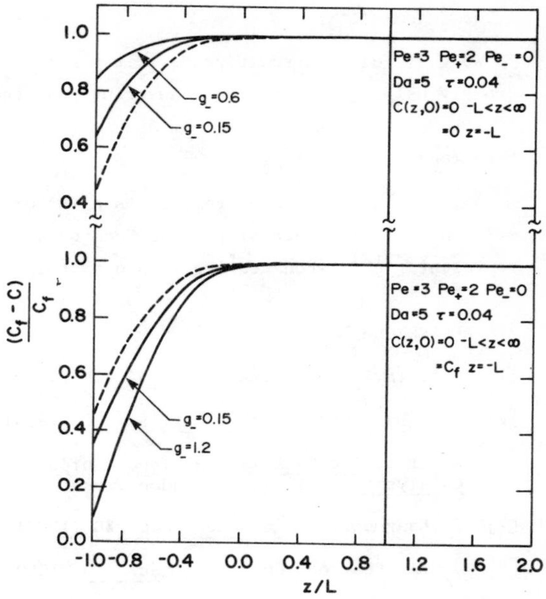

Figure 5.8

Transient reactor profiles with feed from stirred tank. Effect of initial condition. Dashed curves computed with Danckwerts boundary conditions.

Finally, we contend that the use of numerical methods such as finite difference techniques in place of those which we have presented will be difficult, cumbersome and probably time consuming.

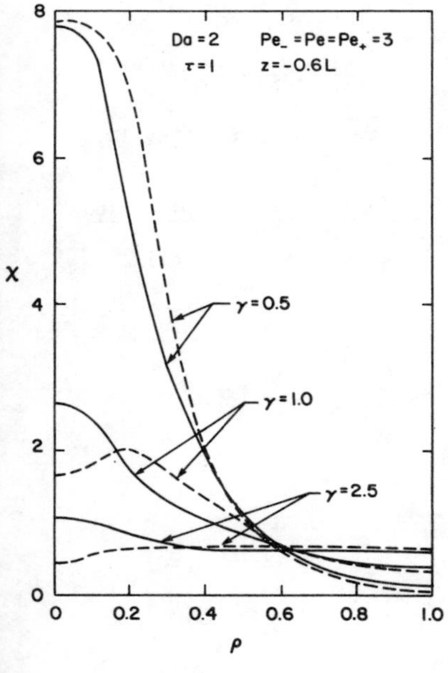

← Figure 5.9

Radial concentration profiles for reactor with radial and axial diffusion.

Acknowledgments:

We gratefully acknowledge Ms. Kitty Rainier and Mrs. Christa Van Etten for vigorously helping us meet the manuscript deadline.

Notation:

A tilda under a symbol represents a vector. Thus $\underset{\sim}{f}$ is a vector and it is also written as $\{f(x)\}$ when written as "components". We also use $\underset{\sim}{f}$ as a vector to represent $\begin{bmatrix} f(x) \\ f_1 \end{bmatrix}$ when dealing with operators $\underset{\sim}{A}^s_+$ and $\underset{\sim}{A}^s_-$.

7. REFERENCES

[1] G.I. Taylor, Proc. Roy. Soc. A 219 (1953) 186.

[2] P.V. Danckwerts, Chem. Eng. Sci. 2 (1953) 1.

[3] R. Aris, The Mathematical Theory of Diffusion and Reaction in Permeable Catalysts - Vol. 1, Clarendon Press, Oxford 1975.

[4] I. Langmuir, J. Am. Chem. Soc. 30 (1908) 1742.

[5] J.R.A. Pearson, Chem. Eng. Sci. 10 (1959) 281.

[6] J.F. Wehner, R.H. Wilhelm, Chem. Eng. Sci. 6 (1955) 89.

[7] H. Brenner, Chem. Eng. Sci. 17 (1962) 229.

[8] N.R. Amundson, Can. J. Chem. Eng. 45 (1965) 49.

[9] D. Ramkrishna, N.R. Amundson, Chem. Eng. Sci. 29 (1974) 1353.

[10] K. Jorgens, Spectral Theory of Second - Order Differential Operators, Lecture Notes Series No. 2, Aarhus University Press 1964.

[11] E.C. Titchmarsh, Eigenfunction Expansions Associated with Second - Order Differential Equations - Part I, Clarendon Press, Oxford 1962.

[12] S.J. Parulekar, Ph.D. Dissertation, Purdue University, West Lafayette, IN, USA (1982).

[13] D. Ramkrishna, S.J. Parulekar, Boundary Value Problems on Axially Dispersed Systems - Solution Via A New Integral Transform, paper presented at the Second World Congress of Chemical Engineering, Montreal, Canada (1981).

APPENDIX I

Here we will present two theorems to prove that the family of axial dispersion to operators $\underset{\sim}{A}$, $\underset{\sim+}{A}$, $\underset{\sim}{A}$, $\underset{\sim+}{A^s}$ and $\underset{\sim-}{A^s}$ is a family of self-adjoint operators. It is interesting to observe that D(A), $D(A_+)$ and $D(A_-)$ are subspaces of the Hilbert spaces $\mathcal{L}_2(-\infty,\infty,r(x)e^{-Pex})$, $\mathcal{L}_2(-1,\infty,r_+(x)e^{-Pex})$ and $\mathcal{L}_2(-\infty,1,r_-(x)e^{-Pex})$ respectively. In general, $\mathcal{L}_2(a,b,w(x)e^{-Pex})$ is the space of all functions u(x) which are such that

$$\int_a^b |u(x)|^2\ w(x)e^{-Pex}\ dx < \infty \tag{1.1}$$

where a,b and w(x) are as defined in Table 3.1. In $\mathcal{L}_2(a,b,w(x)e^{-Pex})$ the inner product is defined as

$$(\underset{\sim}{u},\underset{\sim}{v}) = \int_a^b u(x)v^*(x)w(x)e^{-Pex}\ dx \tag{1.2}$$

where $\underset{\sim}{u} \equiv \{u(x)|-a<x<b\}$ and $v^*(x)$ denotes the complex conjugate of v(x). Next we state the theorem for operators $\underset{\sim}{A}$, $\underset{\sim+}{A}$ and $\underset{\sim}{A}$.

Theorem 1

The differential expressions $\underset{\sim}{A}$, $\underset{\sim+}{A}$ and $\underset{\sim-}{A}$ are formally self-adjoint and the axial dispersion operators $\underset{\sim}{A}$, $\underset{\sim+}{A}$ and $\underset{\sim-}{A}$ are self-adjoint operators with their domains as D(A), $D(A_+)$ and $D(A_-)$ respectively.

Proof

Let $\underset{\sim}{L}$ denote any one of the operators. $\underset{\sim}{A}$, $\underset{\sim+}{A}$ and $\underset{\sim-}{A}$. $\underset{\sim}{L}$ is said to be a self-adjoint operator with respect to the inner product defined in (1.2) if

$$(\underset{\sim}{L}\underset{\sim}{u},\underset{\sim}{v}) = (\underset{\sim}{u},\underset{\sim}{L}\underset{\sim}{v}) \text{ for every } \underset{\sim}{u},\underset{\sim}{v} \in D(L) \tag{1.3}$$

where D(L) is the domain of L. The differential expression for L can be rewritten as

$$L \equiv -\frac{1}{w(x)e^{-Pex}}\frac{d}{dx}(e^{-Pex}\frac{d}{dx}) + \frac{DaY(x)}{r(x)} \tag{1.4}$$

L expressed as shown above is formally self-adjoint. In terms of the inner product (1.2) we can write the following

$$(\underset{\sim}{L}\underset{\sim}{u},\underset{\sim}{v}) - (\underset{\sim}{u},\underset{\sim}{L}\underset{\sim}{v}) = \int_a^b [\frac{d}{dx}(e^{-Pex}\frac{dv^*}{dx})\ u(x) - \frac{d}{dx}(e^{-Pex}\frac{du}{dx})\ v^*(x)]dx$$

which after integration by parts can be written as

$$(\underset{\sim}{L}\underset{\sim}{u},\underset{\sim}{v})-(\underset{\sim}{u},\underset{\sim}{L}\underset{\sim}{v}) = [e^{-Pex}(u(x)\frac{dv^*}{dx} - v^*(x)\frac{du}{dx})]_a^b \tag{1.5}$$

The boundary conditions at $x = a$ and $x = b$ satisfied by functions which belong to the domain of $\underset{\sim}{L}$ are such that the right hand side of equation (1.5) is zero.. Therefore the axial dispersion oprators $\underset{\sim}{A}$, $\underset{\sim}{A}_-$ and $\underset{\sim}{A}_+$ are self-adjoint oprators with $D(A)$, $D(A_-)$ and $D(A_+)$ as their respective domains.

The domains of A_+^s and A_-^s are subspaces of the direct sum spaces† $\mathscr{L}_2(-1,\infty,r_+(x)e^{-Pex}) \oplus \mathcal{R}$ and $\mathscr{L}_2(-\infty,1,r_-(x)\exp(-Pex)) \oplus \mathcal{R}$ respectively. In $\mathscr{L}_2(a,b,w(x)\exp(-Pex)) \oplus \mathcal{R}$ the inner product is defined as

$$(\underset{\sim}{u},\underset{\sim}{v}) = \int_a^b u(x)\ v^*(x)\ w(x)e^{-Pex}\,dx + g\,u_1\,v_1^*\,e^{-Pec} \tag{1.6}$$

where a,b,c and g are defined in Table 3.3, and $\underset{\sim}{u} = \begin{bmatrix} u(x) \\ u_1 \end{bmatrix}$, $a < x < b$.

Note that $u_1 = u(-1)$ if $c = -1$ and $u_1 = u(1)$ if $c = 1$. Next the theorem for $\underset{\sim}{A}_+^s$ and $\underset{\sim}{A}_-^s$ is presented.

Theorem 2

The differential expressions A_+^s and A_-^s are formally self-adjoint and the axial dispersion operators $\underset{\sim}{A}_+^s$ and $\underset{\sim}{A}_-^s$ are self-adjoint operators with $D(A_+^s)$ and $D(A_-^s)$ as their respective domains.

Proof

Let $\underset{\sim}{L}$ denote any one of the operators $\underset{\sim}{A}_+^s$ and $\underset{\sim}{A}_-^s$. $\underset{\sim}{L}$ is said to be a self-adjoint operator with respect to the inner product defined in (1.6) if the relation (1.3) is satisfied. The differential expressions for A_+^s and A_-^s can be conveniently rewritten as

$$A_+^s = \begin{bmatrix} \frac{1}{r_+(x)}\{-\frac{1}{e^{-Pex}}\frac{d}{dx}(e^{-Pex}\frac{d}{dx}) + DaY(x)\} & 0 \\ -\frac{1}{g_-}\{\frac{d}{dx} - Pe\}_{x=-1} & 0 \end{bmatrix}$$

and

$$A_-^s = \begin{bmatrix} \frac{1}{r_-(x)}\{-e^{Pex}\frac{d}{dx}(e^{-Pex}\frac{d}{dx}) + DaY(x)\} & 0 \\ \frac{1}{g_+}\frac{d}{dx}\Big|_{x=1} & 0 \end{bmatrix}$$

which clearly are formally self-adjoint. In terms of the inner product (1.6) we write the following

†See Ramkrishna and Amundson [9] for further details.

$$(\underset{\sim}{A}^s_+ \underset{\sim}{u},\underset{\sim}{v}) - (\underset{\sim}{u},\underset{\sim}{A}^s_+ \underset{\sim}{v})$$

$$= \int_{-1}^{\infty} [\frac{d}{dx}(e^{-Pex} \frac{dv^*}{dx}) u(x) - \frac{d}{dx}(e^{-Pex} \frac{du}{dx}) v^*(x)]dx + e^{Pe}[- \frac{du}{dx} v^* + u \frac{dv^*}{dx}]_{x=-1}$$

$$(\underset{\sim}{A}^s_- \underset{\sim}{u},\underset{\sim}{v}) - (\underset{\sim}{u},\underset{\sim}{A}^s_- \underset{\sim}{v})$$

$$= \int_{-\infty}^{1} [\frac{d}{dx}(e^{-Pex} \frac{dv^*}{dx}) u(x) - \frac{d}{dx}(e^{-Pex} \frac{du}{dx}) v^*(x)]dx + e^{-Pe}[\frac{du}{dx} v^* - \frac{dv^*}{dx} u]_{x=1}$$

which after integration by parts can be rewritten as

$$(\underset{\sim}{A}^s_+ \underset{\sim}{u},\underset{\sim}{v}) - (\underset{\sim}{u},\underset{\sim}{A}^s_+ \underset{\sim}{v})$$

$$= [u(x)e^{-Pex} \frac{dv^*}{dx} - v^*(x) \frac{du}{dx} e^{-Pex}]_{x=\infty} \qquad (1.7)$$

and

$$(\underset{\sim}{A}^s_- \underset{\sim}{u},\underset{\sim}{v}) - (\underset{\sim}{u},\underset{\sim}{A}^s_- \underset{\sim}{v})$$

$$= [v^*(x)e^{-Pex} \frac{du}{dx} - u(x)e^{-Pex} \frac{dv^*}{dx}]_{x=-\infty} \qquad (1.8)$$

The boundary conditions satisfied by the functions belonging to the domains $D(A^s_+)$ and $D(A^s_-)$ at $x = \infty$ and $x = -\infty$ are such that the right hand sides in equations (1.7) and (1.8) are zero which establishes that the axial dispersion operators $\underset{\sim}{A}^s_+$ and $\underset{\sim}{A}^s_-$ are self-adjoint operators.

Since the axial dispersion operators $\underset{\sim}{A}$, $\underset{\sim}{A}_-$, $\underset{\sim}{A}_+$, $\underset{\sim}{A}^s_-$ and $\underset{\sim}{A}^s_+$ are self-adjoint operators, the existence of a spectral representation of each of the operators is guaranteed by the spectral theorem for self-adjoint differential operators [10,12].

APPENDIX II

In the following, we will present the characteristic equations for discrete eigenvalues and expressions for eigenfunctions of the axial dispersion operators $\underset{\sim}{A}$, $\underset{\sim}{A}_+$, $\underset{\sim}{A}_-$, $\underset{\sim}{A}^s_+$ and $\underset{\sim}{A}^s_-$.

II.1 Eigenvalues and Eigenfunctions of $\underset{\sim}{A}$

The number of discrete eigenvalues (N) of the axial dispersion operator $\underset{\sim}{A}$ can be arrived at by using Table 3.2. The continuous spectrum can consist of two portions in each of which the eigenfunction $u(x,\omega)$ has different expressions.

II.1.1. Discrete Eigenvalues and Eigenfunctions.

The discrete eigenvalue $\lambda_j (j=1,2,...,N)$ is the root of the characteristic equation

$$\tan(2\,e) = \frac{e[d+f]}{(e^2-df)} \tag{2.1}$$

where

$$d = \sqrt{\frac{Pe^2}{4} - \lambda\,\frac{Pe_o}{Pe_-}} \qquad e = \sqrt{\lambda\,\frac{Pe_o}{Pe} - \frac{Pe^2}{4} - Da} \tag{2.2}$$

and

$$f = \sqrt{\frac{Pe^2}{4} - \lambda\,\frac{Pe_o}{Pe_+}}$$

The eigenfunction corresponding to the jth eigenvalue can be represented as

$$u_j(x) = \frac{s_j(x)}{\sqrt{\int_{-\infty}^{\infty} |s_j(x)|^2 r(x)dx}}$$

where

$$s_j(x) = \begin{cases} \exp(d_j x) & -\infty < x \leq -1 \\ a_j\,\cos(e_j x) + b_j\,\sin(e_j x) & -1 \leq x \leq 1 \\ c_j\,\exp(-f_j x) & 1 \leq x < \infty \end{cases} \tag{2.3}$$

The constants d_j, e_j and f_j are obtained by replacing λ, d, e and f by λ_j, d_j, e_j and f_j in definition (2.2). The constants a_j, b_j and c_j are given by the expressions

$$a_j = p_j[\frac{f_j}{e_j}\tan(e_j) + 1] \qquad b_j = p_j[\tan(e_j) - \frac{f_j}{e_j}]$$

$$c_j = p_j\,\exp(f_j)/\cos(e_j)$$

where

$$p_j = \frac{\exp(-d_j)}{m_j\,\cos(e_j)} \qquad m_j = [1 - \tan^2(e_j) + 2\,\frac{f_j}{e_j}\,\tan(e_j)]$$

II.1.2. Eigenfunctions Corresponding to Continuous Eigenvalues

In the range $0 \leq \omega \leq \omega_o$, where

$$\omega_o = \frac{Pe}{2}\sqrt{\frac{\max(Pe_+,Pe_-)}{Pe_o} - 1}$$

the eigenfunction $u(x,\omega)$ for the case $Pe_+ \geq Pe_-$ can be expressed as

$$u(x,\omega) = \begin{cases} [\omega(\alpha\cos(2\alpha)+\omega_2\sin(2\alpha))\cos(\omega(x+1))-\alpha\sin(\omega(x+1))(\omega_2\cos(2\alpha)-\alpha\sin(2\alpha))]/\Delta(\omega) & -\infty < x \leq -1 \\ \dfrac{\omega[\alpha\cos(\alpha(x-1)) - \omega_2\sin(\alpha(x-1))]}{\Delta(\omega)}, & -1 \leq x \leq 1 \\ \dfrac{\alpha\omega e^{\omega_2(1-x)}}{\Delta(\omega)}, & 1 \leq x < \infty \end{cases}$$

where

$$\omega_2 = \sqrt{\frac{Pe^2}{4} - (\omega^2 + \frac{Pe^2}{4})\frac{Pe_o}{\max(Pe_-,Pe_+)}} \qquad \alpha = \sqrt{(\omega^2 + \frac{Pe^2}{4})\frac{Pe_o}{Pe} - \frac{Pe^2}{4} - Da}$$

and

$$\Delta(\omega) = \sqrt{\frac{\pi}{2}}\,[\omega^2(\alpha\cos(2\alpha) + \omega_2\sin(2\alpha))^2 + \alpha^2(\omega_2\cos(2\alpha) - \alpha\sin(2\alpha))^2]^{\frac{1}{2}}$$

The eigenfunction $u(x,\omega)$ for the case $Pe_- \geq Pe_+$ is obtained by merely replacing x by $-x$ in the expression for $u(x,\omega)$ for the case $Pe_- \leq Pe_+$.

In the range $\omega_o \leq \omega < \infty$ the eigenfunction $u(x,\omega)$ can be expressed as

$$u(x,\omega)u^*(\xi,\omega) = u_+(x,\omega)u_+^*(\xi,\omega) + \frac{1}{h}u_-(x,\omega)u_-^*(\xi,\omega) \quad , \quad -\infty < x,\xi < \infty$$

For the case $Pe_+ \geq Pe_-$, $u_+(x,\omega)$ and $u_-(x,\omega)$ can be expressed as

$$\sqrt{2\pi}\,u_+(x,\omega) = \begin{cases} e^{i\omega x} + S_-e^{-i\omega x} & , \ -\infty < x \leq -1 \\ A_+e^{i\alpha x} + A_-e^{-i\alpha x} & , \ -1 \leq x \leq 1 \\ Te^{i\omega_1 x} & , \ 1 \leq x < \infty \end{cases}$$

$$\sqrt{2\pi}\,u_-(x,\omega) = \begin{cases} Te^{-i\omega x} & , \ -\infty < x \leq -1 \\ B_+e^{i\alpha x} + B_-e^{-i\alpha x} & , \ -1 \leq x \leq 1 \\ he^{-i\omega_1 x} + S_+e^{i\omega_1 x} & , \ 1 \leq x < \infty \end{cases}$$

where

$$\omega_1 = \sqrt{(\omega^2 + \frac{Pe^2}{4})\frac{Pe_o}{\max(Pe_-,Pe_+} - \frac{Pe^2}{4}} \quad , \quad h = \omega/\omega_1$$

$$\alpha = \sqrt{(\omega^2 + \frac{Pe^2}{4})\frac{Pe_o}{Pe} - \frac{Pe^2}{4} - Da}$$

$$A_- = \frac{(\alpha-\omega_1)\omega\ \exp(i(\alpha-\omega))}{\Delta(\omega)} \qquad A_+ = \frac{(\alpha+\omega_1)\omega\ \exp(-i(\alpha+\omega))}{\Delta(\omega)}$$

$$B_- = \frac{(\alpha+\omega)\ e^{-i(\alpha+\omega_1)}\omega}{\Delta(\omega)} \qquad B_+ = \frac{(\alpha-\omega)\omega\ e^{i(\alpha-\omega_1)}}{\Delta(\omega)}$$

$$S_- = \frac{e^{-2i\omega}}{\Delta(\omega)}[\alpha(\omega-\omega_1)\cos(2\alpha) + i(\alpha^2-\omega\omega_1)\sin(2\alpha)]$$

$$S_+ = \frac{he^{-2i\omega_1}}{\Delta(\omega)}[\alpha(\omega_1-\omega)\cos(2\alpha) + i(\alpha^2-\omega_1\omega)\sin(2\alpha)]$$

and

$$\Delta(\omega) = \alpha(\omega+\omega_1)\cos(2\alpha) - i\sin(2\alpha)(\alpha^2+\omega\omega_1)$$

The expressions for $u_+(x,\omega)$ and $u_-(x,\omega)$ for the case $Pe_- \geq Pe_+$ are obtained from the expressions presented above by merely replacing x by -x in the above expressions..

II.2. Eigenvalues and Eigenfunctions of $\underset{\sim}{A}_+^s$ and $\underset{\sim}{A}_-^s$

II.2.1. Discrete Eigenvalues and Eigenfunctions

The characteristic equation for the discrete eigenvalues λ_j's is

$$\tanh(2\sqrt{e}) = \frac{\sqrt{e}\ [f-d]}{[e-fd]} \qquad \text{if } e > 0$$

or (2.4)

$$\tan(2\sqrt{p}) = \frac{\sqrt{p}\ [d-f]}{[p+fd]} \qquad \text{if } e < 0$$

where

$$d = \sqrt{\frac{Pe^2}{4} - \lambda} \qquad e = \frac{Pe^2}{4} + Da - \lambda\frac{Pe_o}{Pe}$$

$$f = g\lambda - \frac{Pe}{2} \qquad p = -e$$

Note that $Pe_o = Pe_+$ for $g = g_-$ and $Pe_o = Pe_-$ for $g = g_+$. The expressions for eigenfunction $u_j(x)$ of $\underset{\sim}{A}_-^s$($g = g_+$ and $Pe_o = Pe_-$) are

$$u_j(x) = \frac{s_j(x)}{[\int_{-\infty}^{1}\{s_j(x)\}^2\ r_-(x)dx + g_+\{s_j(1)\}^2]}$$

where if $e_j > 0$

$$s_j(x) = \begin{cases} \exp(d_j x) , & -\infty < x \leq -1 \\ a_j \cosh(\sqrt{e_j}\, x) + b_j \sinh(\sqrt{e_j}\, x) , & |x| \leq | \end{cases}$$

and if $e_j < 0$ (i.e., $p_j > 0$)

$$s_j(x) = \begin{cases} \exp(d_j x) , & -\infty < x \leq -1 \\ m_j \cos(\sqrt{p_j}\, x) + n_j \sin(\sqrt{p_j}\, x) , & |x| \leq | \end{cases}$$

The constants d_j, e_j and p_j are obtained by replacing λ, d, e and p by λ_j, d_j, e_j and p_j respectively in definition (2.5). The constants a_j, b_j, m_j and n_j are defined as

$$a_j = \frac{\exp(-d_j)}{\cosh(\sqrt{e_j})[1-\ell_j \tanh(\sqrt{e_j})]} \qquad b_j = \ell_j a_j$$

$$\ell_j = \frac{\{d_j + \sqrt{e_j}\tanh(\sqrt{e_j})\}}{\{d_j \tanh(\sqrt{e_j}) + \sqrt{e_j}\}} \qquad m_j = \frac{\exp(-d_j)}{\cos(\sqrt{p_j})[1-q_j \tan(\sqrt{p_j})]}$$

$$n_j = q_j m_j \qquad q_j = \frac{(d_j - \sqrt{p_j}\tan(\sqrt{p_j}))}{(d_j \tan(\sqrt{p_j}) + \sqrt{p_j})}$$

The eigenfunction $u_j(x)$ of the operator $\underset{\sim}{A}{}^s_+$ ($g = g_-$ and $Pe_o = Pe_+$) can be expressed as

$$u_j(x) = \frac{s_j(x)}{[{}_{-1}\int^{\infty} \{s_j(x)\}^2\, r_+(x)dx + g_-\{s_j(-1)\}^2]}$$

where $s_j(x)$ is obtained by replacing x by -x in the expressions for $s_j(x)$ for the operator A^s_-.

II.2.2 Eigenfunctions Corresponding to Continuous Eigenvalues

The expressions for the eigenfunction $u(x,\omega)$ of th axial dispersion operator $\underset{\sim}{A}{}^s_+$ ($g=g_-$ and $Pe_o = Pe_+$) can be written as

$$u(x,\omega) = \begin{cases} \dfrac{\omega[\alpha\cos(\alpha(x+1)) + (\frac{Pe}{2} - g(\omega^2 + \frac{Pe^2}{4}))\sin(\alpha(x+1))]}{\Delta(\omega)} , & -1 \leq x \leq 1 \\ [\omega\{\alpha\cos(2\alpha) + (\frac{Pe}{2} - g(\omega^2 + \frac{Pe^2}{4}))\sin(2\alpha)\}\cos(\omega(x-1)) - \{\alpha\sin(2\alpha) \\ \quad -(\frac{Pe}{2} - g(\omega^2 + \frac{Pe^2}{4}))\cos(2\alpha)\} \cdot \alpha\sin(\omega(x-1))]/\Delta(\omega) , & 1 \leq x < \infty \end{cases}$$

where

$$\alpha = \sqrt{(\omega^2 + \frac{Pe^2}{4})\frac{Pe_o}{Pe} - \frac{Pe^2}{4} - Da}$$

and

$$\Delta(\omega) = \sqrt{\frac{\pi}{2}}\, [\omega^2\{\alpha\cos(2\alpha) + \sin(2\alpha)(\frac{Pe}{2} - g(\omega^2 + \frac{Pe^2}{4}))\}^2 + \alpha^2\{\cos(2\alpha)(\frac{Pe}{2} - g(\omega^2 + \frac{Pe^2}{4})) - \alpha\sin(2\alpha)\}^2]^{\frac{1}{2}}$$

The expressions for the eigenfunction $u(x,\omega)$ of the axial dispersion operator $\underset{\sim}{A}^s_-$ ($g=g_+$ and $Pe_o = Pe_-$) can be obtained by replacing x by -x in the expressions for $u(x,\omega)$ for the case where $g = g_-$ and $Pe_o = Pe_+$.

Since condition (13) reduces to the Danckwerts 'jump' condition when V_- vanishes, the characteristic equation for eigenvalues and the eigenfuction expressions for the operator $\underset{\sim}{A}_+$ can be obtained from the corresponding relations for $\underset{\sim}{A}^s_+$ by considering g_- as zero. Similarly since condition (14) implies the Danckwerts zero gradient boundary condition when V_+ is zero, the characteristic equation for eigenvalues and the eigenfunction expressions for $\underset{\sim}{A}_-$ can be obtained from the corresponding relations for $\underset{\sim}{A}^s_-$ by considering g_+ as zero.

Nonlinear Adsorption, Reaction, Diffusion and Intraparticle Convection Phenomena in Flow Systems

A. E. Rodrigues

Department of Chemical Engineering,University of Porto,
4099 Porto Codex,Portugal

SUMMARY

This chapter is divided into four sections.In Part 1 an overview of the concept of residence time distribution and its applications is presented.Examples of diagnosis of equipment operation based on tracer methodology,determination of hydrodynamic parameters in multiphase systems and prediction of conversion in real reactors are presented.

In Part 2 the importance of intraparticle forced convection in large pore catalysts is discussed with regard to catalyst diffusivity measurements and its implication in reactor design.Experimental data for effective diffusivity of hydrogen tracer in a partial oxydation catalyst are reported and reactor design considerations are made for first and zero order reactions (which are relevant in biofilm reactors).

Part 3 deals with the coupling between nonlinear adsorption and chemical reaction in adsorbent/catalyst particles which occurs in chemical engineering systems such as: removal of organics by activated carbon (where adsorption and biodegradation take place simultaneously),catalytic reactions in supported catalysts and determination of equilibrium and kinetic data by chromatographic methods.

Finally in Part 4 a brief reference to the percolation concept as an alternative way of describing fluid flow through reactors is made and areas of application of the residence time distribution theory are mentioned.

1. RESIDENCE TIME DISTRIBUTIONS:HOW USEFUL ARE THEY?

The concept of residence time distribution (RTD) has deeply contributed to chemical engineering science,mainly due to the lumped methodology used to describe fluid or solid flow through vessels. The theoretical framework of RTD was given by Danckwerts (1) and recent reviews on this subject are available (2,3).

We will follow the definition of a chemical reactor presented by Levenspiel and Bischoff (4) which includes also mass and heat exchangers; the output of the system is then a function of input (step,impulse,etc), kinetics (of chemical reaction, heat and mass transfer),nature of fluid and solid flow and state of mixing.It is obvious that RTD theory is not restricted to chemical engineering;it finds applications in areas such as biomedicine,pharmacokinetics,hydrology and environmental sciences.

Let us first summarize the basic notions of RTD theory;we will assume that a fluid element once entered the system can not leave and reenter it again (closed to diffusion boundaries) and steady state RTD holds.Two populations of fluid elements are considered:those inside the reactor -population A and those leaving the reactor -population B. Each element of these populations is identified by some characters: age,t_α and life expectation,t_λ for elements of population A and residence time,t_r for elements of population B.By analogy with population studies we easily accept the following definitions: age- the time spent by a fluid element since it entered the reactor; life expectation- time it will spend within the reactor before leaving it and residence time- time that a fluid element spent in the reactor from the moment it entered until it left the system. It results that $t_r=t_\alpha+t_\lambda$.

1.1. Age distribution,I(t),residence time distribution,E(t) and life expectation distribution,Λ(t)

For each character a density function (improperly called in the literature "distribution" function) can be defined: I(t) for the internal age, Λ(t) for the life expectation and E(t) for the residence time.Then, for the RTD, the fraction of the population leaving the system with residence time between t_r and t_r+dt_r is $E(t_r)dt_r$ or simply E(t)dt.The moments of the RTD are given by:

$$\mu_n=\int_0^\infty t^n\, E(t)\, dt \qquad |1|$$

and we can show that there are some important relationships between these distributions, namely:

$$\Lambda(t) = \frac{E(t)}{\tau\, I(t)} \qquad |2|$$

and

$$E(t) = -\tau \frac{d\, I(t)}{dt} \qquad |3|$$

For systems operating in steady state and for a multicomponent feed the mean residence time of species i, $\bar{t}_{ri}$ is the ratio between the total holdup of species i and the overall flowrate through the system (5):

$$\bar{t}_{ri} = \frac{H_i}{Q} \qquad |4|$$

For a single tracer in homogeneous reactors, $H_i = V$ and $\bar{t}_r = \tau$, where τ is the space time.

Now we have to find an experimental technique for getting information about these theoretical distributions. The main idea for the study of phase (fluid or solid) flow through reactors is to "trace" the fluid or solid elements and look at the response of the system to a given input of tracer. For us a tracer is simply any substance which does not modify the reactor hydrodynamics and is easily detected at the outlet. A tracer should be a non adsorbable substance (hydrodynamic tracer) but it can be adsorbable (linear or nonlinearly adsorbed) or even a reactive tracer.

Different tracer inputs can be considered: step, Dirac impulse, purge, etc which lead to similar information. The response of a system to a step input of tracer, normalized by the step magnitude, is called F-curve of Danckwerts. Since tracer elements leaving at time t are all younger than t it appears that F(t) is the cumulative RTD, i.e.,

$$F(t) = \int_0^t E(t)\, dt \qquad |5|$$

It can also be shown that

$$F(t) + \tau\, I(t) = 1 \qquad |6|$$

If we consider now a Dirac input of n moles of tracer, the inlet concentration can be expressed by $c_{in}(t) = c^o \tau \delta(t)$ where c^o is the amount of tracer injected divided by the volume accessible to the fluid. The outlet concentration normalized by c^o is the so-called C(t) curve of Danckwerts. The area below the C-curve is the space time, τ and since at time t the tracer elements which left the reactor had residence times lower than t, we get:

$$C(t) = \tau E(t) \qquad |7|$$

We have now an experimental technique for getting the residence time distribution from C or F curves. In many problems, however, it is difficult to obtain an analytical expression for E(t); then we should use the relationship between RTD and the transfer function of the system, G(s) defined as $\bar{c}_{out}(s) / \bar{c}_{in}(s)$:

$$G(s) = L\{E(t)\} \qquad |8|$$

The transfer function is the Laplace transform of the RTD and also the generating function of the moments of E(t); this results from a Taylor series development of G(s) and enables us to calculate the moments of E(t) from G(s) :

$$\mu_n'\{E(t)\} = (-1)^n \left.\frac{\partial^n G}{\partial s^n}\right|_{s=0} \qquad |9|$$

For homogeneous reactors the steady state outlet concentration, if a step input of reactant A and first order reaction $r=kc_A$ takes place, is simply G(k); this result is derived from the fact that the transfer function when reaction occurs, $G_r(s)$ is G(s+k) and then applying the final value theorem we get:

$$\lim_{t\to\infty} c_{out}(t)/c_{in} = G(k) \qquad |10|$$

1.2. Diagnosis of equipment operation and prediction of chemical conversion in real reactors.

The usefulness of the information contained in a tracer experiment depends on the knowledge of some quantities (mass of tracer injected, flowrate), calibration of the detector, etc.

The diagnosis of equipment operation is based on the comparison of the measured (experimental) mean residence time, $\bar{t}_r$ and the space time, τ. Two main situations can occur:

a- $\bar{t}_r > \tau$

This indicates a bypass of fluid; the fraction of flowrate bypassed is $1-\tau/\bar{t}_r$.

b- $\bar{t}_r < \tau$

This indicates the existence of dead zones; the volume fraction occupied by dead regions is $1-\bar{t}_r/\tau$.

As an example we present some data taken from a tracer experiment in a polymer reactor (2). The reactor has a volume V=6400 liters and the flowrate used was Q=6000 l/h.Sulphuric acid was injected as a tracer (impulse input) and the pH at the outlet was recorded.From the curve of pH as a function of time a short-circuit was observed as suspected.The real reactor was modelled by a stirred tank with a fraction α of the feed flowrate,Q being bypassed.The RTD of the model is then:

$$E(t) = \alpha\delta(t) + \frac{1-\alpha}{\tau} \exp(- \frac{1-\alpha}{\tau} t) \qquad |11|$$

and $\bar{t}_r=\tau/(1-\alpha)$.The experimental mean residence time can be calculated from the slope of the line pH vs time,say m, by $\bar{t}_{r,exp}=1/2.3$ m.We got $\bar{t}_{r,exp}=68$ min and so a fraction of flowrate bypassed $\alpha=6.25\%$.

Besides this application of RTD it is important to be able to predict the conversion in real reactors.From a model which considers the real reactor as an ensemble of small plug flow reactors (streamlets) in paralel having different space times,t_r and assuming no interchange between fluid elements flowing through each streamlet (completely segregated flow hypothesis) we get,after writing a mass balance at the node where outlet streams are connected,the following result:

$$\langle c_{out}\rangle = \int_0^\infty c(t_r)\ E(t_r)\ dt_r \qquad |12|$$

since the fraction of flowrate passed through each element is $\frac{dQ}{Q}=E(t)dt$ and $c(t_r)$ is the kinetic law of the chemical reaction (obtained in a batch reactor).

From Eq.(12) we can get the conversion in a chemical reactor,for any kind of kinetic law and for segregated flow;this requires information about the RTD.For linear systems we just need to know the transfer function of the system,G(s);this brings us to the problem of modelling chemical reactors.An enormous literature has been published on this area and we just want to emphasize that any model can be built from some nuclei-elements (stirred tank,plug flow reactor,laminar flow reactor) and consideration of recycle and bypass streams,dead and stagnant zones.With different arrangements we get more or less complex models but in any case we should be able to calculate the transfer function of the whole system by some algebra involving association of elements with transfer function $g_i(s)$,such as:

a- association in series , $G(s)= \prod_i g_i(s)$

b- association in paralel, $G(s)= \sum_i \omega_i\ g_i(s)$ where ω_i is the flowrate fraction in each branch.

One of the most well-known models for describing fluid flow in chemical reactors is the dispersion model.Many papers tackled the question of the boundary conditions for the dispersion equation.Following the basic assumption we made - closed to diffusion boundaries- the only transfer function from which the residence time distribution is obtained by inverse Laplace transform, is:

$$G(s)=\frac{4\beta\ e^{\frac{Pe}{2}(1-\beta)}}{(1+\beta)^2-(1-\beta)^2\ e^{-\beta Pe}} \qquad |13|$$

where Pe is the Peclet number and $\beta=\sqrt{1+4\tau s/Pe}$ .This result is obtained by using the so-called Danckwerts boundary conditions.If we keep the assumptions made at the begining of the development of RTD theory one can calculate transfer functions for infinite,semi-infinite reactors,etc but can not say that the RTD is the inverse transform of those transfer functions.The question of boundary conditions for flow systems has been revisited by Kreft and Zuber (6) while Gibilaro (7) and Nauman (8) extended the concept of RTD to open boundaries systems.

Now it is well known that the conversion obtained with associations in series of a CSTR and a plug flow reactor,in which we just change the order of the reactors,is not the same for nonlinear kinetics.Since the systems have the same residence time distribution we conclude that the RTD is not sufficient to characterize the state of mixing of the fluid.

Zwietering (9) considered two limiting cases of micromixing:complete segregation and maximum mixedness (Figure 1).In this last situation we can calculate the steady state outlet concentration,c_{out} by solving the ODE:

$$\frac{dc(t)}{dt} = r(c) + \Lambda(t)\ \{c(t)-c_{in}\} \qquad |14|$$

with the boundary condition $(dc/dt)_{t=\infty}=0$.The outlet concentration is then $c(t=0)$.Equation (14) can be derived from a mass balance around a volume element as shown in Figure 1.The inputs of such element are the flowrates $QE(t)dt$ and $Q\int_t^\infty E(t)dt$ with concentrations c_{in} and $c(t)$,respectively;the output flowrate is $Q\int_{t-dt}^\infty E(t)dt$ at a concentration $c(t-dt)$ while the reaction term is $Q(1-F(t))r(c)$.In general we can then calculate the conversion in a real reactor for the bounds of complete segregated flow and maximum mixedness.

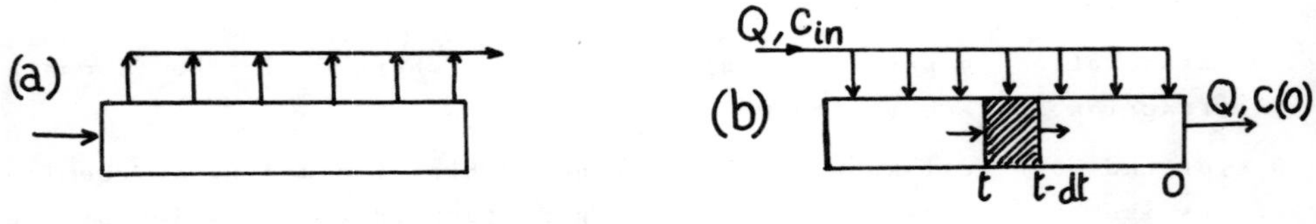

Figure 1 - States of mixing; a-complete segregation, b-maximum mixedness.

1.3. Measure of hydrodynamic parameters in multiphase systems

When we move from homogeneous to heterogeneous reactors the concept of RTD should be replaced by the concept of Contact Time Distribution,CTD; this is so since what is important now is the sojourn time inside the catalyst pellet.Two main ideas have been used to get the CTD,$\xi(t_c)$:

a- Use of tracer experiments with differently adsorbable tracers.

The idea is due to Nauman and Collinge (10) who considered the retention time of a fluid element,t_R as the sum of the time spent in the fluid phase,t_r and the time spent in the catalyst surface,t_a.The adsorption time,t_a is related to the contact time,t_c by $t_a=Kt_c$,so finally $\bar{t}_R=(1+K)\bar{t}_r$. If we carry out two experiments (negative steps) with differently adsorbed tracers we get from the responses of the reactor, $\bar{t}_{R1}=(1+K_1)\bar{t}_r$ and $\bar{t}_{R2}=(1+K_2)\bar{t}_r$; for the same value of ordinate,P(t) we get $t_{R1}=t_r+K_1t_c$ and $t_{R2}=t_r+K_2t_c$ and finally

$$t_c = \frac{t_{R2} - t_{R1}}{K_2 - K_1} \qquad |15|$$

The contact time distribution,$\xi(t_c)$ is then obtained from

$$1-P(t_c) = \int_0^{t_c} \xi(t_c)dt_c \qquad |16|$$

and the residence time,t_r is simply

$$t_r = \frac{K_2t_{R1}-K_1t_{R2}}{K_2 - K_1} \qquad |17|$$

The above treatment is limited to linear adsorption isotherms and infinitely fast mass transfer between solid and fluid phases.

b- Use of reactive tracers undergoing first order irreversible reaction

We already know that in homogeneous systems and first order irreversible reactions,the steady state outlet concentration is simply G(k) as derived in Equation(10).

For heterogeneous reactors Shinnar (11) extended this statement by writing:

$$\frac{c_{out}(\infty)}{c_{in}} = G(k) \qquad |18|$$

where G(k) is the Laplace transform of the CTD. G(k) can be measured by doing runs at different temperatures,so changing k.

Tracer methodology has been used for the determination of hydrodynamic parameters in multiphase systems namely in trickle beds.In this case we are interested in the total liquid holdup (fraction of reactor volume occupied by the liquid phase),H_T which for porous catalysts is the sum of the external holdup,H_E and the intraparticle holdup,H_I.Moreover,the external holdup is divided into dynamic holdup,H_D and static holdup,H_S. It is also of interest the measure of the contacting efficiency- catalyst area contacted by liquid- since it determines the reactor performance.The contacting efficiency can be defined in many ways;however for nonporous particles it is the fraction of external area wetted by the liquid,η_{ce} while for porous pellets it is the fraction of external plus internal area contacted by the liquid,η_c and the fraction of catalyst pore volume filled with liquid is η_I.

Dudukovic and his group (12,13) developed elegant tracer methods for the obtention of these parameters.They first injected a liquid tracer in the trickle bed,which is not adsorbed by the catalyst (I);from the mean residence time of the inert tracer we get:

$$\bar{t}_I = H_T V/Q_L \qquad |19|$$

Now the experiment is repeated with an adsorbable tracer (A),which is linearly adsorbed;the mean residence time is higher:

$$\bar{t}_A = H_T V/Q_L + A_w K/Q_L \qquad |20|$$

where K is the adsorption equilibrium constant and A_w the total wetted area.

From Eqs.(19) and (20) we get A_w if K is known from an independend experiment and then $\eta_c = A_w/A_T$ (A_T -total catalyst area).

Alternatively we can run experiments in a liquid filled column at the same Q_L used in the trickle bed;then the holdup and contacting efficiency are :

$$H_T = \bar{t}_I/(\bar{t}_A)_{LF} \qquad |21|$$

$$\eta_c = \frac{\bar{t}_A - \bar{t}_I}{(\bar{t}_A)_{LF} - (\bar{t}_I)_{LF}} \qquad |22|$$

In order to account for the volatility of an adsorbable tracer,Schwar et al.(12) derived,for isothermal,isobaric,linear adsorption and plug flow of the liquid phase,the following relationship,Eq.(23),where K_{VL} is the vaporization equilibrium constant and h_T is the total vapor holdup.

Some authors got the static holdup after reducing liquid flow rate to zero;however,as Hofmann (14) correctly stated the only way of obtaining H_S is via tracer experiments by using appropriate mathematical models.

2. THE ROLE OF INTRAPARTICLE FORCED CONVECTION IN REACTOR PERFORMANCE

Let us now move to the problem of intraparticle forced convection;this transport mechanism can be relevant in large pore catalysts.Although a brief reference was made by Wheeler (15) only recently a nice theoretical analysis on the effect of intraparticle convection on catalyst effectiveness factor,for single reactions,was reported by Nir and Pismen (16) and extended for complex reactions by Nir (17).Intraparticle convection should be considered when measuring effective diffusivities:experimental evidence of apparent effective diffusivity,$\tilde{D}_e$ changes with flowrate were reported by Ahn (18) and explained by Rodrigues et al(19) on the basis of an intraparticle convection effect.Also Cogan et al(20) published some results on depolymerization of paraldehyde showing the role of intraparticle convection on effectiveness factor.

2.1. The importance of intraparticle convection in catalyst diffusivity measurements.

We will briefly describe the basis for the analysis of experimental results when measuring effective diffusivities by dynamic physical method using either perfectly mixed reactors or fixed beds (single pellet string reactor).

- The perfectly mixed reactor

Let us consider a nonadsorbable tracer and isothermal operation;the unsteady state mass balance for the tracer over the reactor and the mass balance for the catalyst particle are respectively:

$$c_{in} = c + \varepsilon \frac{dc}{d\theta} + \beta\ (1-\varepsilon)\ \frac{d\langle c'\rangle}{d\theta} \qquad |23a|$$

$$\frac{\partial^2 c'}{\partial \rho^2} - \lambda \frac{\partial c'}{\partial \rho} = \alpha \frac{\partial c'}{\partial \theta} \qquad |23b|$$

Boundary conditions:

$$\rho=0,\ c'=c'_s \qquad |23c|$$
$$\rho=2,\ c'=c'_s \qquad |23d|$$
$$\theta=0,\ c=c'=0 \qquad |23e|$$

In the above equations c_{in} is the inlet tracer concentration,c is the outlet tracer concentration, c' the tracer concentration inside the particle, ρ the dimensionless radial coordinate (assuming slab geometry), θ the reduced time (by the space time $, V/Q=\tau$), $\lambda=\ell v_o/D_e$ is the intraparticle Peclet number (v_o is the intraparticle convective velocity), comparing time constants for convection inside the particle and in the reactor and $\alpha=\tau_d/\tau$ compares time constant for intraparticle diffusion and space time.

The transfer function relating particle surface concentration and average concentration inside the particle is:

$$g_p(s)=\frac{\overline{<c'>}}{\overline{c'_s}(s)}=\frac{(e^{2r_2}-1)(e^{2r_1}-1)}{e^{2r_2}-e^{2r_1}}\;\frac{\sqrt{(\lambda/2)^2+\alpha s}}{\alpha s}=\frac{M(s)}{\alpha s} \qquad |24|$$

with $r_{1,2}=\lambda/2\pm\sqrt{(\lambda/2)^2+\alpha s}$. Since $<\bar{c}'>=\overline{<c'>}$ and $\overline{c'_s}=\bar{c}$ the tranfer function for the whole reactor is:

$$G(s)=\frac{\bar{c}}{\bar{c}_{in}}=\{1+\varepsilon s+(1-\varepsilon)\beta s\,\frac{\sqrt{(\lambda/2)^2+\alpha s}}{\alpha s}\,\frac{(e^{2r_2}-1)(e^{2r_1}-1)}{(e^{2r_2}-e^{2r_1})}\}^{-1} \qquad |25|$$

The moments of the impulse response are obtained from Eq.(9):

$$\mu_o=1$$
$$\mu_1=\varepsilon+(1-\varepsilon)\beta=\gamma$$
$$\mu_2=2\mu_1^2+\frac{2}{3}(1-\varepsilon)\beta\alpha f(\lambda)$$

where

$$f(\lambda)=\frac{3}{\lambda}\{\frac{1}{th\lambda}-\frac{1}{\lambda}\} \qquad |26|$$

The variance of the impulse response is then:

$$\sigma^2=\gamma^2+\frac{2}{3}(1-\varepsilon)\alpha\ f(\lambda) \qquad |27|$$

In the absence of intraparticle forced convection, $\lambda=0$; then $f(\lambda)=1$ and we get:

$$\tilde{g}_p(s)=\{th\sqrt{\alpha s}\}/\sqrt{\alpha s} \qquad |24a|$$

$$\tilde{G}(s)=\{1+\varepsilon s+(1-\varepsilon)\beta s\,\frac{th\sqrt{\alpha s}}{\sqrt{\alpha s}}\}^{-1} \qquad |25a|$$

$$\tilde{\sigma}^2=\gamma^2+\frac{2}{3}(1-\varepsilon)\ \beta\tilde{\alpha} \qquad |27a|$$

If we compare Eqs(27a) and (27b) we see that the authors who got valu of effective diffusivities (apparent) by neglecting intraparticle conve tion, measured in fact $\tilde{\alpha}$ (or $\tilde{D}_e$) which is related with the true α (or D by:

$$\tilde{\alpha}=\alpha\ f(\lambda)\quad\text{or}\quad\tilde{D}_e=D_e/f(\lambda) \qquad |28|$$

At this point we can understand why apparent effective diffusivities, $\tilde{D}_e$ can change with flowrate ,if we note that the intraparticle Peclet number increases with Re and $f(\lambda)=1$ for $\lambda=0$ and $f(\lambda)=0$ when $\lambda\to\infty$.

If film mass transfer resistance is taken into account

$$k_f a\ (c-c_s) = \beta \frac{d\langle c'\rangle}{dt} \qquad |29|$$

where a is the specific area of the particle ($a=1/\ell$ for slab geometry) and k_f is the film mass transfer coefficient.Then the transfer function for the reactor is:

$$G_1(s)=\{1+\varepsilon s+\beta(1-\varepsilon)s \frac{M(s)}{\alpha s\left|1+\frac{M(s)}{Bi_m}\right|}\}^{-1} \qquad |30|$$

The variance of the impulse response is now:

$$\sigma^2= \gamma^2+ \frac{2}{3}\ \beta(1-\varepsilon)\ \alpha\{f(\lambda)+\frac{3}{Bi_m}\} \qquad |31|$$

In Figure 2 we show the influence of model parameters: λ, α and Bi_m on the impulse response of a nonadsorbable tracer in a two-phase perfectly mixed reactor.These results were obtained by using the Fast Fourier Transform to calculate the inverse of the transfer function.

If now a first order irreversible reaction is carried out in this system we should extend with caution the result obtained in Equation(10). In fact the reaction will take place only in the catalyst particles and then,assuming no film mass transfer resistance,the transfer function at the particle level is:

$$g_{pr}(s+Da) = \frac{M(s+Da)}{\alpha(s+Da)} \qquad |32|$$

which results from Eq(24) by replacing s by s+Da (Da is the Damkholer number $Da=k\tau$).Taking into account the reaction term in the overall mass balance for the whole reactor we get now the transfer function,relating outlet and inlet concentrations in the presence of reaction:

$$G_r(s)=\{1+\varepsilon s+\beta(1-\varepsilon)s\ \frac{M(s+Da)}{\alpha(s+Da)}\ +Da\ \frac{M(s+Da)}{\alpha(s+Da)}\}^{-1} \qquad |33|$$

The steady state outlet concentration,for a step input,is then:

$$\frac{c_{out}(\infty)}{c_{in}} = \{1+\ Da\ \frac{M(Da)}{\alpha\ Da}\}^{-1} \qquad |34|$$

We should notice that $\alpha Da=\phi^2$ (where ϕ is the Thiele modulus, $\phi=\ell\sqrt{k/D_e}$)

and since $M(Da) = \sqrt{(\lambda/2)^2+\phi^2}\,\{1/th\sqrt{\lambda^2+4\phi^2} - ch\lambda/sh\sqrt{\lambda^2+4\phi^2}\}$ we get, in the absence of intraparticle convection ($\lambda=0$; $M(Da)=\phi\ th\phi$):

$$\frac{c_{out}(\infty)}{c_{in}} = \frac{1}{1+\frac{Da\ th\phi}{\phi}} = \frac{1}{1+\eta Da} \qquad |34a|$$

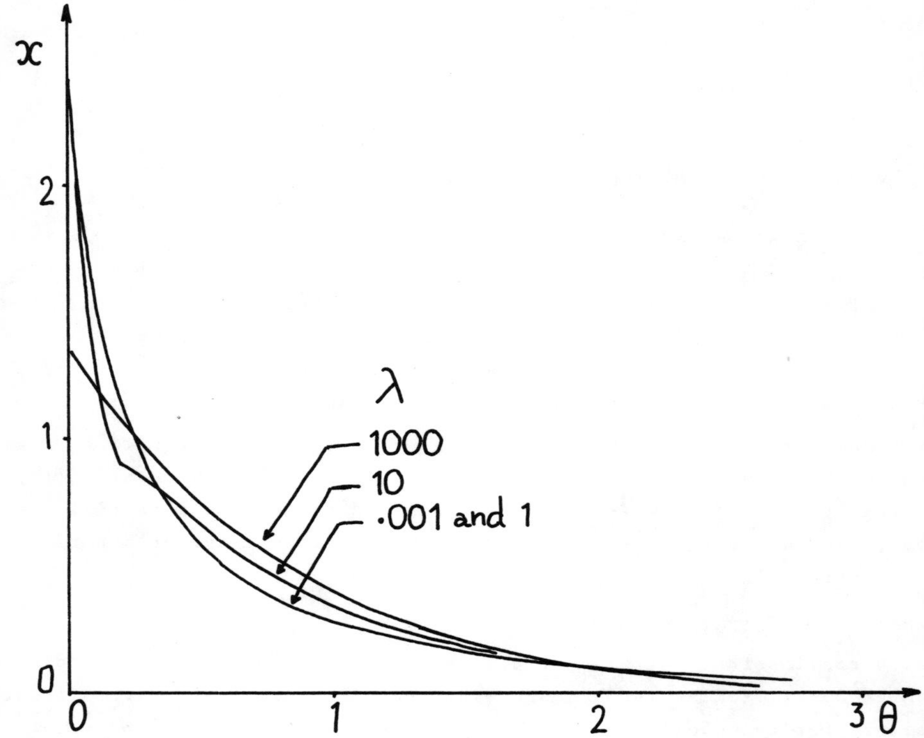

Figure 2a- Impulse response of a nonadsorbable tracer; reduced outlet concentration as a function of reduced time

Influence of the intraparticle Peclet number, λ
($\varepsilon=0.4$, $\beta=0.537$, $\alpha=1$, $Bi_m=\infty$)

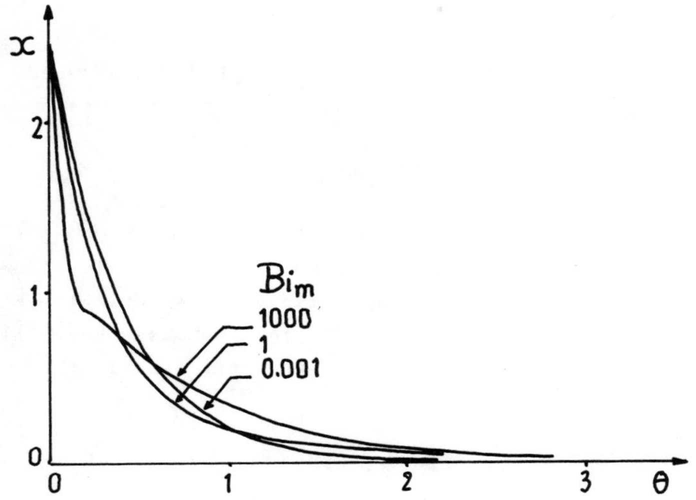

Figure 2b- Influence of mass Biot number on the impulse response of a nonadsorbable tracer in a CSTR (ε=0.4, β=0.537, α=1, λ=10)

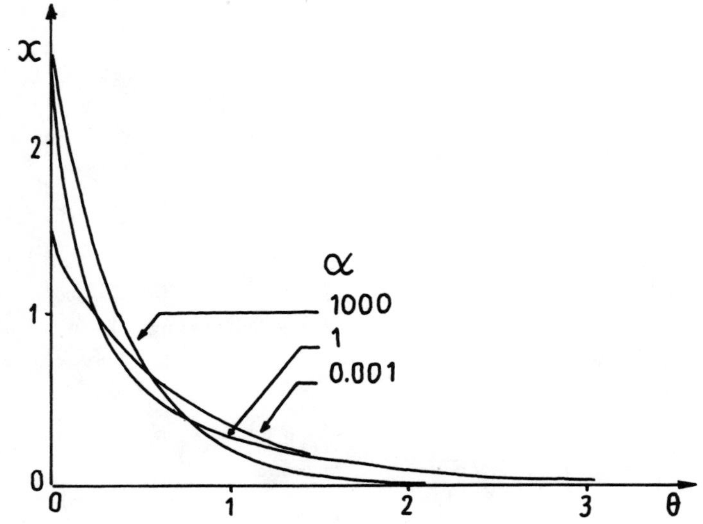

Figure 2c- Impulse response of a nonadsorbable tracer in a CSTR in absence of intraparticle convection; influence of α . (ε=0.4, β=0.537, λ=0, $Bi_m=\infty$)

- The fixed bed

Let us consider now a fixed bed reactor in which flows a nonadsorba ble tracer according to the axial dispersion model;the mass balance in a volume element is :

$$\varepsilon D_{ax} \frac{\partial^2 c}{\partial z^2} = u_o \frac{\partial c}{\partial z} + \varepsilon \frac{\partial c}{\partial t} + (1-\varepsilon)\beta \frac{\partial \langle c' \rangle}{\partial t} \qquad |35|$$

where D_{ax} is the axial dispersion coefficient,u_o the superficial veloc ty and t the time coordinate.Introducing dimensionless variables,$z^*=z/l$ $\theta=t/\tau$ and $Pe=u_o L/\varepsilon D_{ax}$ (Peclet number) we get,for the case where film ma transfer resistance is important,an overall transfer function:

$$G(s)= \exp\left\{\frac{Pe}{2}\left(1-\sqrt{1+\frac{4N(s)}{Pe}}\right)\right\} \qquad |36|$$

with $N(s)=\varepsilon s+(1-\varepsilon)\beta s \dfrac{M(s)}{\alpha s\left(1+\dfrac{M(s)}{Bi_m}\right)}$.

The moments of the impulse response are now:

$$\mu_1=\gamma$$
$$\mu_2=\gamma^2\left(1+\frac{2}{Pe}\right)+\frac{2}{3}(1-\varepsilon)\beta\ \alpha\left\{f(\lambda)+\frac{3}{Bi_m}\right\}$$

The limiting cases are:

- $\lambda=0$;absence of intraparticle convection
- $Pe=\infty$;plug flow of the fluid phase
- $Bi_m=\infty$;film mass transfer negligible

In Figures 3 we show the effect of the model parameters on the impulse response of a nonadsorbable tracer;results were computed by taking the inverse of G(s) with FFT technique.

Again if a first order irreversible reaction is taking place in the catalyst,the tranfer function is $G_r(s)$ obtained from G(s) by replacing N(s) by $N_r(s)$,where:

$$N_r(s)=\varepsilon s+(1-\varepsilon)\beta s \frac{M(s+Da)}{\alpha(s+Da)\left(1+\dfrac{M(s+Da)}{Bi_m}\right)} + Da\frac{M(s+Da)}{\alpha(s+Da)}$$

The steady state outlet concentration is,for the case of infinite Bi_m

$$\frac{c_{out}(\infty)}{c_{in}} = \exp\left\{\frac{Pe}{2}\left(1-\sqrt{1+\frac{4\ Da\ M(Da)}{Pe\ \phi^2}}\right)\right\} \qquad |37|$$

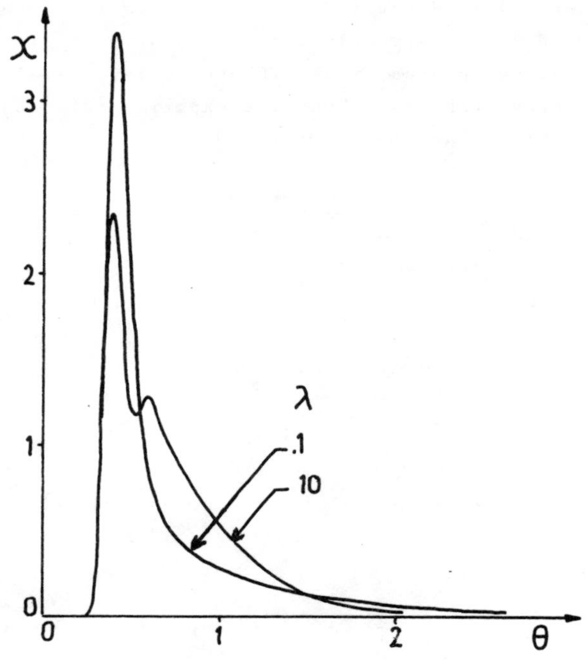

Figure 3a- Response of a fixed bed to a Dirac impulse of nonadsorbable tracer :influence of intraparticle Peclet number (ε=0.4, β=0.537,α=1, Bi_m=10,Pe=100)

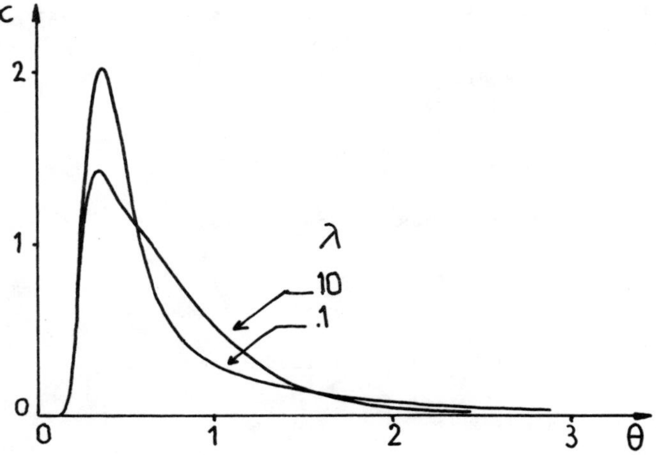

Figure 3b- Response of a fixed bed to a Dirac input of nonadsorbable tracer:influence of λ (ε=0.4,β=0.537,Pe=20,Bi_m=10,α=1)

Experiments were carried out in a SPSR in order to measure the effective diffusivity of a nonadsorbable tracer - hydrogen - in a catalyst based on vanadium and phosphorus oxydes (Rhone-Poulenc catalyst BM329) used for partial oxydation of hydrocarbons. The experimental conditions were reported by Ahn (18) and are listed below:

catalyst:

particle diameter =0.45 cm
intraparticle porosity =0.537
true solid density =2.84 g/cc
apparent solid density =1.31 g/cc
particle pore volume =0.41 cm^3/g
S_{BET} =4.3 m^2/g
mean pore diameter =10^4 Å

reactor :

tube diameter =2.12 cm
length =30 cm
porosity =0.676
T =293 K

Experimental data were treated by using a model which neglected intraparticle convection; from the variance of the impulse response Ahn (18) got $\tilde{\tau}_d=f(Re)$, i.e., the time constant for diffusion decreases with the Reynolds number. These observations were explained by our complete model namely by Equation (28). Moreover we were able to predict the changes of apparent effective diffusivity from the knowledge of basic quantities such as permeability of the catalyst.

In fact the pressure drop across the bed is

$$\frac{\Delta P}{L} = a\, u_o + b\, u_o^2 \qquad |38|$$

while the pressure drop across the pellet is:

$$\frac{\Delta p}{\ell} = \mu v_o / B \qquad |39|$$

The equality of Eqs (38) and (39) leads to:

$$v_o = a_1 B\, u_o + a_2\, B\, u_o^2 \qquad |40|$$

or

$$\tilde{\tau}_d(Re) = f\,(Re; B, \tau_d) \qquad |41|$$

Given the experimental points ($\tilde{\tau}_d$,Re) and Eq(41) a two parameter optimization by the Rosenbrock method leads to the values of τ_d=1.216 sec and B=1.275×10^{-5} cm^2 :finally D_e=4.61×10^{-3} cm^2/s. Once the permeability B is known we can plot the calculated intraparticle convective velocity v_o as a function of the superfitial velocity,u_o and compare the predicted values with the experimental results (since $\tilde{\tau}_d = \tau_d f(\lambda)$,from an experimental point ($\tilde{\tau}_d$,Re) we get $\lambda$and then v_o).

Figure 4 compares the experimental and calculated curve v_o versus u_o.

Similar trends on changes of apparent effective diffusivities with flowrate were reported by Boersma-Klein and Moulijn (21) and Hsu and Haynes (22) .

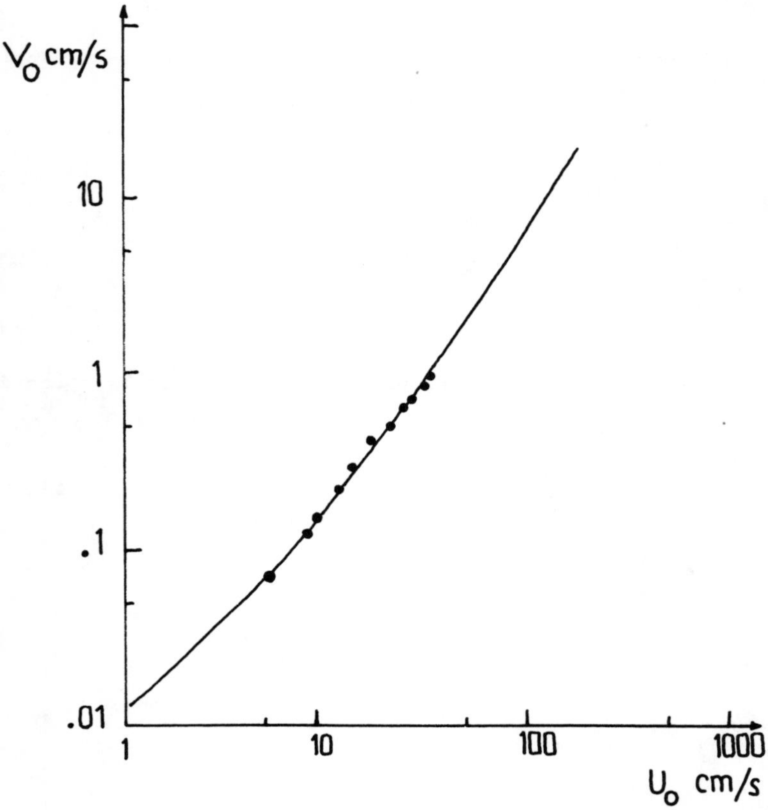

Figure 4- Intraparticle convective velocity,v_o versus superficial velocity,u_o in a fixed bed.

2.2. Practical importance of intraparticle forced convection in reactor design.

Let us consider a first order irreversible reaction in an isothermal catalyst particle (slab geometry) and that the transport mechanisms inside the pellet are diffusion and convection. Nir and Pismen (16) derived an effectiveness factor, η_{d-c} given by:

$$\eta_{d-c} = \frac{1/\alpha_1 \quad -1/\alpha_2}{\coth\alpha_1 \ -\coth\alpha_2} \qquad |42|$$

with $\alpha_{1,2} = \lambda/2 \pm \sqrt{(\lambda/2)^2 + \phi^2}$. They show that there is an intermediate range of Thiele modulus for which the effectiveness factor is enhanced by the action of intraparticle convection.

The analysis starts with the steady state mass balance of a reactive species in a volume element of catalyst

$$\frac{d^2 f}{d\rho^2} - \lambda \frac{df}{d\rho} - \phi^2 f = 0 \qquad |43|$$

with boundary conditions

$$f=1, \quad \rho=0 \qquad |43a|$$

$$f=1, \quad \rho=2 \qquad |43b|$$

where f is the reduced concentration and ρ the reduced catalyst coordinate. The solution of eq(43) leads to the concentration profile:

$$f = \frac{e^{\alpha_1(\rho-1)}\ \mathrm{sh}\alpha_2 - e^{\alpha_2(\rho-1)}\ \mathrm{sh}\alpha_1}{\mathrm{sh}(\alpha_2 - \alpha_1)} \qquad |44|$$

and finally to the effectiveness factor.

In the absence of intraparticle convection we already know that:

$$\eta_d = \frac{\mathrm{th}\phi}{\phi} \qquad |45|$$

and thus the enhancement factor, as defined by Nir and Pismen, is:

$$E = \eta_{d-c} / \ \eta_d \qquad |46|$$

However in order to quantify the errors made in current design practice we should compare η_{d-c} with the apparent effectiveness factor, $\tilde{\eta}_d$ based on an apparent effective diffusivity, $\tilde{D}_e$ measured at a given flowrate (19).

Since then $\tilde{\phi} = \phi \sqrt{f(\lambda)}$ we get:

$$\tilde{\eta}_d = \frac{th\{\phi \sqrt{f(\lambda)}\}}{\phi \sqrt{f(\lambda)}} \quad |47|$$

and finalyy we define a new enhancement factor:

$$\tilde{E} = \eta_{d-c} / \tilde{\eta}_d \quad |48|$$

Figure 5 shows $\tilde{E}$ factor as a function of the intraparticle Peclet number for fixed values of Thiele modulus:it can be seen that errors of 100 % can be made by neglecting intraparticle convection in reactor design.

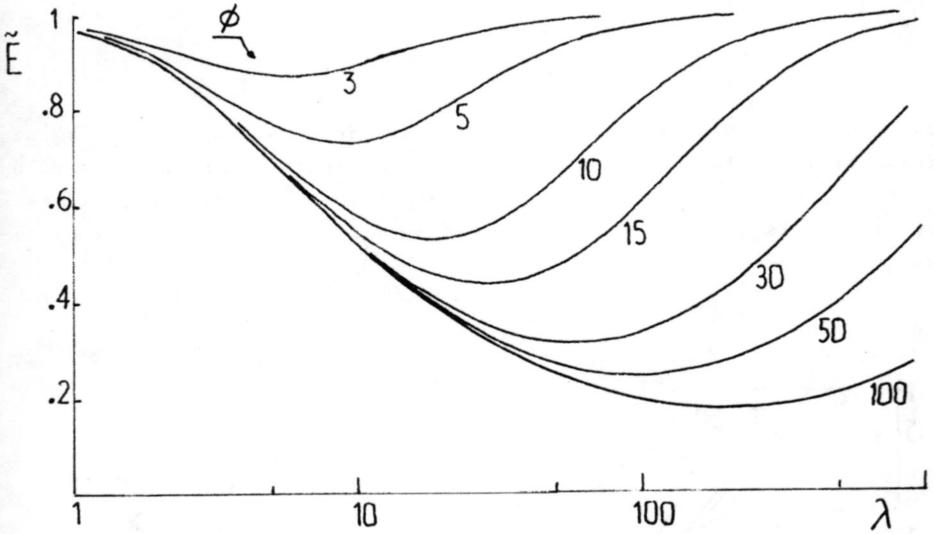

Figure 5- $\tilde{E}$ factor versus intraparticle Peclet number with the Thiele modulus as parameter

We can extend this **analysis** for zero order reactions which often occur in biological wastewater treatment. We should be careful when writing the mass balance for the catalyst pellet:in fact the true reaction rate is a constant,k provided there is a positive reactive concentration. If no reactive reached a point inside the catalyst then the reaction rate is zero (23).Having this in mind we can calculate the points inside the catalyst for which the concentration profile reach zero values, ρ^* and ρ' from the equations:

$$e^{-\lambda\rho^*} + \lambda\rho^* = 1 + \frac{\lambda^2}{\phi^2} \tag{49a}$$

and

$$e^{\lambda(2-\rho')} - (2-\rho')\lambda = 1 + \frac{\lambda^2}{\phi^2} \tag{49b}$$

The reactive concentration is positive provided $\phi < \phi_c$ with:

$$\phi_c = \lambda \Big/ \sqrt{\left\{\frac{2\lambda}{e^{2\lambda}-1} - 1 - \ln\frac{2\lambda}{e^{2\lambda}-1}\right\}} \tag{50}$$

and finally:

$$\eta_{d-c} = 1 \quad , \phi < \phi_c \tag{51a}$$

$$\eta_{d-c} = 1 - \frac{\rho' - \rho^*}{2} \quad , \phi \geqslant \phi_c \tag{51b}$$

In Figure 6 we plot η_{d-c} as a function of the Thiele modulus with the intraparticle Peclet number as a parameter. Again it can be seen that in an intermediate range of ϕ there is an enhancement in the effectiveness factor. This is also shown by ploting E as a function of ϕ for fixed values of λ (Figure 7).

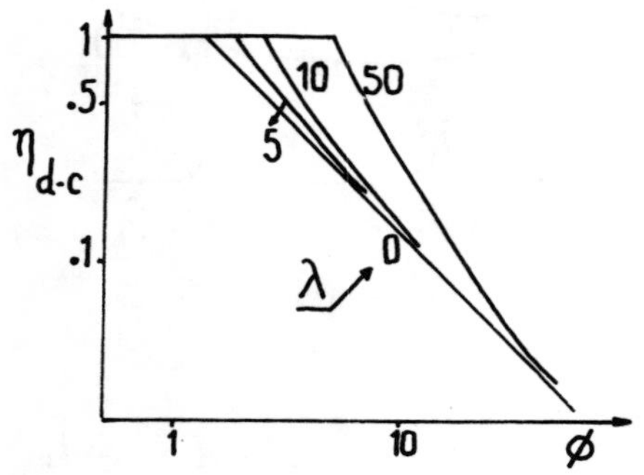

Figure 6- η_{d-c} versus ϕ, with λ as a parameter

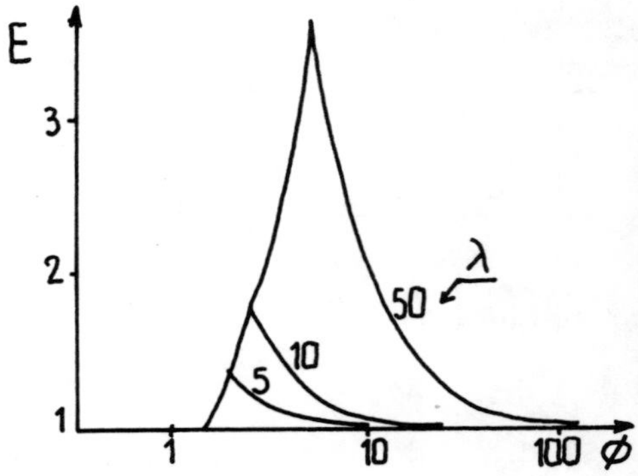

Figure 7- E factor versus ϕ, with λ as parameter

Following the methodology developed above for first order reactions we can compare η_{d-c} with the calculated effectiveness factor based on an apparent effective diffusivity, $\tilde{\eta}_d$ and then plot $\tilde{E}=\eta_{d-c}/\tilde{\eta}_d$ as a function of the model parameters, as shown in Figure 8.

These concepts can be applied in the design of biological reactors. Just as an example we will consider a two phase perfectly mixed reactor. The overall mass balance in steady state operation is

$$Qc_{in} = Q\,c_{out} + (1-\varepsilon)V\,\eta\,k \qquad |52|$$

which coupled to Eqs (51a) and (51b) enables us to calculate the substrate conversion as a function of $N_r=(1-\varepsilon)k\tau/c_{in}$ (number of reaction units), $N_b=(1-\varepsilon)D_e\tau/\ell^2$ (number of diffusion units for the biofilm) and $N_c=(1-\varepsilon)v_o\tau/\ell$ (number of convection units). These results are shown in Figure 9.

If convection is not important then the effectiveness factor for zero order reactions is simply:

$$\eta=1 \;, \quad \phi<\sqrt{2} \quad \text{(chemical regime)} \qquad |53a|$$
$$\eta=\sqrt{2}/\phi; \quad \phi>\sqrt{2} \quad \text{(diffusional regime)} \qquad |53b|$$

and then the substrate conversion, X_A is:

$$X_A=N_r \quad \text{(chemical regime)} \qquad |54a|$$
$$X_A=\sqrt{\alpha^2+2\alpha}-\alpha \quad \text{(diffusional regime)} \qquad |54b|$$

where $\alpha=N_rN_b$.

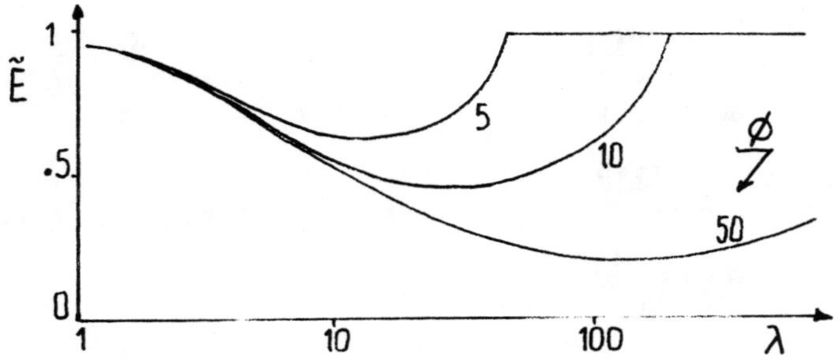

Figure 8 - $\tilde{E}$ factor versus intraparticle Peclet number; zero order reaction.

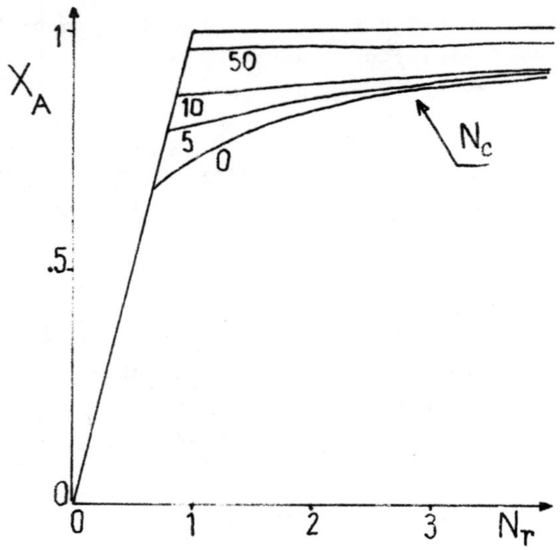

Figure 9- Conversion or efficiency, X_A of a CSTR versus N_r, with N_c as a parameter (N_b=1).

3. NONLINEAR ADSORPTION AND REACTION IN ADSORPTIVE REACTORS

In a number of chemical engineering systems one is faced with the problem of simultaneous adsorption and chemical reaction. This is the case of the operation of activated carbon columns in wastewater treatment, where removal of organics by adsorption is coupled with biodegradation and chromatographic reactors.

At the laboratory level the problem arises when measuring equilibrium and kinetic data by chromatographic techniques; the usual way to get kinetic parameters from the ratio of outlet and inlet peaks is not adequate unless the adsorption equilibrium isotherm is linear.

Because of these implications let us analyse the propagation of concentration waves in fixed beds, using the method of characteristics as a mathematical tool.

We will start with the case of nonlinear adsorption alone in fixed beds before tackling the more complex problem of nonlinear adsorption coupled with chemical reaction.

We will assume an equilibrium model, plug flow of the fluid phase and isothermal operation.

- Nonlinear adsorption in fixed beds

The model equations are the mass balance and the adsorption equilibrium isotherm,respectively:

$$\frac{\partial x}{\partial z^*} + \frac{\partial x}{\partial \theta^*} + \xi \frac{\partial y}{\partial \theta^*} = 0 \qquad |55|$$

$$y=f(x)= \frac{Kx}{1+(K-1)x} \qquad |56|$$

where $x=c/c_o$ and $y=q/Q$ are the reduced fluid and solid concentrations, respectively, $\xi=(1-\varepsilon)Q/\varepsilon c_o$ is the mass capacity factor, z^* is the reduced axial coordinate and $\theta^*=t/\tau^*$ is the reduced time (τ^* is the space time defined as the ratio of the void volume in the reactor and flowrate).

Combining Eqs (55) and (56) and considering a parameter $\underline{s}$ running along the characteristic curve σ_i, the method of characteristics leads to:

$$\frac{dz^*}{d\theta^*} = \frac{1}{1+ \xi f'(x)} \qquad |57a|$$

$$\frac{dx}{d\theta^*} = 0 \qquad |57b|$$

Equation (57a) is the characteristic direction along which Eq.(57b) is integrated. Eq.(57a) also states that the velocity of a concentration, x is inversely proportional to the slope of the adsorption equilibrium isotherm at that point.The general equation of characteristics is then:

$$\theta^*= \{1 + \frac{K}{|1+(K-1)x|^2}\} z^*+ \text{const.} \qquad |58|$$

Different solutions can be obtained for different inputs:step,pulse or Dirac.As an example let us consider the case of step input;since at $\theta^*=0, x=0$ the characteristics leaving the z^*-axis are:

$$\theta^*=(1+ \xi K)z^* + \text{const} \qquad |58a|$$

and as at $z^*=0, x=1$ the characteristics leaving the θ^*-axis are:

$$\theta^*=(1+ \frac{\xi}{K})z^* + \text{const} \qquad |58b|$$

In the case of unfavorable isotherms, $f''(x)> 0$ higher concentrations move slower than lower concentrations and then a dispersive wave occurs.

If the isotherm is favorable, $f''(x) < 0$ the inverse situation occurs and then a shock is formed; the shock velocity is:

$$\frac{dz^*}{d\theta^*} = \frac{1}{1+\frac{y^- - y^+}{x^- - x^+}} \qquad |59|$$

where superscripts - and + denote concentrations behind and ahead the shock. Thus the shock velocity is inversely proportional to the slope of the chord between points representing the feed state (x^-, y^-) and the presaturation state of the bed (x^+, y^+).

The practical implications of these results should be stressed: for favorable isotherms the equilibrium model predicts a breakthrough time, θ^*_{Bp} equal to the stoechiometric time, θ^*_{st}, i.e.,

$$\theta^*_{Bp} = \theta^*_{st} = 1+\xi \qquad |60|$$

while for unfavorable isotherms ($K < 1$) we get:

$$\theta^*_{Bp} = 1 + K\xi \qquad |61|$$

The useful time of operation strongly depends of the nature of the whole adsorption equilibrium isotherm and not only on the value of the capacity, Q corresponding to the inlet concentration, c_o.

- <u>First order irreversible reaction, $A \xrightarrow{k} B$ coupled with nonlinear adsorption of A only.</u>

Now let us consider a first order irreversible reaction occuring at the active sites of a supported catalyst and simultaneously A is adsorbed in the support according to a nonlinear equilibrium adsorption isotherm.

Under similar assumptions the model equations are the mass balances for components A and B, respectively:

$$\frac{\partial x_A}{\partial z^*} + \{1+\xi f'(x_A)\}\frac{\partial x_A}{\partial \theta^*} + Da\, x_A = 0 \qquad |62a|$$

$$\frac{\partial x_B}{\partial z^*} + \frac{\partial x_B}{\partial \theta^*} - Da\, x_A = 0 \qquad |62b|$$

The method of characteristics leads to:

$$\frac{d\theta^*}{dz^*} = 1 + \xi f'(x_A) \qquad |63a|$$

$$\frac{dx_A}{dz^*} = - Da\ x_A \qquad |63b|$$

Integrating Eq(63b) and substituting in Eq(63a) we get finally the directions of characteristics:

$$(1+\xi K)z^* + \frac{K'}{Da}\{\ln|1+(K-1)C_1 e^{-Da\ z^*}| - \frac{1}{1+(K-1)C_1 e^{-Da\ z^*}}\} = \theta^* + \text{const} \qquad |64|$$

Now for the step input the boundary conditions are: $\theta^*=0, x_A=0$, $\forall z^*$ and $z^*=0, x_A=1$, $\forall\theta^* > 0$;then the characteristics leaving z^*-axis are obtained for $C_1=0$ and those leaving θ^*-axis result from $C_1=1$.

Again a shock will be formed;the shock equation is :

$$\theta^* = z^* + \xi K\{z^* + \frac{1}{Da}\ln|\frac{1+(K-1)\exp(-Da\ z^*)}{K}|\} = g(z^*) \qquad |65|$$

The concentration of component A is then:

$$x_A(z^*,\theta^*) = \exp(-Da\ z^*)\ H\{\theta - g(z^*)\} \qquad |66|$$

Similarly for component B,which is not adsorbed,we get:

$$x_B(z^*,\theta^*) = \{1-e^{-Da\ \tilde{z}^*}\}\{H(\theta^*-z^*) - H(\theta^*-g(z^*)\} + \{1-e^{-Daz^*}\}H\{\theta^*-g(z^*)\} \qquad |67|$$

with

$$\tilde{z}^* = \frac{1}{Da}\ln\{K\exp|Da(\theta^*-z^*)/K\xi| - (K-1)\}$$

Figures 10 and 11 show the diagram of characteristics and concentration profiles,for components A and B,respectively.

Let us now calculate the breakthrough time in the case of nonlinear adsorption coupled with reaction;from Eq(65) at $z^*=1$ we get:

$$\theta^*_{Bp} = 1 + \xi K'\{1 + \frac{1}{Da}\ln|\frac{1+(K-1)\exp(-Da)}{K}|\} \qquad |68|$$

For favorable isotherms the breakthrough time is always higher if adsorption is coupled with chemical reaction and then the number of sorption/desorption cycles for a given operation is reduced.In terms of the average of the chord slopes linking the point (0,0) and the moving

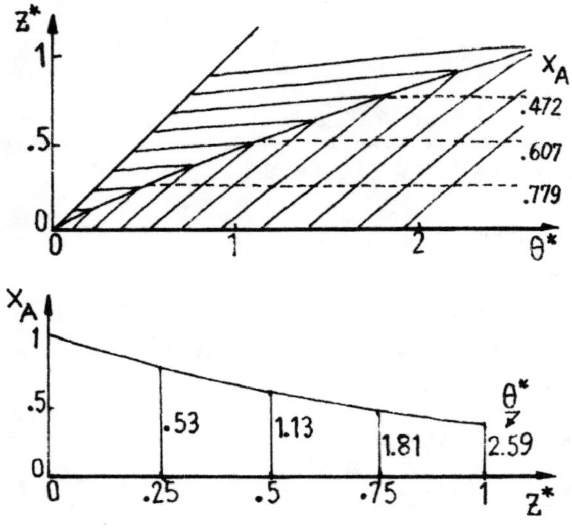

Figure 10- Nonlinear adsorption and irreversible reaction;A adsorbed. Characteristics and concentration profiles of A (K=10,Da=1 and ξ=1).

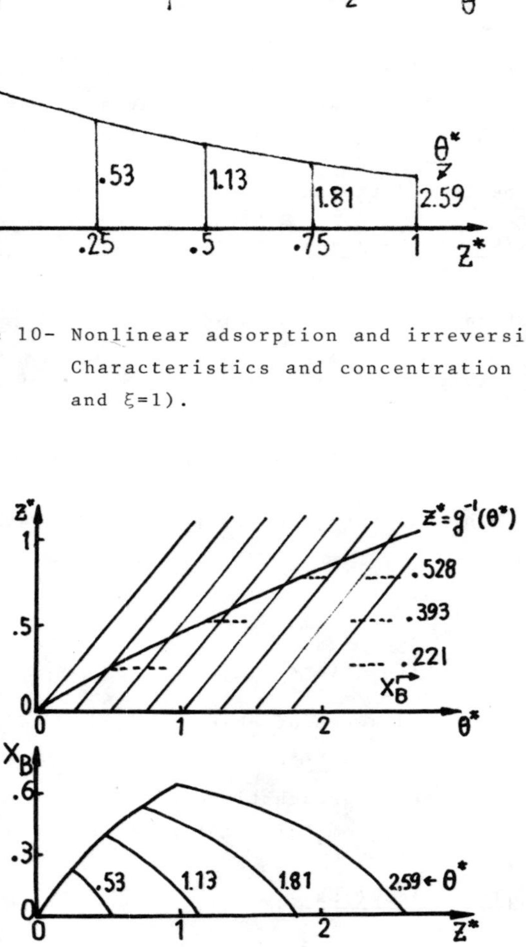

Figure 11- Characteristics and concentration profiles for the non-adsorbed component,B.

point (x,y) ,i.e., < y/x> we obtain:

$$\theta^*_{Bp} = 1+\xi \{ K - \frac{(K-1)(1-\exp(-Da))}{Da} \langle \frac{y}{x} \rangle \} \qquad |69|$$

Figure 12 shows the reduced breakthrough time as a function of K (which measures the nonlinearity of the equilibrium isotherm) and Da (Damkholer number, $Da=k\tau^*$) for a fixed value of the capacity parameter.

The increase in the breakthrough time, predicted by our model, agrees with recently reported experimental observations (24,25,26).

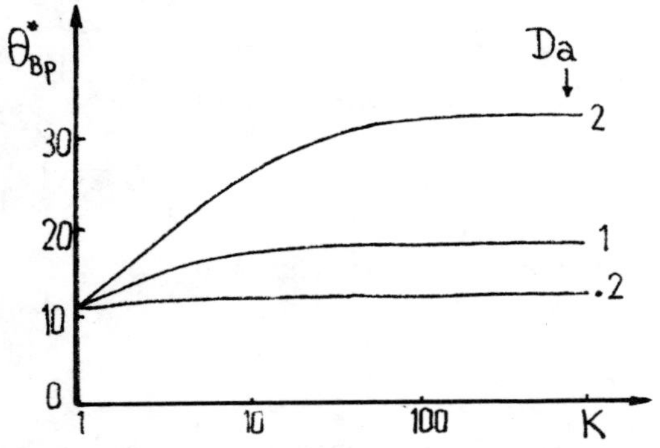

Figure 12- Breakthrough time as a function of K and Da (ξ=10)

The above treatment can be extended to other type of input and reversible reactions ,with one or both components adsorbed (27,28).

If we consider now a step input but adsorption of both components A and B according to the equilibrium adsorption isotherm:

$$y_i = \frac{K_i x_i}{1+ \sum_i K_i x_i} \qquad (i=A,B) \qquad |70|$$

the model equations are the mass balances for A and B, respectively:

$$\frac{\partial x_A}{\partial z^*} + \frac{\partial x_A}{\partial \theta^*} + \xi \frac{\partial y_A}{\partial \theta^*} + Da\ x_A = 0 \qquad |71a|$$

$$\frac{\partial x_B}{\partial z^*} + \frac{\partial x_B}{\partial \theta^*} + \xi \frac{\partial y_B}{\partial \theta^*} - Da\ x_A = 0 \qquad |71b|$$

This system is hyperbolic and non reducible. However if A is more adsorbed than B we can assume that until the shock of A (which takes place after the shock of B at a given position z*) the ratio between concentrations of A and B is equal to the ratio which occurs in a plug flow reactor without adsorption, i.e., before the shock of A (at each z*) the concentration reached a steady state value.

For a step input the characteristics for component A are:

-characteristics leaving z*-axis

$$\theta^* + \text{const} = (1+\xi K_A) z^* \qquad |72a|$$

-characteristics leaving θ*-axis

$$\theta^* + \text{const} = z^* + \frac{\xi K_A}{(1+K_B)Da}\left\{ \frac{1}{1+K_B} \ln\left| \frac{(1+K_B)+(K_A-K_B)e^{-Da\, z^*}}{\exp(-Da\, z^*)} \right| + \frac{1}{(1+K_B)+(K_A-K_B)\exp(-Da\, z^*)} \right\} \qquad |72b|$$

The shock equation for component A is:

$$\theta^* = z^* + \frac{K_A}{(1+K_B)Da} \ln \frac{(1+K_B)+(K_A-K_B)e^{-Da\, z^*}}{(1+K_A)\exp(-Da\, z^*)} = g(z^*) \qquad |73|$$

and from Eq(73) we easily obtain the concentration of A, i.e.,

$$x_A(z^*,\theta^*) = \exp(-Da\, z^*)\, H\{\theta^* - g(z^*)\} \qquad |74|$$

Now since B is less adsorbed than A, component B exists ahead of A (at fixed time) and Eq.(71b) is still valid: the characteristics for B will be then:

- $\theta^* < g(z^*)$; x_B is constant along the characteristics

$$\theta^* + \text{const} = \left\{1 + \frac{\xi K_B}{(1+K_B x_B)^2}\right\} z^* \qquad |75|$$

- $\theta^* > g(z^*)$; $x_B = C_2 - \exp(-Da\, z^*)$ along the characteristics

$$\theta^* + \text{const} = z^* + \frac{\xi K_B}{(1+K_B C_2)Da}\left\{ \frac{1}{1+K_B C_2} \ln \frac{(1+K_B C_2)+(K_A-K_B)e^{-Da\, z^*}}{\exp(-Da\, z^*)} + \frac{1}{(1+K_B C_2)+(K_A-K_B)\exp(-Da\, z^*)} \right\} \qquad |76|$$

Since these characteristics are only valid at θ*> g(z*) they will leave the θ^*-axis until $\theta^*=g(z^*)$;as at $z^*=0, x_B=0$ then $C_2=1$ .The characteristics leaving θ^*-axis are given by Eq(76) with $C_2=1$.At $\theta^*=g(z^*)$ a shock of B exists together with a shock of A;this implies that:

$$\left.\frac{d\theta^*}{dz^*}\right|_{\text{shock of A}} = \left.\frac{d\theta^*}{dz^*}\right|_{2^{nd}\text{ shock of B}} \qquad |77|$$

This is the second shock of B which leaves the fixed bed.From Eq.(77) we can get the value of the concentration of component B at the right of $g(z^*)$, i.e., x_B^+ .With this value we can derive the characteristics for $\theta^* < g(z^*)$ which are straight lines.After $z^*=g^{-1}(\theta^*), x_B^+$ is carried out without change until the first shock of B ;the characteristics which carry $x_B^+(z^*)$ are:

$$\theta^* = \{1+ \frac{\xi\ K_B}{|1+K_B x_B^+(\tilde{z}^*)|^2}\}\ z^* + \text{const} \qquad |78|$$

and the first shock of B has a velocity given by:

$$\left.\frac{d\theta^*}{dz^*}\right|_{1^{st}\text{ shock of B}} = 1 + \frac{\xi\ K_B}{1 + K_B x_B^+(\tilde{z}^*)} \qquad |79|$$

Eliminating θ^* between Eqs (78) and (79) we get,after some algebra,the equation for the first shock of B,i.e.,

$$h(z^*) = \{1+ \frac{\xi\ K_B}{|1+K_B x_B^+(\tilde{z}^*)|^2}\}(z^*-\tilde{z}^*)+g(\tilde{z}^*) \qquad |80|$$

The concentration of component B is finally :

$$x_B(z^*,\theta^*)=x_B^+(\tilde{z}^*)\ \{H|\theta^*-h(z^*)|-H|\theta^*-g(z^*)|\}\ -(1-e^{-Da\ z^*})H|\theta^*-g(z^*)|$$

|81|

Figures 13 and 14 show the diagram of characteristics for components A and B,respectively.Figures 15 and 16 present the concentration profiles and history of concentrations for those components.

Besides the practical importance of increasing the breakthrough time in adsorptive reactors,as a result of the coupling between nonlinear adsorption and chemical reaction, the above theory provides a tool for obtaining equilibrium and kinetic data from dynamic chromatographic experiments.

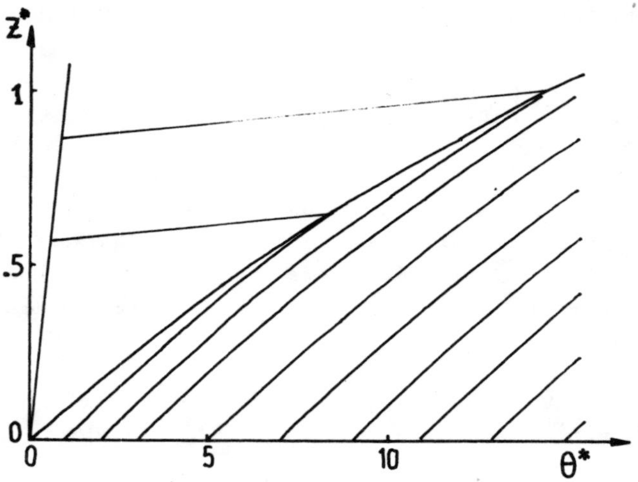

Figure 13- Nonlinear adsorption and irreversible reaction;both components adsorbed. Characteristics for component A (K_A=10,K_B=1,Da=1,ξ=10)

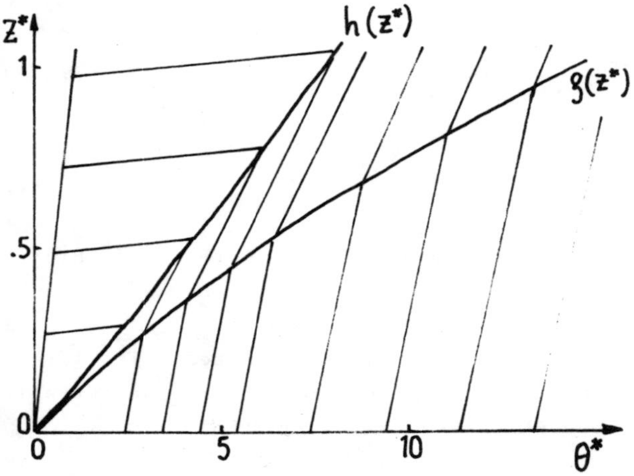

Figure 14- Characteristics for component B.

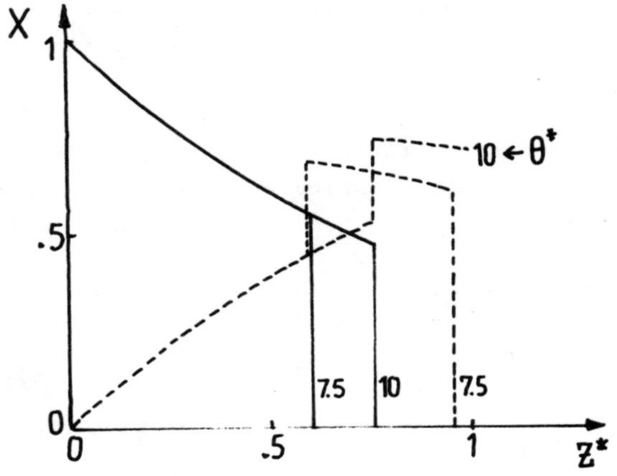

Figure 15- Concentration profiles for components A (——) and B(---).

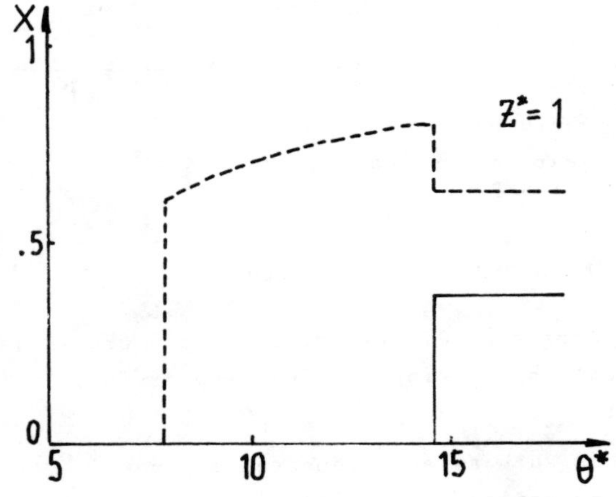

Figure 16- Histories of concentrations for components A and B

A ———— ; B -------

In fact the current methods are only valid for linear equilibrium: in that case the ratio of outlet and inlet peaks is directly related to the kinetic constant.This is no longer valid if the equilibrium is non-linear:however model parameters can be obtained from the breakthrough time,outlet plateau concentration and overall mass balance in the case of a step input. For Dirac input kinetic data can be obtained from similar experimentally measured quantities.

Figure 17 shows the response of the column in the case of adsorption alone and in the case of adsorption coupled with reaction;the parameter values used were: $K=10, \xi=2, Da=1$ (only A adsorbed) and $a=1$ (unit impulse).

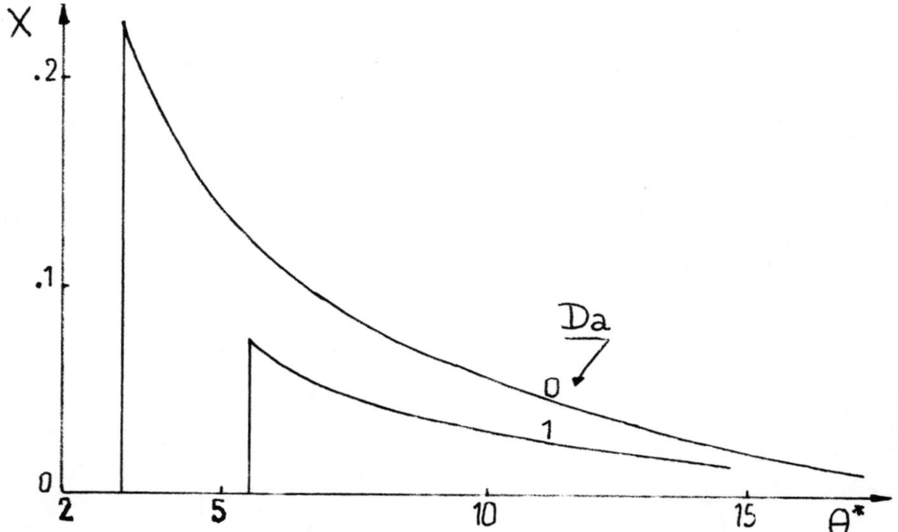

Figure 17- Chromatographic peaks

—— nonlinear adsorption

---- adsorption and reaction

4. CONCLUDING REMARKS.THE CONCEPT OF PERCOLATION

The concept of residence time distribution already proved its usefulness in areas of chemical engineering ranging from drying,clarifiers, twin screw extrusion,etc.

Also in adjacent areas such as environmental engineering tracer studies have been used to determine dispersion of pollutants in rivers,estuaries and locate sources of pollution.In such large systems one is faced with multiple inlets,multiple outlets and then detailed analysis of internal age distributions should be of interest.

In biomedicine tracer techniques have been largely used under the terminology of "dilution technique",in order to get information on circulating blood volume,etc.

In reaction engineering one should ask if he concept of residence time distribution is really useful.It can be said that one can not describe the fine texture of fluid flow through a reactor by using RTD measurements.This is specially true for multiphase reactors;however tracer experiments coupled to the measure of flowrates in different points of a section give some insights on problems of fluid mal-distribution.

New concepts are now being applied to chemical engineering such as the concepts of percolation and fractal.

Of particular interest is the work done by the group of Prof L'Homme in Liège (29,30) using the peocolation concept to predict hydrodynamics of trickle-bed reactors.

They start the analysis by making the observation that in a trickle--bed the liquid flow texture is formed by trickling films,stagnant pockets and nonirrigated particles.Then since the spatial distribution of these zones determines the reactor behavior they take two levels of description: particle level (elementary tranport cell) and reactor level. At that moment a percolation process is defined by ascribing to each cell a property (hydrodynamican connection) following some stochastic distribution:it was considered that the liquid flow inside a cell is determined by the local irrigation rate and the cell hydrodynamic surrounding. They took as basic parameters the mean overlaping rate between trajectories leading to and leaving the cells and the relative amount of the isotropic and anisotropic flow structures.Moreover they were able to correlate dynamic hold-up with those parameters introduced by percolation theory.

However the coupling of hydrodynamics,heat and mass transfer and chemical reaction was not solved yet in the framework of percolation theory. This approach and obviously the detailed description through fluid dynamics (measure of local velocities,local porosities,etc) should prove very important in the near future.

ACKNOWLEDGMENTS

Financial support from NATO Scientific Affairs Division,Research Grant 138/82 and INIC is gratefully acknowledged.

Contribution and friendship of my coworkers J.Loureiro,C.Costa and J.Õrfão and Prof. A.Zoulalian UTC) made this work possible.

REFERENCES

1 P.V.Danckwerts,Chem.Eng.Sci.,2(1953),1

2 A.E.Rodrigues,"Theory of Residence Time Distributions" in Multiphase Chemical Reactors,ed.A.Rodrigues,J.Calo and N.Sweed,M.Nijhoff(1981)

3 E.B.Nauman,Chem.Eng.Commun.,8(1981),53

4 O.Levenspiel and K.Bischoff,Adv.Chem.Eng.,4(1963),95

5 B.Buffham,Proc.Royal Soc.London,A333(1973),89

6 A.Kreft and A.Zuber,Chem.Eng.Sci.,33(1978),471

7 L.Gibilaro,Chem.Eng.Sci.,33(1978),487

8 E.B.Nauman,Chem.Eng.Sci.,36(1981),957

9 T.Zwietering,Chem.Eng.Sci.,11(1959),1

10 E.Nauman and C.Collinge,Chem.Eng.Sci.,23(1968),1309

11 R.Shinnar,Levich Conference,Oxford(1977)

12 J.Schwartz,E.Weger and M.Dudukovic,AIChEJ,22(1976),894

13 A.El-Hisnawi,M.Dudukovic and P.Mills,7th ISCRE,Boston(1982)

14 H.Hofmann,"Fluiddynamics,mass transfer and chemical reaction in multiphase catalytic fixed bed reactors",NATO ASI "Mass tranfer with chemical reaction in multiphase systems",Izmir(1981)

15 A.Wheeler,Adv.Cat.,3(1951),249

16 A.Nir and L.Pismen,Chem.Eng.Sci.,32(1977),35

17 A.Nir,Chem.Eng.Sci.,32(1977),925

18 B.Ahn,Thesis,Université Techonologie Compiègne(1980)

19 A.Rodrigues,B.Ahn and A.Zoulalian,AIChEJ,in press

20 R.Cogan,G.Pipkos and A.Nir,Chem.Eng.Sci.,37(1982),147

21 W.Boersma-Klein and J.Moulijn,Chem.Eng.Sci.,34(1979),959

22 L.Hsu and H.Haynes,AIChEJ,27(1981),81

23 A.Rodrigues,J.Orfão and A.Zoulalian,submitted to Chem.Eng.Commun.

24 G.Andrews and C.Tien,AIChEJ,27(1981),396

25 J.Lowry and C.Burkhead,JWPCF,52(1980),389

26 W.Weber,"Concepts and principles of carbon applications in wastewater treatment" in Applications of adsorption to wastewater treatment, ed.W.Eckenfelder,Enviro Press(1981)

27 A.Rodrigues,J.Loureiro and C.Costa,2nd World Congress Chem.Eng.,vol. III (1981),237

28 J.Loureiro,C.Costa and A.Rodrigues,submitted to AIChEJ

29 M.Crine and P.Marchot,Entropie,in press

30 M.Crine,P.Marchot and G.L'Homme, Comp.Applic.Chem.Eng.,Montreux(1979).

Influence of Bed Structure and Tracer Sorption on the R.T.D. in Fluidized Bed Reactors

H. Schlingmann, M. Thoma, D. Wippern*, H. Helmrich*, K. Schügerl*

Institut für Regelungstechnik der Universität Hannover,
D-3000 Hannover, West Germany

* Institut für Technische Chemie der Universität Hannover,
D-3000 Hannover, West Germany

SUMMARY

Based on bed structure and adsorption measurements a mathematical model was developed for fluidized bed reactors with gas volume change along the reactor due to chemical reaction. The model consists of bubble gas and emulsion gas phases as well as wake solid and emulsion solid phases. It takes into account for the convective and diffusive mass exchanges between the gas phases and the nonlinear sorption process. The variation of the bed structure and mass exchange coefficients along the bed and the solid circulation are also taken into account. The RTD of Argon and CO_2 were simulated using model parameters which were determined by separate measurements and compared with the measured RTD values. Only with nonlinear sorption satisfactory agreement between simulated and measured data was found.

INTRODUCTION

Several papers have been published on the distribution of residence times in fluidized reactors. However, only few of them investigated the influence of adsorption /1-11/. None of them has developed a satisfactory model to describe the distribution of residence time behavior under different operational conditions, especially at different temperatures. The aim of the present paper is to develop a model for fluidized bed reactors which also takes care of the sorption effects. To test the developed model extensive measurements were carried out on a continuously operated bench-scale fluidized bed 19.5 cm in diameter and 70 cm in maximum bed height with a porous plate gas distributor. The solid particles were fed to the reactor at a rate of up to 6 g/s and the solid was continuously discharged alternately through two different overflows corresponding to height to diameter ratios of H/D = 3 and/or 1 /12/. This fluidized bed has already been described in /13/.

The axial and radial concentration profiles of the gas in the reactor were measured by a mass spectrometer, those of solid particles by sampling and analyzing them. The bubble size distributions at four different distances from the aerator were measured as functions of the radial position. The gas flow rate, the solid feed rate and the wall heating were controlled by direct digital control (DDC) by a process computer (PDP 11/40).

Since the conversion of sodium hydrogencarbonate to sodium carbonate was investigated in this bed and the solid in the reactor mainly consisted of sodium carbonate, pure sodium carbonate (mean particle diameter d_p = 100 μm, true solid density ρ_s = 2.52 g/cm^3, apparent solid density ρ_{app} = 1.52 g/cm^3, bulk density ρ_b = 0.754 g/cm^3) was used as bed material. This bed had a minimum fluidization velocity u_{mf} = 1.63 cm/s at a porosity of ε_{mf} = 0.52.

The distribution of residence times of nonadsorbing Argon and strongly adsorbing CO_2 were measured by the pulse technique and a mass spectrometer detector. The distribution of residence times of solids was also measured by the pulse technique by using the radionuclide ^{24}Na and a NaJ scintillator detector and on-line signal analysis.

HYDRODYNAMICAL BEHAVIOR

As usual, it was assumed that the bed consists of bubble and emulsion phases. The bubble probability is higher at the wall near the gas distributor and it shifts to the center of the bed with increasing distance from the gas distributor. This nonuniform gas distribution causes a solid circulation as shown in Fig. 1

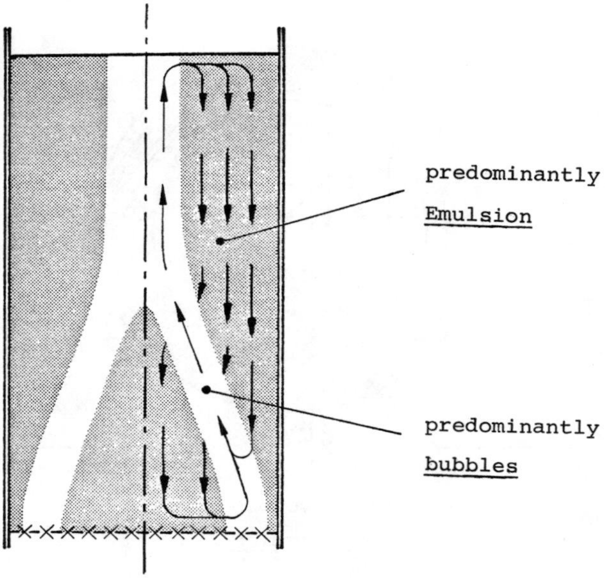

Figure 1: Solid circulation

One can also recognize from this figure that the vortices of gas bubbles and solid particles cross each other. In this cross flow range increased exchange rates between these phases can be expected. The following assumptions were made:

- the bed is isotherm
- the emulsion phase is radially and angularly homogeneous and has a porosity ε and a height L_f.
- the axial component of the gas velocity dominates
- a steady-state flow pattern prevails
- at the gas distributor as well as at the top of the bed thin layers of indefinite thicknesses exist in which the perfect gas mixing state prevails.
- wall effects can be neglected
- the pressure drop along the bed is neglected
- the influence of cross flow on mass transfer is neglected

It is generally accepted /14/ that a rising bubble transports a wake and a cloud of solid particles according to Figure 2 as long as the bubble velocity v_b is higher than the gas velocity in the emulsion phase v_e.

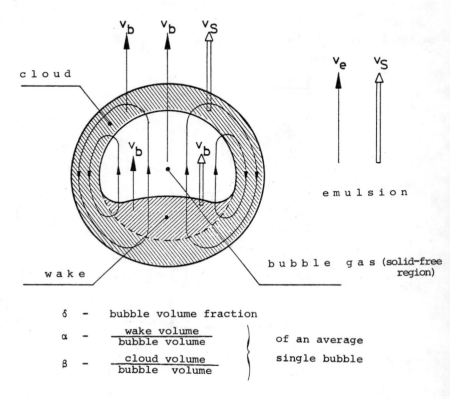

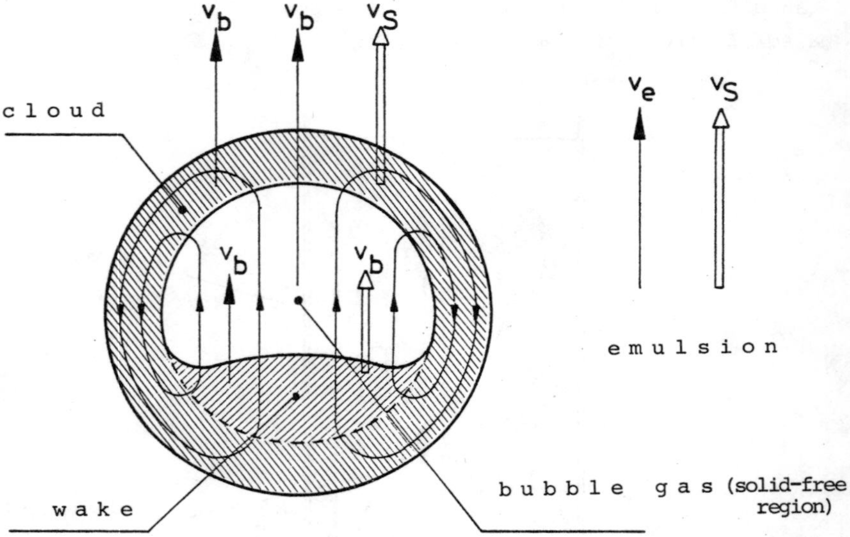

δ - bubble volume fraction

α - $\dfrac{\text{wake volume}}{\text{bubble volume}}$ } of an average single bubble

β - $\dfrac{\text{cloud volume}}{\text{bubble volume}}$

Figure 2: Bubble model

The solid particles do not remain in the cloud of the bubble to which they belong after the bubble formation but they are exchanged between cloud and emulsion phase during the passage of the bubble through the bed. Therefore the solid particles in the cloud belong to the emulsion phase.

The bubble volume fraction $\delta(x)$ gives the fraction of the bubbles in the reactor cross section as a function of the distance from the gas distributor. The average bubble has an average wake fraction α and cloud fraction β in every cross section of the reactor. All of them vary with the distance from the gas distributor. The porosity ε is the same in the wake, cloud and emulsion phase.

If A_R is the constant reactor cross section area, the following cross section fractions prevail:

wake solid	:	$A_w^S / A_R = \alpha\delta(1-\varepsilon)$	(1)
wake gas	:	$A_w^G / A_R = \alpha\delta\varepsilon$	(2)
bubble gas	:	$A_b^G / A_R = \delta$	(3)
cloud gas	:	$A_c^G / A_R = \beta\delta\varepsilon$	(4)
cloud solid	:	$A_c^S / A_R = \beta\delta(1-\varepsilon)$	(5)
emulsion solid	:	$A_e^S / A_R = [1-\delta(1+\alpha+\beta)](1-\varepsilon)$	(6)
emulsion gas	:	$A_e^G / A_R = [1-\delta(1+\alpha+\beta)]\,\varepsilon$	(7)

All of these ranges (together with their velocities) are plotted in the upper part of Figure 3.

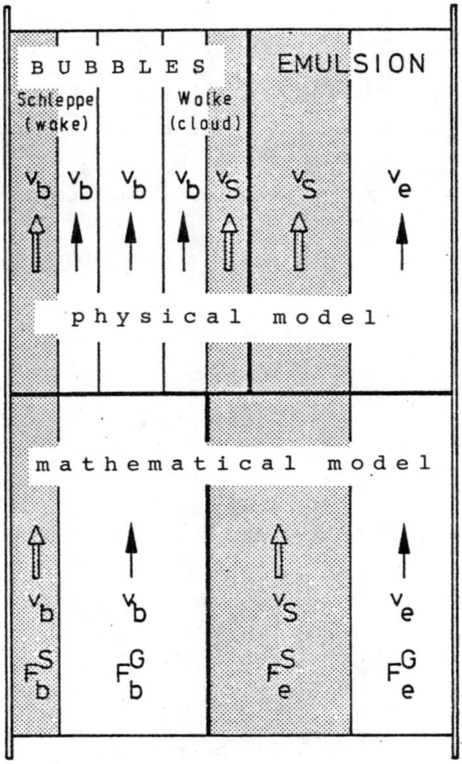

Figure 3: Phase ranges of fluidized beds

It is assumed that the gas mixing in the bubble, wake and cloud ranges are high enough to combine them to a bubble gas with the cross section area fraction F_b^G. By that the seven ranges are reduced to four ranges (lower part of Figure 3). These four phases are used in the model considered in the present paper: the cross-sectional fractions and velocities are

$$F_b^G = \delta[1 + \varepsilon(\alpha + \beta)] \qquad v_b \tag{8}$$

$$F_b^S = (1 - \varepsilon)\cdot\alpha\cdot\delta \qquad v_b \tag{9}$$

$$F_e^G = \varepsilon[1 - \delta(1 + \alpha + \beta)] \qquad v_e \tag{10}$$

$$F_e^S = (1 - \varepsilon)[1 - \delta(1 + \alpha)] \qquad v_S \tag{11}$$

The necessary parameters and velocities are determined as follows:

- The porosity at the minimum fluidization corresponds to the porosity of the emulsion phase

$$\varepsilon = \varepsilon_{mf} \tag{12}$$

- The bubble cross section fraction δ and the bubble rise velocity v_b were measured as functions of the distance from the gas distributor /12,13/.
- The relative wake volume α can be determined from the backmix measurements /8,15/.
- The absolute emulsion gas velocity v_e is given by

$$v_e = v_s + v_{rel} \tag{13}$$

where v_s is the solid particle velocity,
v_{rel} the relative velocity, calculated by

$$v_{rel} = u_{mf}/\varepsilon_{mf} \tag{14}$$

- β and v_s are calculated from the gas and solid particle balances

$$u_G = F_b^G\, v_b + F_e^G\, v_e \tag{15}$$

$$u_S = F_b^S\, v_b + F_e^S\, v_S \tag{16}$$

Kunii and Levenspiel /14/ neglect β in their model. This assumption does not hold for the reactor considered here.

In Figure 4 characteristic behavior of the fluidized bed is shown at $u^+ = u/u_{mf} = 3$ and T = 425 k without chemical reaction.

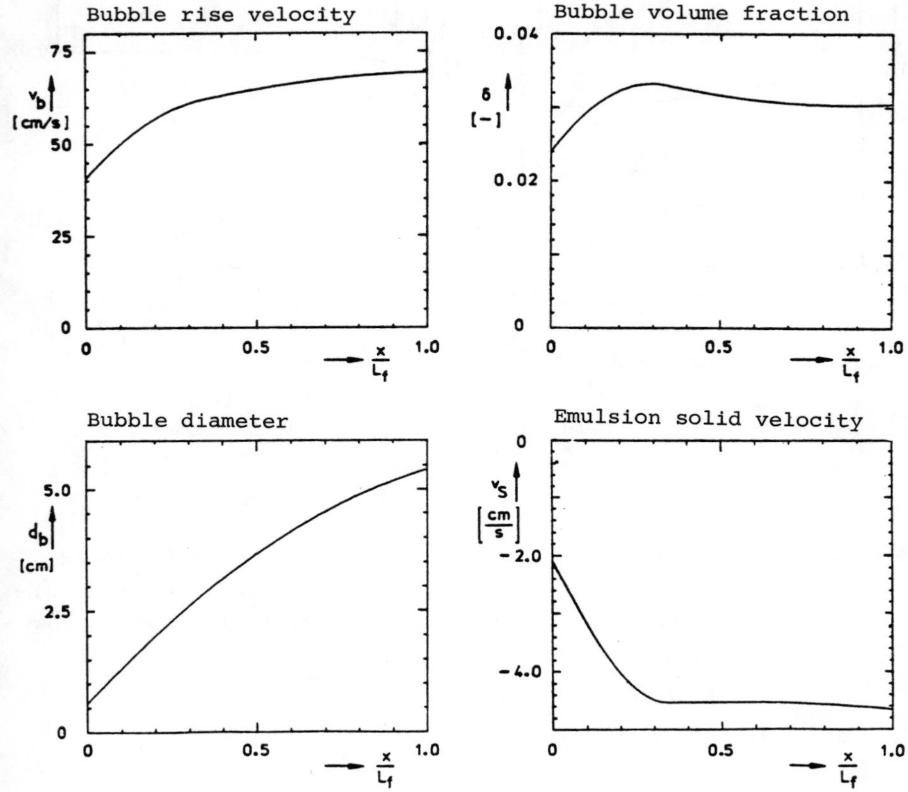

Figure 4: Steady-state flow pattern
($u^+ = 3$, $T_B = 425$ K, without reaction)

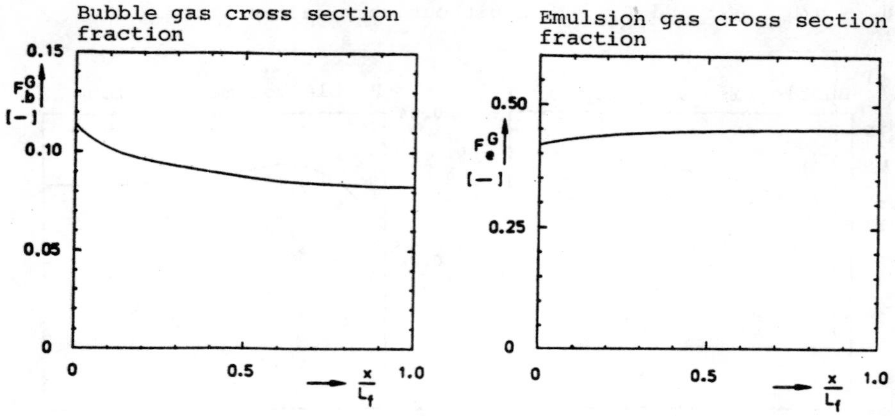

to Fig. 4: Steady-state flow pattern ($u^+ = 3$, $T_B = 425$ K, without reaction)

MASS TRANSFER PROCESSES

Different assumptions were recommended in the literature with regard to the mass exchange coefficient between the bubble and emulsion phases. Kunii and Levenspiel (K/L) assumed the validity of the following relationships /14/ for gas (G) diffusion:

$$k^{G,K/L} = 6,78 \cdot \delta \cdot \sqrt{\frac{\varepsilon_{mf}\, D_G\, v_b}{d_b^3}} \tag{17}$$

and for the diffusion of solid particles (s)

$$k^{S,K/L} = 3\, \frac{\delta \cdot u_{mf}}{d_b \cdot \varepsilon_{mf}} \cdot \frac{1 - \varepsilon_{mf}}{1 - \delta} \tag{18}$$

These relationships were used in the model. However, because d_b is a function of the distance from the gas distributor, $k^{G,K/L}$ and $k^{S,K/L}$ also vary along the reactor height. With the measured functions $d_b(x)$ and $\delta(x)$ diminishing volumetric mass transfer coefficients were found as functions of the relative distance from the gas distributor (Fig. 5).

However, experimental evidence of convective gas exchange (additive to diffusive gas exchange) was proved /16/. It can be calculated from the balance of bubble gas (Figure 6):

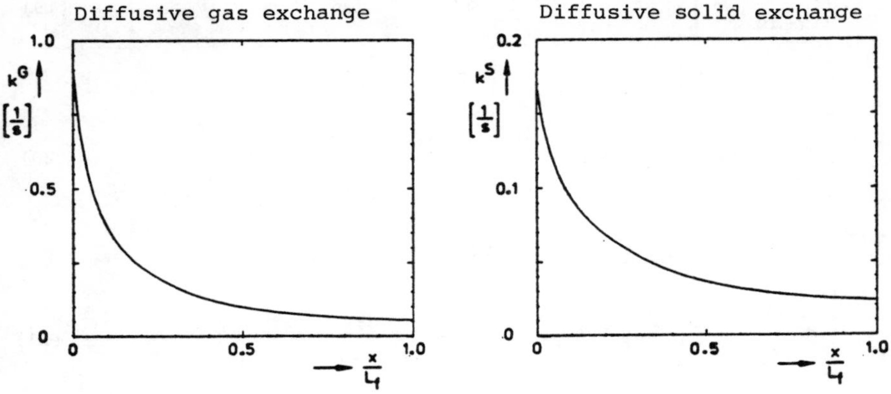

Figure 5: Diffusive mass exchange coefficients ($u^+ = 3$, $T_B = 425$ K, without reaction

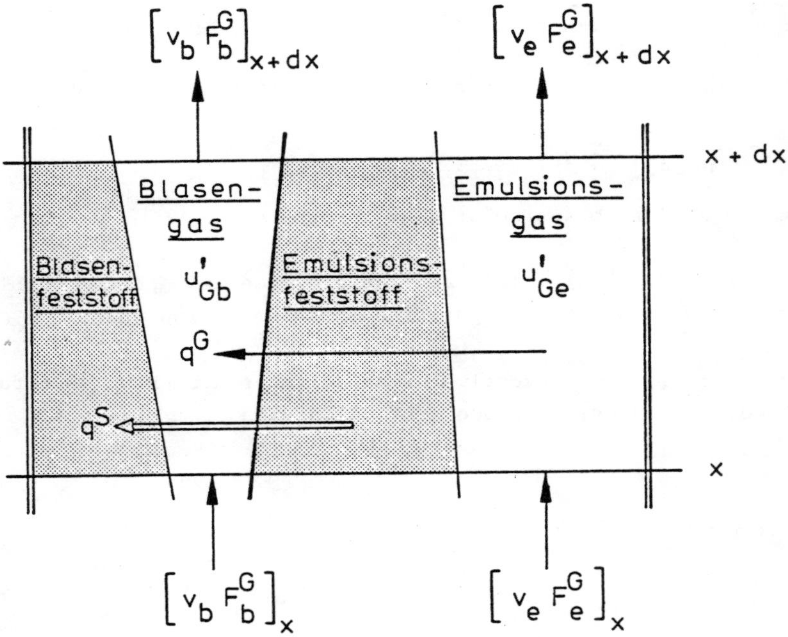

Figure 6: Convective mass exchange

$$\left[v_b\ F_b^G\right]_{x+dx} = \left[v_b\ F_b^G\right]_x + u'_{Gb}\ dx + q^G\ dx\ , \tag{19}$$

$$q^G = \frac{d}{dx}\left(v_b\ F_b^G\right) - u'_{Gb}\ . \tag{20}$$

or from the balance of the emulsion gas

$$q^G = -\frac{d}{dx}\left(v_e\ F_e^G\right) + u'_{Ge} \tag{21}$$

where u'_{Gb} is the gas source term in the bubble phase and
u'_{Gl} the gas source term in the emulsion phase with regard to the reactor length due to chemical reaction with gas production.

The increase in the gas flow rate u_G follows from eq. (20) and (21):

$$\frac{d}{dx}\left(v_b\ F_b^G\right) + \frac{d}{dx}\left(v_e\ F_e^G\right) = u'_{Gb} + u'_{Ge} = \frac{du_G}{dx} \tag{22}$$

The mass transfer rate for the solid particles is given by

$$q^S = \frac{d}{dx}\left(v_b\ F_b^S\right)\ , \tag{23}$$

since for solids no source or sink is assumed.

Positive q^G and q^S values alter the composition in the bubble ranges. Their values change the composition in the emulsion phase.

In Figure 7, the convective exchange rates are shown as a function of the dimensionless distance x/Lf calculated from Figure 4.

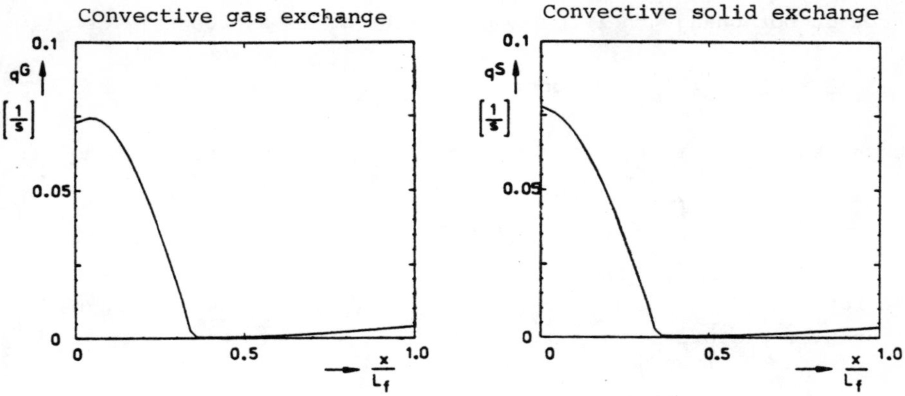

Figure 7: Convective mass exchange coefficient ($u^+ = 3$, $T_B = 425$ K, without reaction)

SORPTION

Yoshida and Kunii /17/ assumed that the following sorption equilibrium prevails:

$$c_S = m\, c_G \tag{24}$$

between a particular component in the gas phase and in the solid phase (adsorbed moles per solid volume).

Neither eq. (24) nor the linear relationship (25)

$$\frac{dc_S}{dt} = k_{ad}(m\, c_G - c_S) \tag{25}$$

are suitable to describe the measured course of the distribution of the residence time. At higher coverage the linear relationship does not hold. According to Aris /18/ and Clark /19/ Langmuir-Isotherm is fairly suitable to describe the nonlinear sorption process:

$$\frac{dc_S}{dt} = k_{ai}\, c_G \left[\left(c_o^* - \sum_{j\neq i}^{n} c_{Sj}\right) - c_S\right] - k_{di}\, c_S \tag{26}$$

where k_{ai} is the adsorption rate coefficient,
k_{di} the desorption rate coefficient and
c_o^* the maximal possible concentration of the adsorbed gas on the solid surface.

The assumption that except for the tracer gas i all other adsorbed gases do not change their coverage on the solid surface yields

$$c_o = c_o^* - \sum_{j \neq i}^{n} c_{Sj} = \text{const} \tag{27}$$

Hence, eq. (26) gives the following three-parameter sorption model:

$$\frac{d\, c_S}{dt} = k_d \left[\frac{k_a}{k_d} (c_o - c_S) \cdot c_G - c_S \right] \tag{28}$$

The rate coefficients $k_a = k_{ai}$ and $k_d = k_{di}$ and the storage constant C_o are temperature dependent.

A comparison of the linear model (25) with the nonlinear model (28) yields for m:

$$m(c_S) = \frac{k_a}{k_d}(c_o - c_S) \tag{29}$$

m can be interpreted as the storage ability of the solid. It is equal to the gas volume with regard to the solid volume. The use of the non-linear model yields the long tailing of the distribution of residence times which were measured in the reactor and could not be simulated by the linear sorption model (25).

REACTION KINETICS

The kinetics of the reaction

$$2\,Na\,H\,CO_3 \longrightarrow Na_2CO_3 + CO_2 + H_2O \tag{30}$$

was determined in /20/. The reaction rate

$$\frac{dc_H}{dt} = -\,k(T) \cdot c_H \tag{31}$$

rate constant:

$$k(T) = k_o \cdot e^{-\frac{E}{\mathcal{R}\,T}} \tag{31a}$$

and heat demand

$$\dot{Q} = \frac{dc_H}{dt} \cdot \Delta H \cdot V_S \tag{32}$$

hold true. Here $k_0 = 1{,}76 \cdot 10^7$ 1/s,

$E = 75350$ W s

$\Delta H = 129500$ W s /mol

During reaction in the solid volume V_s product gas is formed which consists of one part CO_2 and one part H_2O vapor. This yields the gas formation rate:

$$\frac{dV_G}{dt} = -\frac{1}{2} \cdot \frac{dc_H}{dt} V_S \cdot 2 \cdot V_M \tag{33}$$

$$2 \cdot V_M = V_{M\ H_2O} + V_{M\ CO_2} \tag{34}$$

In eq. (31–34) C_H is the concentration of $NaHCO_3$,
E the apparent activation energy,
R_G the gas constant,
ΔH the molar reaction enthalpy and
V_M the mol volume

Hence, the convective mass transfer during reaction is given by (35) and (36) in the bubble phase:

$$u'_{Gb} = k(T)\ c_b^H\ F_b^S\ V_M \tag{35}$$

in the emulsion phase

$$u'_{Ge} = k(T)\ c_e^H\ F_e^S\ V_M \tag{36}$$

MODEL EQUATIONS

The distributed parameter model is the first model to take into account the measured spacial variation of the bed structure, the convective mass flows between the phases and the nonlinear sorption process.

Mass Balances

For the description of the chemical reaction 6 balances in 4 phases are necessary. For the description of CO_2 tracer behavior 4 balances in 4 phases are needed. For the description of solid distribution of residence time 2 balances in the two solid phases are sufficient.

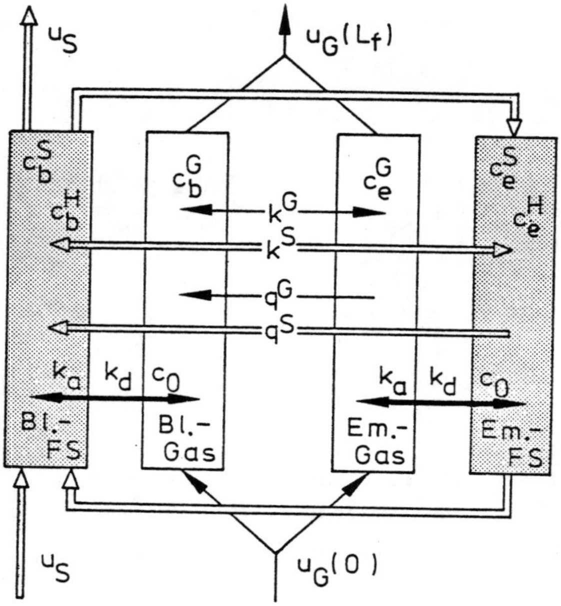

Figure 8: 4-phase model

In Figure 8 the 4-phase model with the mass flows into and out of the system and the different exchange processes is presented. The concentration profiles of CO_2 in emulsion and bubble gas C_e^G and C_b^S and the sodium hydrogencarbonate in the solid phases C_e^H and C_b^H control the reactor state.

The longitudinal dispersion within the phases is taken into account by the dispersion coefficients.

Goedecke et al. /5/ have already shown that the fitting of the distributions of the residence time which was calculated by means of the Kunii-Levenspiel model, could be better fitted to the measurements if the longitudinal dispersion of the phases is taken into account.

In Figure 9 the volume element of the fluidized bed and the mass transfer between the phases are shown. This yields the following mass balance:

$$F_e^G \frac{\partial c_e^G}{\partial t} = \frac{\partial}{\partial x}\left[D_e^G \cdot F_e^G \frac{\partial c_e^G}{\partial x}\right] - \frac{\partial}{\partial x}\left[v_e \cdot F_e^G \cdot c_e^G\right] - k^G\left(c_e^G - c_b^G\right)$$

$$- q_{eb}^G \cdot c_e^G + q_{be}^G \cdot c_b^G - k_d \left[\frac{k_a}{k_d}\left(c_o - c_e^G\right) c_e^G - c_e^S\right] \cdot F_e^S \tag{37}$$

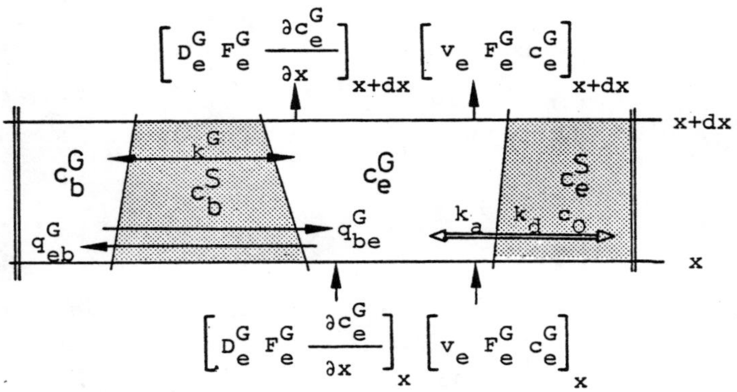

Figure 9: Volume element of the fluidized bed and mass transfer between the phases

The convective exchange rate coefficients are

$$q_{eb}^G = \begin{cases} q^G & \text{for} \quad q^G > 0 \\ 0 & \text{for} \quad q^G \leq 0 \end{cases} \tag{38}$$

$$q_{be}^G = \begin{cases} 0 & \text{for} \quad q^G \geq 0 \\ -q^G & \text{for} \quad q^G < 0 \end{cases} \tag{39}$$

Hence the CO_2 balance in bubble gas is given

$$F_b^G \frac{\partial c_b^G}{\partial t} = \frac{\partial}{\partial x}\left[D_b^G \cdot F_b^G \frac{\partial c_b^G}{\partial x}\right] - \frac{\partial}{\partial x}\left[v_b \cdot F_b^G \cdot c_b^G\right] - k^G\left(c_b^G - c_e^G\right)$$

$$- q_{be}^G \cdot c_b^G + q_{eb}^G \cdot c_e^G - k_d \left[\frac{k_a}{k_d}\left(c_o - c_b^S\right) c_b^G - c_b^S\right] F_b^S \tag{40}$$

and the adsorbed CO_2 in the emulsion solid

$$F_e^S \frac{\partial c_e^S}{\partial t} = \frac{\partial}{\partial x}\left[D_e^S \cdot F_e^S \frac{\partial c_e^S}{\partial x}\right] - \frac{\partial}{\partial x}\left[v_S \cdot F_e^S \cdot c_e^S\right] - k^S\left(c_e^S - c_b^S\right)$$

$$- q_{eb}^S \cdot c_e^S + q_{be}^S \cdot c_b^S + k_d\left[\frac{k_a}{k_d}\left(c_O - c_e^S\right) c_e^G - c_e^S\right] F_e^S$$

$$+ F_e^S \frac{k(T)}{2} c_e^H \tag{41}$$

The convective solid exchange rate coefficients are

$$q_{eb}^S = \begin{cases} q^S & \text{for} \quad q^S > 0 \\ 0 & \text{for} \quad q^S \leq 0 \end{cases} \tag{42}$$

$$q_{be}^S = \begin{cases} 0 & \text{for} \quad q^S \geq 0 \\ -q^S & \text{for} \quad q^S < 0 \end{cases} \tag{43}$$

The hydrogencarbonate balance in the emulsion solid is given by

$$F_e^S \frac{\partial c_e{}^H}{\partial t} = \frac{\partial}{\partial x}\left[D_e^S \cdot F_e^S \frac{\partial c_e^H}{\partial x}\right] - \frac{\partial}{\partial x}\left[v_S \cdot F_e^S \cdot c_e^H\right] - k^S\left(c_e^H - c_b^H\right)$$

$$- q_{eb}^S \cdot c_e^H + q_{be}^S \cdot c_b^H - F_e^S \cdot k(T) \cdot c_e^H \tag{44}$$

The balances of CO_2 and hydrogencarbonate in bubble solid are analog to these balances.

It can be shown /21/ that for

$$q_{eb}^G = - \frac{\partial}{\partial x}\left(F_e^G \cdot v_e\right) > 0 \tag{45}$$

$$\frac{\partial c_e^G}{\partial t} = 0 \tag{46}$$

and for

$$q_{be}^G = \frac{\partial}{\partial x}\left(F_e^G \cdot v_e\right) > 0 \tag{47}$$

holds true

$$F_e^G \frac{\partial c_e^G}{\partial t} = - F_e^G \cdot v_e \frac{\partial c_e^G}{\partial x} + q_{be}^G \cdot (c_b^G - c_e^G) \tag{48}$$

<u>Boundary Conditions</u>

The boundary conditions are given in Table I for the gas phase and Table II for the solid phase.

<u>Table I:</u> Boundary conditions in the gas phase

	v_e	$x = 0$	$x = L_f$
c_e^G - balance	≤ 0	$\frac{\partial c_e^G}{\partial x} = 0$	$D_e^G \frac{\partial c_e^G}{\partial x} - v_e \cdot c_e^G = - v_e \cdot c_b^G(L_f,t)$
	> 0	$- D_e^G \frac{\partial c^G}{\partial x} + v_e \cdot c_e^G = v_e \cdot c_{Gein}$	$\frac{\partial c_e^G}{\partial x} = 0$
c_b^G - balance	≤ 0	$- D_b^G \frac{\partial c_b^G}{\partial x} + v_b \cdot c_b^G = v_b \cdot \tilde{c}^G$ $\tilde{c}^G = \frac{u_G \cdot c_{Gein} - v_e \cdot F_e^G \cdot c_e^G(o,t)}{u_G - v_e F_e^G}$	$\frac{\partial c_b^G}{\partial x} = 0$
	> 0	$- D_b^G \frac{\partial c_b^G}{\partial x} + v_b \cdot c_b^G = v_b \cdot c_{Gein}$	$\frac{\partial c_b^G}{\partial x} = 0$

Table II: Boundary conditions in the solid phase

	v_S	$x = 0$	$x = L_f$
c_e^S - balance	≤ 0	$\frac{\partial c_e^S}{\partial x} = 0$	$D_e^S \frac{\partial c_e^S}{\partial x} - v_S \cdot c_e^S = - v_S \cdot c_b^S(L_f,t)$
	> 0	$- D_e^S \frac{\partial c_e^S}{\partial x} + v_S \cdot c_e^S = v_S \cdot c_{Sein}$	$\frac{\partial c_e^S}{\partial x} = 0$
c_b^S - balance	≤ 0	$-D_b^S \frac{\partial c_b^S}{\partial x} + v_b \cdot c_b^S = v_b \cdot \tilde{c}^S$ $\tilde{c} = \frac{u_S \cdot c_{Sein} - v_S \cdot F_e^S \cdot c_e^S(0,t)}{u_S - v_S \cdot F_e^S}$	$\frac{\partial c_b^S}{\partial x} = 0$
	> 0	$-D_b^S \frac{\partial c_b^S}{\partial x} + v_b \cdot c_b^S = v_b \cdot c_{Sein}$	$\frac{\partial c_b^S}{\partial x} = 0$

Model Parameter

Besides the hydrodynamical parameters which have already been discussed, the model includes 12 more parameters. Three of them, the reaction rate constant k(T) and the convective mass exchange rate coefficients q^G and q^S are already known. In the following the remaining nine parameters will be determined by independent methods.

Longitudinal dispersion coefficients

The simulations indicated that the solution of the D.E. system (37) to (44) is slightly sensitive to the variations of longitudinal dispersion coefficients. The dynamic behavior mainly depends on the mass transfer coefficients.

Wippern et al. determined the longitudinal gas dispersion coefficient by using different models /8/. The emulsion gas dispersion coefficient with a two-phase model yields values between 1 and 250 cm^2/s depending on the operational conditions.

Wittmann measured the distributions of residence times of solid particles in the same system /12/ and calculated the longitudinal solid dispersion coefficients. They vary between 0.6 and 14.1 cm^2/s depending on the operational conditions.

For the longitudinal gas dispersion coefficient in the bubble gas phase values between 0.35 to 0.5 cm/s /15/ were found. Therefore this longitudinal dispersion was neglected.

Mass transfer between the phases

The determination of the convective mass transfer coefficients has already been discussed. The diffusive mass transfer coefficients were calculated according to Kunii and Levenspiel /14/

$$k^G = k^{G,K/L} \tag{49}$$

$$k^S = \eta \cdot k^{S,K/L} \tag{50}$$

However, the simulations indicated that $K^{S,K/L}$ results in values which are too high. Therefore k^S was identified by fitting the calculated values to the measured ones. For all simulations the fitting parameter η = 0.4 gave satisfactory results.

Sorption parameters

The parameters k_a, k_d and C_o of the dynamic sorption models (28) were identified by means of the tailing of the RTD. By assuming a CSTR model for the reactor (Figure 10) the total gas volume

$$V_G = A_R \cdot \int_o^{L_f} (F_e^G + F_b^G)\, dx \tag{51}$$

and the apparent solid volume

$$V_S = A_R \cdot \int_o^{L_f} (F_e^S + F_b^S)\, dx, \tag{52}$$

are ideally mixed.

The tracer gas concentration in solid c_s can only change due to sorption, since during the RTD measurements the solid feed u_s was stopped.

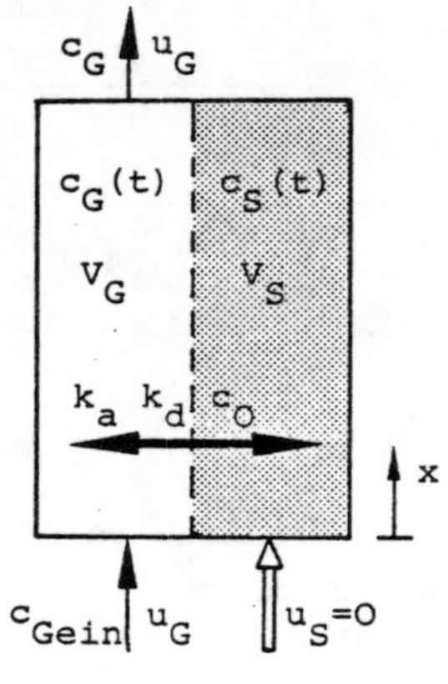

simplifying assumptions

i) ideal mixing

$c_e^G = c_b^G = c_G \neq \text{fkt}(x)$

$c_e^S = c_b^S = c_S \neq \text{fkt}(x)$

ii) sorption is the rate determining step

Figure 10: Simplified fluidized bed model for identification of sorption parameters

$$\frac{dc_S}{dt} = k_d \left[\frac{k_a}{k_d} (c_o - c_S)\, c_G - c_S \right] \tag{53}$$

The gas concentration c_G is measured (at the exit)

$$\frac{dc_G}{dt} = - \frac{V_S}{V_G} \frac{dc_S}{dt} + \frac{1}{\tau_L} \left(c_{G\,in} - c_G \right) \tag{54}$$

where τ_L is the mean residence time of the gas

$$\tau_L = \frac{V_G}{A_R\; u_G} \tag{55}$$

The integration of the measured tracer gas concentration $C_{Gm}(t)$ over the tailing from the starting time t_o yields the initial value $c_s(t_o)$

$$c_S(t_o) = \frac{V_G}{V_S} \left[\frac{1}{\tau_L} \cdot \int_{t_o}^{\infty} [c_{Gm}(t) - c_{Gein}(t)]\, dt - c_{Gm}(t_o) \right] \tag{56}$$

$$c_G(t_o) = c_{Gm}(t_o) \tag{57}$$

The sorption parameters were identified by the method of Nelder and Mead /22/ and the following values were found:

	k_d [1/s]	k_a [cm^3/mol s]	c_o [mol/cm^3]
Argon	0,1	$3{,}9 \cdot 10^4$	$7{,}6 \cdot 10^{-6}$
CO_2	0,049	$7{,}45 \cdot 10^3$	$5{,}1 \cdot 10^{-5}$

Remarkable are the relatively slight differences between the sorption parameters of Ar and CO_2. This might be explained by the pore diffusion.

SIMULATION OF RTDs

The DSCT (= discrete space, continuous time) method was used for simulation /21,23/. Tracer pulses of a 1:1 mixture of Argon and CO_2

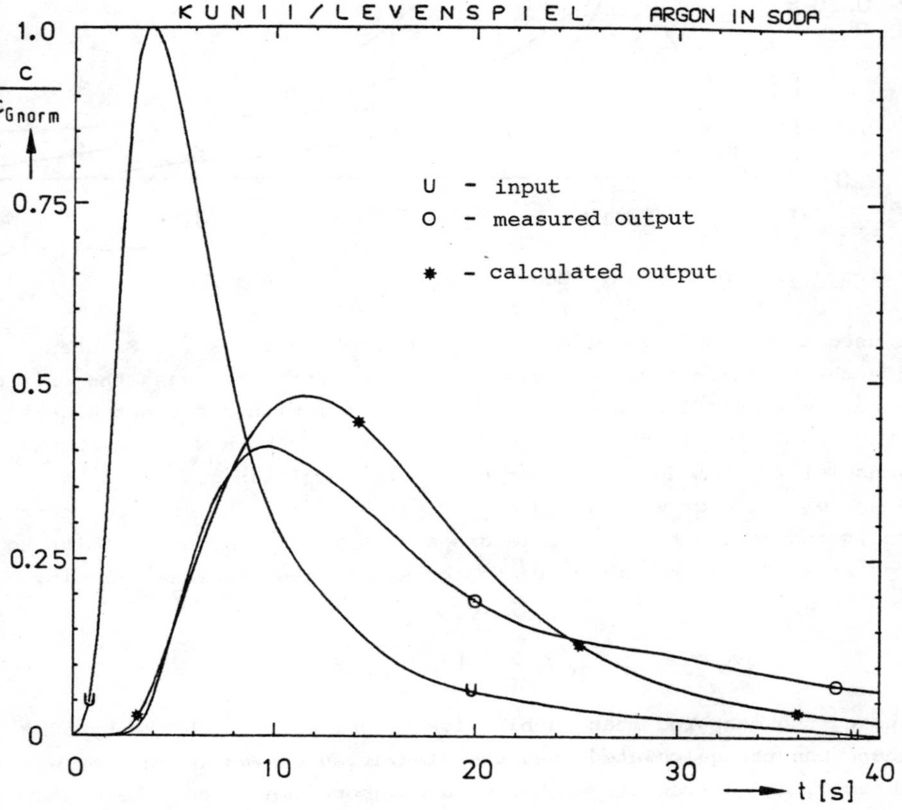

Figure 11: Argon-RTD (K/L-Modell) ($u^+ = 3$, $T_B = 425$ K)

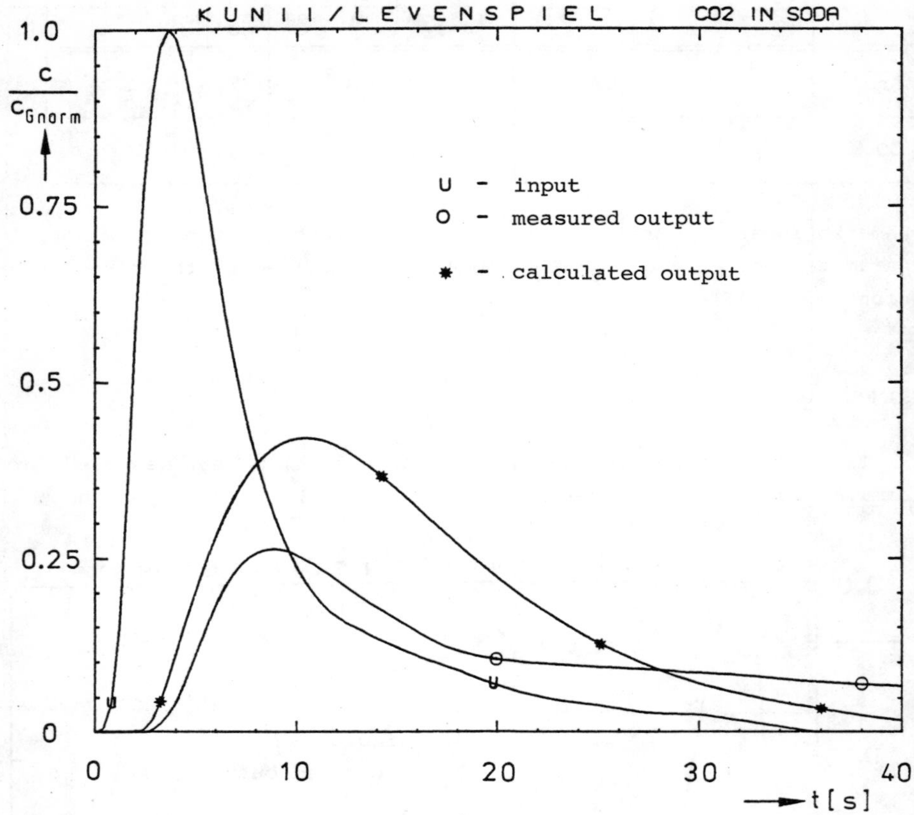

Figure 12: CO_2-RTD (K/L-Modell) ($u^+ = 3$, $T_B = 425$ K)

was used as an input function at $u^+ = 3$ and $T_B = 425$ k. In Figures 11 to 14 the measured input and exit tracer concentrations and the exit concentration simulations are shown as calculated with different models. In Figures 11 and 12 the Argon and CO_2 RTDs are shown with the Kunii-Levenspiel (K/L) model. Since at $u^+ = 3$ the emulsion gas flows back to the gas distributor with the downstreaming solids, the exit concentration is controlled by the bubble gas alone. The K/L model exhibits too large mean residence time due to too small a bubble rise velocity calculated by

$$v_b = u_G - u_{mf} + 0{,}711 \sqrt{g\, d_b} \tag{58}$$

By using the measured mean bubble rise velocities, which are by 50 % higher than the calculated ones the simulation curves (marked by *) in Figures 11 and 12 result. With increasing sorption effect the measured and calculated curves differ more and more. The difference is especially

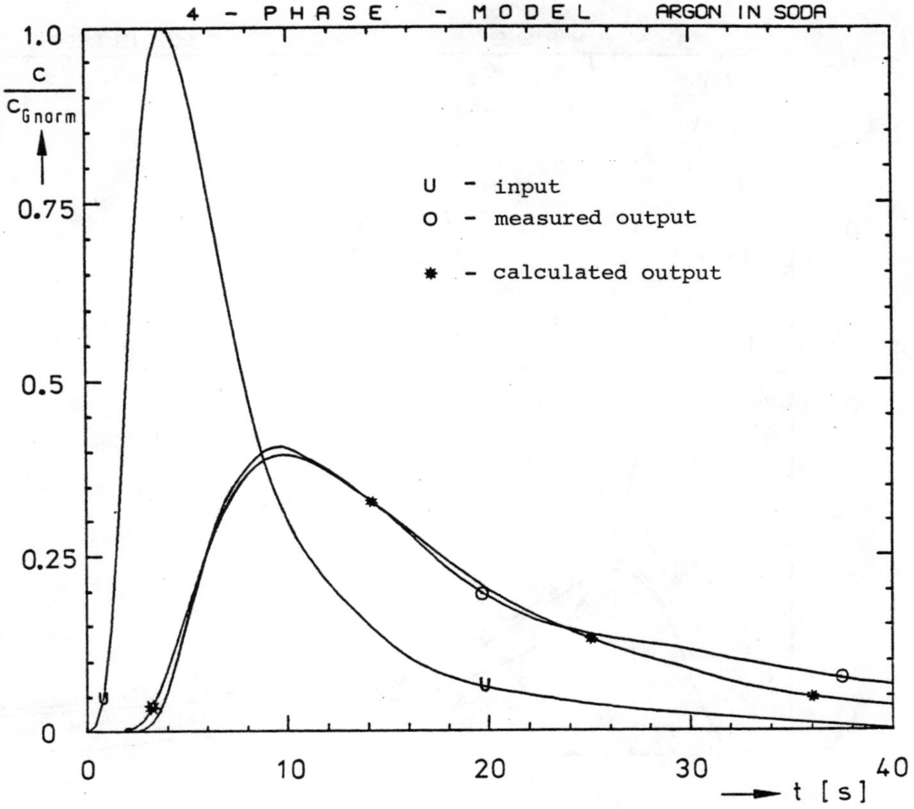

Figure 13: Argon-RTD (4-phase model) (u^+ = 3, T_B = 425 K)

large in the tailing section. The large differences in the RTDs of Argon and CO_2 cannot be rendered by the K/L model. Also the temperature dependence of the RTD cannot be described by this model. The RTD calculated by the K/L model exhibits a much higher concentration maximum and less tailing than the measured one (Fig. 12) due to the missing sorption effect.

In Figures 13 and 14 the RTDs were calculated by the 4-phase model presented in this paper. The excellent agreement between measured and calculated RTDs is obvious.

In Figures 15a to 15d the longitudinal CO_2 concentration profiles are shown in the emulsion gas. c_e^G, in the bubble gas, c_b^G, in the emulsion solid, c_e^S and in the wake solid, c_b^S, at 4, 8, 16 and 24 secs after the injection of the tracer gas into the reactor.

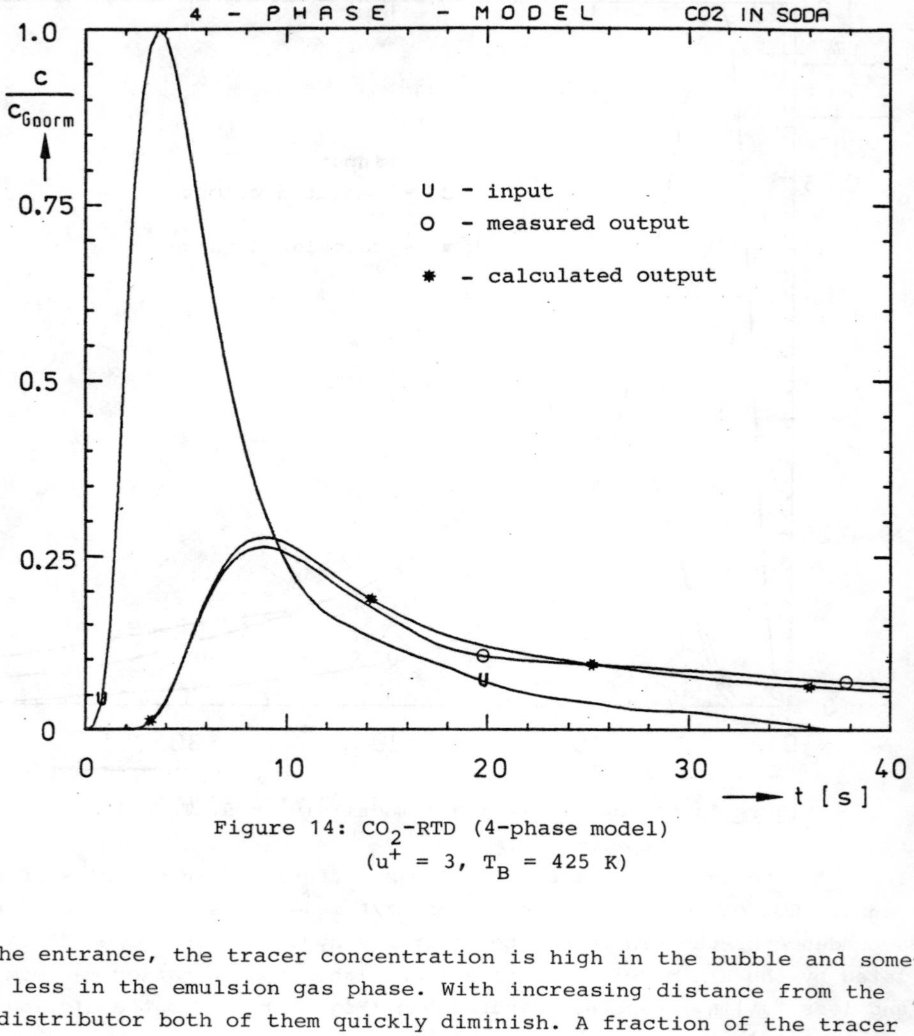

Figure 14: CO_2-RTD (4-phase model)
($u^+ = 3$, $T_B = 425$ K)

At the entrance, the tracer concentration is high in the bubble and somewhat less in the emulsion gas phase. With increasing distance from the gas distributor both of them quickly diminish. A fraction of the tracer is adsorbed in the wake solid, transported to the top and after the escape of the bubbles it is delivered to the emulsion solid. With the downflowing emulsion solid it comes back from the top to the center of the bed, whereas the bubble gas and emulsion gas gradually lose their tracer (Figure 15b). After 16 s a nearly constant low level of tracer concentration is established in the bubble and emulsion gases whereas the concentration of the adsorbed gas in the emulsion and wake solids remain fairly high (Figure 15c). At t = 24 s the tracer concentration in bubble and emulsion gas drops further, but it does not disappear, since it is supplied by the desorption from the solid. The tracer concentration level in the emulsion and wake solids diminishes only slowly

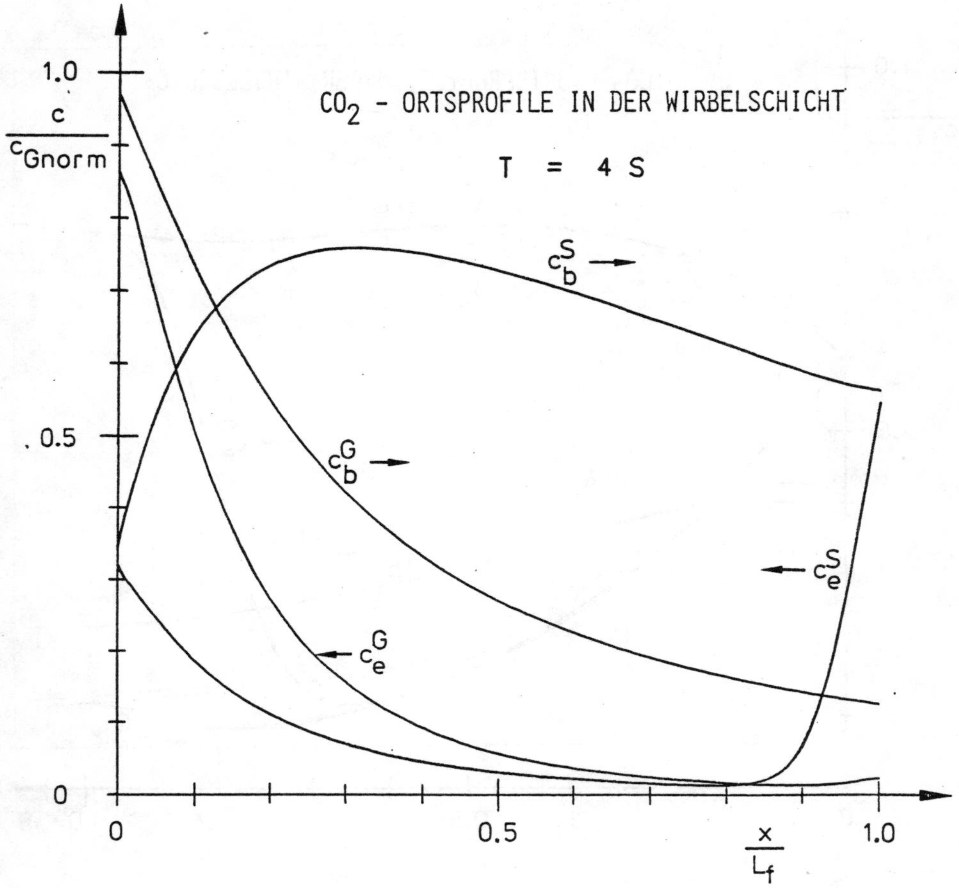

Figure 15 a: Longitudinal CO_2 profiles after 4 s

due to desorption (Figure 15 d). After 30 sec. the tracer concentration at the exit is controlled by desorption alone. The long tailing begins.

To display the entire dynamical process of the RTD the tracer concentrations are plotted as functions of the time and length coordinate in the bubble gas, (Figure 16), emulsion gas (Figure 17), wake solid (Figure 18), and emulsion solid (Figure 19).

These figure clearly indicate that the nonadsorbed tracer rapidly disappears from the bed (its concentration in the bubble and emulsion gases quickly approach zero). The adsorbed gas is held back in the emulsion solid and the wake solid. Since this solid is transported to the top as

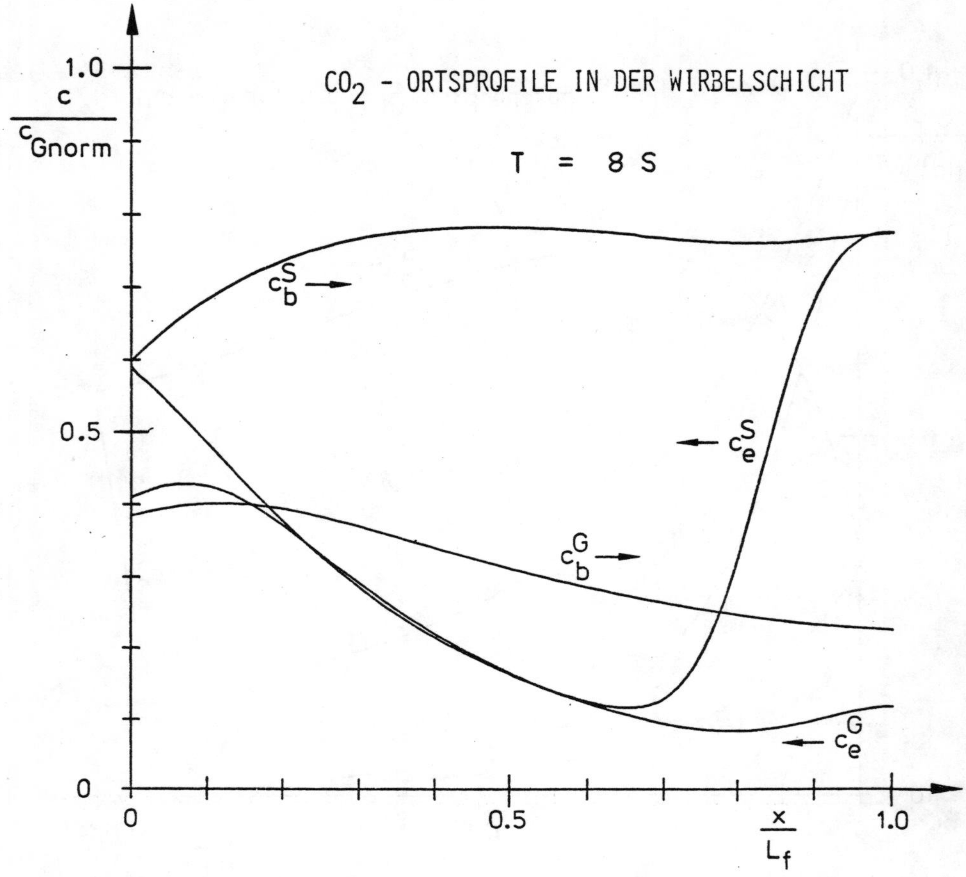

<u>Figure 15 b:</u> Longitudinal CO_2 profiles after 8 s

wake solid by the bubbles and returns to the bulk as back flowing emulsion solid, the solids circulate in the bed. Thus the adsorbed tracer is also recirculated and well mixed. Hence the assumption of well-mixed tracer in the gas and solid phase in the tailing phase holds true fairly well.

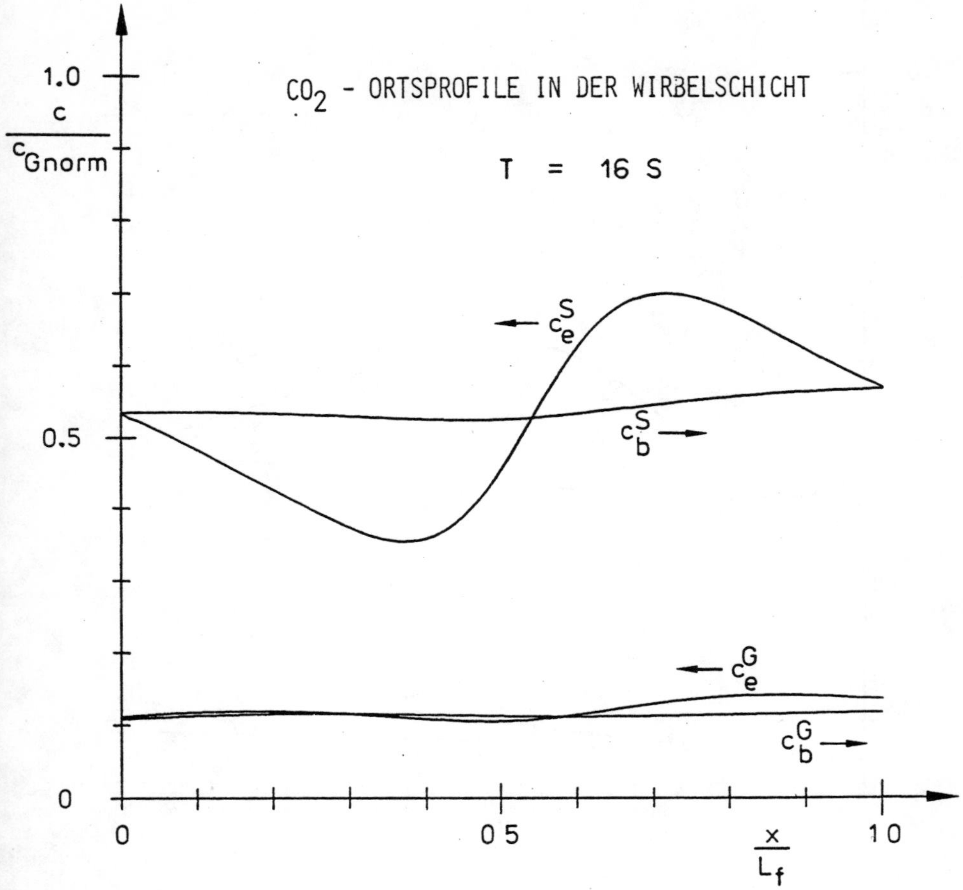

Figure 15 c: Longitudinal CO_2 profiles after 16 s

CONCLUSIONS

The two- and three-phase dispersion models with space independent bed structure and linear sorption kinetics is not suited to describe the dynamical behavior of fluidized beds.

The four-phase dispersion model presented in this paper, which takes into account the longitudinal variation of the bed structure, the solid circulation and nonlinear sorption, well describes the fluidized bed performance without adjustable parameters when using model parameters determined by separate measurements.

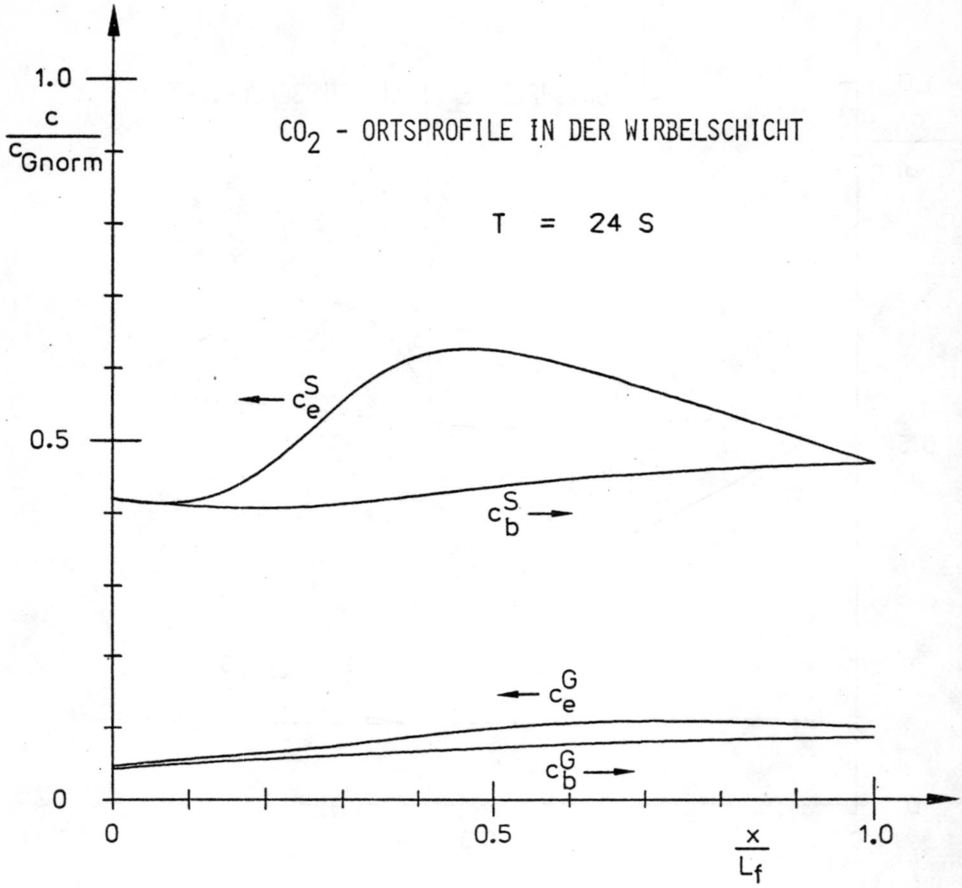

Figure 15 d: Longitudinal CO_2 profiles after 24 s

ACHNOWLEDGMENT

The authors gratefully acknowledge the financial support of the Stiftung Volkswagenwerk.

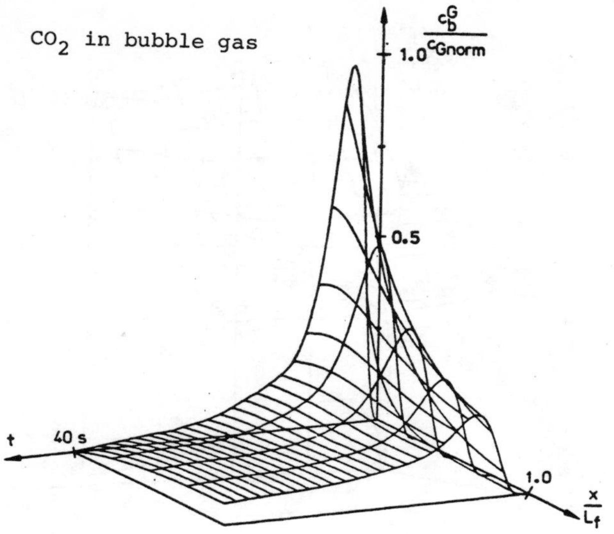

Figure 16: CO_2-RTD simulation (bubble gas)

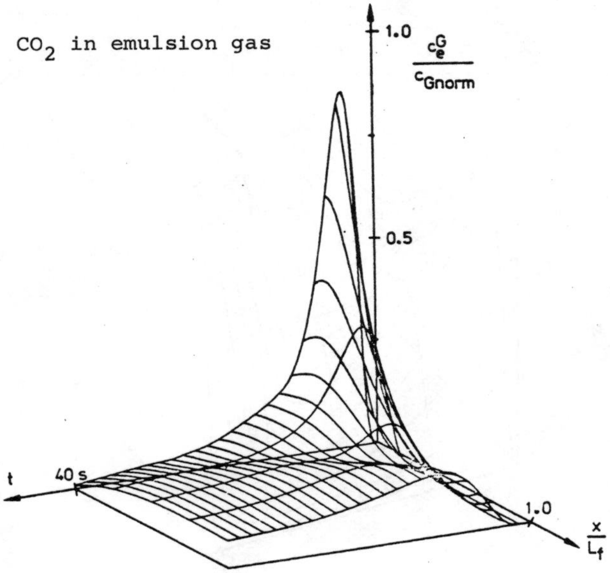

Figure 17: CO_2-RTD simulation (emulsion gas)

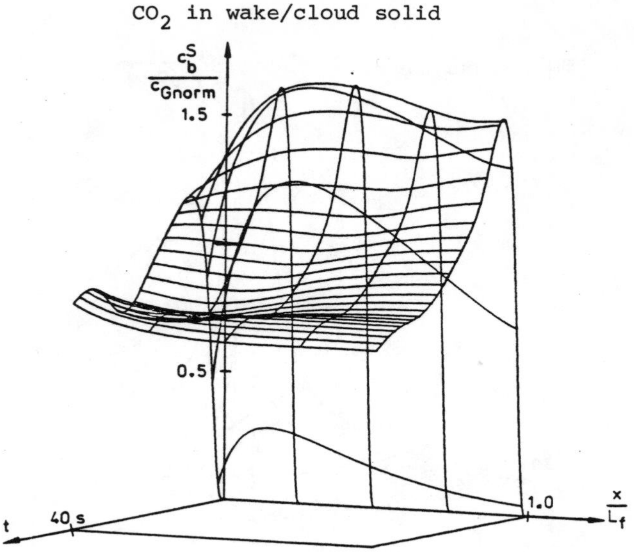

Figure 18: CO_2-RTD simulation (wake solid)

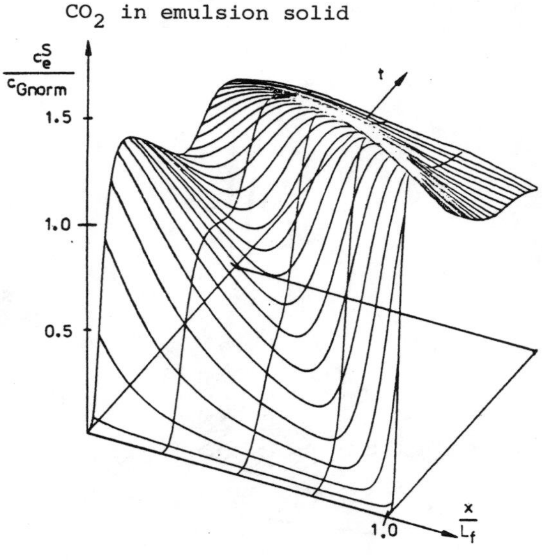

Figure 19: CO_2-RTD simulation (emulsion solid)

LIST OF SYMBOLS

a	[cm^2/cm^3]		volumetric interfacial area
A	[cm^2]		surface area
		A_R	reactor cross-sectional area
		A_M	reactor mantle surface area
		A_a	interfacial area
		$A_w^G, A_c^G, A_e^G, A_b^G$	cross-sectional area fractions of wake, cloud, emulsion and bubble gases
		A_w^S, A_c^S, A_e^S	cross-sectional area fractions of wake , cloud and emulsion solids
c	[mol/cm^3]		concentration
		c_e^G, c_b^G	tracer gas in emulsion gas, bubble gas
		c_e^S, c_b^S	adsorbed tracer in emulsion solid
		c_e^H, c_b^H	hydrogencarbonate in solid
		c_G, c_S	tracer averaged over gas and solid phases
		c_H	hydrogencarbonate averaged over the solid phases
		$c_{G\ in}, c_{S\ in}, c_{H\ in}$	inlet concentrations
		c_O^*, c_O	storage capacity of solids for all adsorbing gas components
		c_{Gm}	measured outlet concentration in the gas phase
		c_{Gnorm}	reference concentration
C_p	[Ws/g K]		specific heat
		$C_{pS}, C_{pH}, C_{pLuft}$	soda, hydrogencarbonate, air
C_m	[Ws/mol K]		molar specific heat
		C_{mH_2O}, C_{mCO_2}	water, CO_2
C_{Bett}	[Ws/K]		heat capacity of reactor
d_b	[cm]		mean bubble diameter
D	[cm^2/s]		diffusion or dispersion coefficient
		D_e^G, D_b^G	tracer in emulsion, bubble gas
		D_e^S, D_b^S	emulsion, wake/cloud solid
		D_G	tracer in air
E	[Ws]		apparent activation energy

f	[1/s]	bubble frequency
F	-	cross section area fraction
F_e^G, F_b^G		emulsion, bubble gas
$F_e^S . F_b^S$		emulsion, bubble solid
g	[cm/s²]	acceleration of gravity
H/D	-	reactor height to diameter ratio
ΔH	[Ws/mol]	reaction enthalpy
k	[1/s]	mass exchange coefficient
k^G, k^S		diffusive mass exchange
$k^{G,K/L}, k^{S,K/L}$		diffusive mass exchange according to Kunii and Levenspiel (eqs. 17,18)
k_{ad}		sorption coefficient
k_a	[cm³/mol s]	sorption coefficient
k_d	[1/s]	desorption coefficient
k_O	[1/s]	frequency factor
$k(T)$	[1/s]	reaction rate constant
K	[cm/s]	diffusive mass exchange coefficient
L	[cm]	length
$L_f, L_{Schütt}$		fluidized bed, packed bed
m	-	sorption equilibrium constant
M	[g/mol]	mol weight
M_S, M_H		soda, hydrogencarbonate
n	[mol]	mol number
Δp	[bar]	pressure drop in the bed
q	[1/s]	convective mass exchange coefficient
q^G, q^S		gas, solid
q_{eb}^G, q_{eb}^S		emulsion to bubble phase
q_{be}^G, q_{be}^S		bubble to emulsion phase
$\dot{Q}$	[Ws/s]	heat flux
r_a, r_d	[1/s]	specific adsorption, desorption rate
$\mathcal{R}$	[Ws/mol K]	gas constant
$R(\,.\,)$	[mol/cm³ s]	reaction rate

$R(T_B, c_H)$	[mol/cm^3 s]	reaction rate
$S(c_S, c_G)$	[mol/cm^3 s]	sorption rate
t	[s]	time
T	[K]	temperature
T_B		bed temperature
u	[cm/s]	superficial velocity
u_{mf}		minimum fluidization velocity
u_G, u_S		gas, solid superficial velocity
u'_G, u'_{Ge}, u'_{Gb}	[cm/s·cm]	velocity increase due to reaction
$\Delta u_G, \Delta u_e, \Delta u_b$	[cm/s]	velocity increase due to tracer injection
u^+	-	u/u_{mf} fluidization index
v	[cm/s]	absolute velocity
v_e, v_b, v_s		emulsion gas, bubble gas, emulsion solid
v_{rel}		relative velocity
V	[cm^3]	volume
V_R, V_g, V_S		reactor, gas, solid volume
V_M	[cm^3/mol]	mole volume
V_{MH_2O}, V_{MCO_2}		water, CO_2
$\dot{V}_b$	[cm^3/s]	bubble volume flow
x	[cm]	longitudinal coordinate
$x_E, \Delta x$		longitudinal position of tracer injection, injection range
X_H	-	mol fraction of hydrogencarbonate in solid
z	-	normalized longitudinal coordinate with regard to bed length
α	-	wake volume fraction
α_W	[W/K]	heat transfer coefficient
β	-	cloud volume fraction
δ	-	bubble volume fraction
ε	-	bed porosity
ε_{mf}		bed porosity at minimum fluidization
η	-	fitting parameter
ρ	[g/cm^3]	density

ρ_W		true density of soda
$\rho_{Scheinb}$		apparent density of soda particle
$\rho_{Schütt}$		bulb density of bed
τ	[s]	mean residence time

REFERENCES

(1) O.E. Potter. Mixing,in:"Fluidization". Ed. J.F. Davidson, D. Harrison, Acad. Press 1971, p. 292

(2) H.V. Nguyen, O.E. Potter. Adsorption effects in fluidized beds. In: "Fluidization Technology" Vol. II. Ed. D. Keairns, Hemisphere Publ. Corp. Washington 1976 (Asilomar Conference), p. 193

(3) R. Goedecke, K. Schügerl. "Influence of the interparticle flow, intraparticle diffusion and adsorption of the gas on its distribution of residence times in fluidized beds. In: "Fluidization Technology" Vol. I. Ed. D. Keairns, Hemisphere Publ. Corp., Washington 1976, p. 305

(4) R. Goedecke, O. Vrbata, K. Schügerl. Chem. Ing. Techn. 49 (1977) 585.

(5) R. Goedecke, K. Schügerl, J. Todt. Powder Technology 21 (1978) 227

(6) O. Vrbata, K. Schügerl. Powder Technology 22 (1979) 179

(7) O. Vrbata, K. Schügerl. Powder Technology 22 (1979) 207

(8) D. Wippern, K. Wittmann, J. Kühne, H. Helmrich, K. Schügerl. Chem. Eng. Communications 10 (1981) 307

(9) T. Miyauchi, H. Kaji, K. Saito. J. Chem. Eng. Japan 1 (1968) 72

(10) P. Sagetong, H. Gibert, H. Angelino. Chimie et industrie 105 (1973) 1825

(11) K. Yoshida, D. Kunii, O. Levenspiel. Ind. Eng. Chem. Fundam. 8 (1969) 402

(12) K. Wittmann, Doctoral Thesis, University of Hanover 1979

(13) K. Wittmann, H. Helmrich, K. Schügerl. Chem. Eng. Sci. 36 (1981) 1673

(14) D. Kunii, O. Levenspiel. Fluidization Engineering. Wiley & Sons, New York 1969

(15) D. Wippern, Doctoral Thesis. University of Hanover 1979

(16) J. Werther. Die Bedeutung der Blasenkoaleszenz für die Auslegung von Gas/Feststoff-Wirbelschichten. GVC-Jahrestagung, Karlsruhe 1975

(17) K. Yoshida, D. Kunii. J. of Chem. Eng. Japan 1 (1968) 11

(18) R. Aris. The mathematical theory of diffusion and reaction in permeable catalysts. Clarendon Press, Oxford 1975

(19) A. Clark. The theory of adsorption and catalysis. Academic Press, New York 1970

(20) H. Helmrich, H. Kröger, K. Schügerl, K. Wittmann. Chem. Ing. Techn. 50 (1978) 139

(21) H. Schlingmann. Doctoral Thesis, University of Hanover 1980

(22) J.A. Nelder, R. Mead. The Computer Journal 7 (1965) 308

(23) H. Schlingmann. Diplomarbeit, Technische Universität Hannover 1975

Measurement of Liquid and Solid Residence Time Distribution in Biological Reactors

S. Elmaleh, S. Papaconstantinou

Laboratoire de Génie Chimique Appliqué aux Biotechnologies, Université des Sciences et Techniques du Languedoc, 34060 Montpellier Cedex, France.

SUMMARY

The liquid and solid flow in biological reactors has not yet been investigated thoroughly lacking of experimental and numerical methods. In this work, tracers for both of the phases have been tested and numerical methods for RTD calculation even for recycled reactors have been proposed allowing RTD determination in an activated sludge unit. A quantification of mixing in a spouted multiphasic biological reactor through a residence probability has been considered.

INTRODUCTION

Only a few works have been devoted to residence time distribution (RTD) in biological reactors. As in liquid-solid catalytic reactors, the flow and the mixedness degree of two phases are determinant on conversion. RTD measurements of both of the phases are indeed difficult :

1) many usual tracers are toxic or degradable ;
2) the solid phase mass is varying with microbial growth ;
3) in many reactors the effluent is partly recycled, i.e. activated sludge in wastewater treatment.

A methodology for RTD measurements in biological reactors will de discussed here ; it is mostly based on work by Hornut et al. (1, 2).

LIQUID PHASE

1. Tracers

Biological reactors are sensitive and reactive to most usual tracers. Among coloured or fluorescent compounds, fluoresceine only is weakly degraded, i.e. 3 % in 25 hours ; this can be compared to rhodamine B degradation : 20 % in 25 hours. Besides, rhodamine B has tensio active properties and this compound is of poor utilization in aerated reactors ; the accuracy of RTD determinations with rhodamine B in an activated sludge pilot plant by Murphy et al. is not therefore evident (3, 4).
As the main fluid is water, the best tracer is a hydrogen isotope tritium. Bromine 82 which is easier to handle can be used too even in polluted waters (5).

2. RTD measurements

Liquid RTD measurements is uneasy when a fraction of the effluent is recycled in the reactor. Fig. 1 shows the flow-sheet of an activated sludge unit with its aeration tank and its clarifier. No recycle during the RTD measurement could induce a wash out of the microbial culture. Moreover, one of the aim is the research of short circuits or dead volumes in real working conditions.

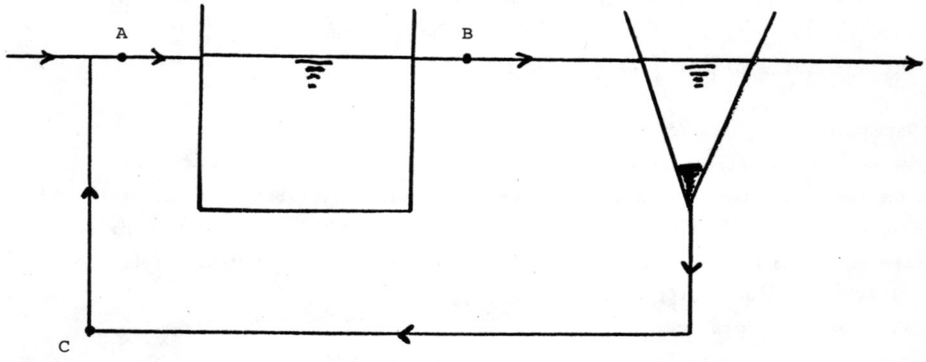

FIGURE 1

If x and y are the input and output variables at points A and B, i.e. tracer mass flow rates, the aeration tank RTD g (t) is such that :

$$y(t) = \int_0^t g(t-u)\, x(u)\, du \qquad \{1\}$$

When the system is forced by an unit impulse which introduces a mass m of tracer :

$$y(t) = m\, g(t) + \int_0^t g(t-u)\, z(u)\, du \qquad \{2\}$$

where z is the output variable at point C.
Equation {2} is a second type Volterra equation. Three numerical methods are generally used for solving {1} or {2}.

2.1. Fourier integral

The Fourier integral $X(i\omega) = \int_{-\infty}^{\infty} x(t) \exp(i\omega t)\, dt$ transforms the convolution product {1} in a simple algebraic product from which :

$$G(i\omega) = \frac{Y(i\omega)}{X(i\omega)}$$

The RTD is then calculated by the inverse Fourier transform.

2.2. Minimization of a structural distance

The convolution integral {1} is written under a discrete form :

$$y(n) = \sum_{i=1}^{n} x(i)\, g(n-i) \text{ or}$$

$$y(n) = \underline{X}^T(n)\ \underline{G(n)}$$

where $\underline{X}^T(n)$ and $\underline{G(n)}$ are line or column matrices with x(i) or g(i) elements.
An Euclidean distance between observed values and an assumed model is :

$$D(n) = \left[\underline{G(n)} - \underline{Go}\right]^T \left[\underline{G(n)} - \underline{Go}\right] \qquad \{3\}$$

$\underline{G(n)}$ represents the system impulse response and $\underline{Go}$ the observation impulse response. As the latter is not known, D (n) cannot be measured ; the following algorithm, nevertheless, ensures the decreasing of D (n) (6) :

$$\underline{G}(n+1) = \underline{G}(n) - \frac{\varepsilon(n)}{\underline{X}^T(n) - \underline{X}(n)}\ \underline{X}(n) \qquad \{4\}$$

where $\varepsilon(n)$ is the instant difference between the model and the observed value.

2.3. Resolution by recurrence

Equation {2} is re-written :

$$g(t) = \frac{y(t)}{m} - \frac{1}{m} \int_0^t g(t-u)\, z(u)\, du$$

$$g\ (i) = \frac{y\ (i)}{m} - \frac{1}{m} \sum_{k=1}^{i-1} \left[g\ (i-k)\ z\ (k)\ \ \Delta t \right]$$

3. Application

Those three methods have been used to RTD determination of a 3.5 liters aeration tank.

The same curve has been got is the three cases and it is identical to the one which can be traced without recycle and suspended solids (1, 2). However, some oscillations have been noted in using the Fourier integral which seems the less adapted method. In fact, each case is different and it is impossible to predict the accurate method (7).

SOLID PHASE

1. Tracers

In a suspended-floculated cell reactor, it is conceivable to inject a mineral compound having the same mechanical behaviour than the biological solids. Many experiments have shown that kieselguhr behaves in this way in an aeration tank and that some retention occurs on the bioflocs. Kieselguhr can then be used, the forced variable being the mineral suspended solids concentration (2). Biological solids can be followed too by using a gold isotope Au 198 (2). Metallic gold is irradiated then solved in HCL - HNO_3 leading to the complex auritetrachlorhydric acid H $(AuCl_4)$. This complex is reduced by simple contact with activated sludge inducing an immobilization of $AuCl_4^-$ on the sludge. The reaction time is 10 to 15 seconds and 0.25 g of gold can be fixed on 1 kg of dry matter. Au 198 is a gamma emitter.

2. RTD measurement

The situation is identical to the precedent : the observed output results from the initial perturbation and a recycled sighal. But here, the problem is still complicated because the tracer does not leave the system and solid phase can be growing. It has been shown that the first part only of the RTD curve can be calculated with accuracy (2). The whole curve is then only extrapolated.

Nevertheless, the method is accurate enough to calculate the mean residence time of the solid phase in the aeration tank which is not generally equal to the liquid mean residence time even in perfect mixing : this is due to a non uniform porosity distribution in the reactor.

3. Solid phase mixing

Attached-cells reactors provide excellent efficiency on pollution abatement owing to the large biomass concentration they are able to develop (8). A good example is given by the high compacting multiphasic reactor (HCMR) designed to mix many fluid phases with one or many solid phases (9). This reactor can be used in fermentation the cells being attached on big disk particles of 2 cm diameter and 0.5 cm height spouted by air injection (fig. 2).
Tracer experiments have shown that the liquid phase is in perfect mixing for all operational values of liquid and solid phase fraction volume and gas flow-rate. The mixedness of the solid phase is quantified by following one coloured particle. The reactor is divided in three zones (fig. 2) ; residence time of the coloured particle in each one is measured. The probability of residence in a zone is defined by $P_r(A)$ = (residence time in A)/(total observation time).
By this way, it has been shown that A is a partial stagnant zone ; in C, particles are transported by gaz bubbles and they can cross up the zone by direct motion or by swirling up. They go then down to A crossing B or through swirling movements in C.

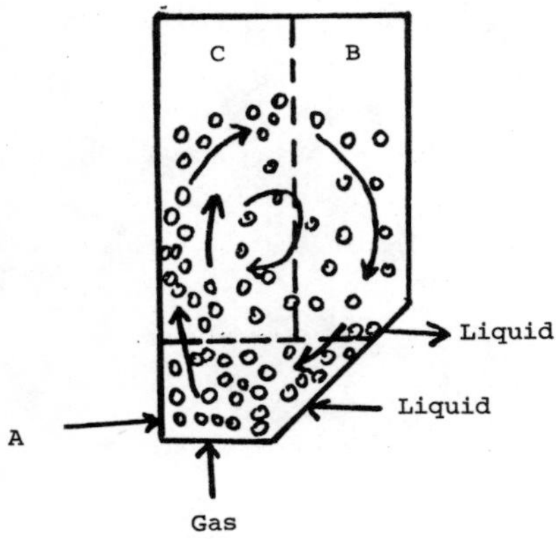

FIGURE 2

REFERENCES

1 J.M. Hornut, Etude des Ecoulements des Phases Liquide et Solide en milieu biologique, Docteur Ingenieur Thesis, Montpellier 1978

2 J.M. Hornut, S. Elmaleh and R. Ben Aïm, Chem. Eng. J. 19 (1980), 19

3 K.L. Murphy and P.L. Timpany, J. Sanit. Eng. Div., SA5 (1967), 1

4 K.L. Murphy and B.I. Boyko, J. Sanit. Eng. Div., SA2 (1970), 211.

5 P. Corompt, J. Guizerix, R. Margrita and J. Molinari, Etude des Conditions Hydrauliques de fonctionnement de l'Aérateur de la Station d'Achères II, CEA-CENG 1971

6 J. Richalet, R. Rault and R. Pouliquen, Identification des processus par la Méthode du Modèle, Gordon and Breatch, New-York 1970

7 P. Corompt, Application de quelques Méthodes de Déconvolution, CEA-CENG 1968

8 S. Elmaleh, Les Réacteurs à Biomasse Fixée, in Point 81, Lavoisier 1982

9 G.M. Rios et al, French Patent n° 79 17430.

Pseudorandom Technique for Measuring Residence Time Distributions

A. Lübbert, J. Diekmann, G. Rotzoll

Institut für Technische Chemie der Universität Hannover,
D-3000 Hannover, West Germany

SUMMARY

A method of measuring the gas phase residence time distribution (RTD) in bubble columns and gas/solid reactors is proposed. The RTD is obtained as the weighting function of the system 'reactor' from the measured response on a pseudorandom input function. The main advantage of this technique is the possibility of using very low tracer input flow rates which lead to very low system disturbances. Modern microprocessors permit an extremely inexpensive implementation of the method.

INTRODUCTION

Most practical measurements of residence time distributions use the response on special system input functions like Dirac's Delta pulse or step functions; using white noise inputs is still another method mentioned in many textbooks, but there are only very few applications, mostly because of expensive hardware requirements.

Here we propose a method of obtaining gas phase residence time distributions by measuring the response of a reactor to a continuous pseudorandom input function. The mean tracer input flow rate can be held extremely low, thus minimizing disturbances of the system. Because of the continuous tracer input, the total measuring time can be extended until a required signal-to-noise ratio has been obtained. The method is similar to a technique which has been successfully used in time-of-flight measurements in nuclear physics (1) and molecular beam research.

The tracer input concentration can be reduced to the point where it suffices to modulate the He-content in the air using an aerated water column to obtain the required distribution from the He-concentration fluctuations in the outlet gas stream.
Very cheap microprocessor equipment can be used to control the tracer input during data acquisition and calculation of the required algorithms.

THEORETICAL BACKGROUND

The method can be described in terms of random data analysis (2). Basic descriptive functions in this theory are auto- and cross-correlation functions for signals and weighting functions for constant parameter linear systems. An essential input-output relationship relating the cross-correlation function R_{xy} between the input signal x(t) and the output y(t) and the autocorrelation function R_x of the input signal x(t) with the system property $h(\tau)$ is

$$R_{xy}(\tau) = \int_{-\infty}^{\infty} h(\tau) R_x(t-\tau) dt \tag{1}$$

which reduces to

$$R_{xy}(\tau) = h(\tau) \tag{2}$$

in the case of an input signal x(t) having an autocorrelation function equal to Dirac's Delta function. White noise is one theoretical example for such a signal. This relation forms the theoretical basis for the determination of the weighting function from the cross-correlation function between a statistical test function and the measured system response y(t).

The practical application of this relation requires a device producing a known, i.e. measured, random input function having white noise characteristics. This can be done by means of a noise generator and an appropriate measuring device, but there is the much simpler method of using pseudostatistical sequences.

A pseudostatistical sequence is a finite sequence of N real numbers a_i which, repeated periodically, satisfies the autocorrelation condition

$$A = \Sigma a_i a_{i+j} = \alpha \delta_{i(\mathrm{mod}\, N)} + \beta \tag{3}$$

If the input signal to the system is considered as being divided into time slices of width d, during which the tracer concentration is switched on or off, this signal can be described as a superposition of rectangular-shaped pulses O(t) shifted by integer multiples of the time increment d along the time axis. The input signal then has the form

$$x(t) = \sum_{i=1}^{N} a_i O\left(t-\left(i-\frac{1}{2}\right)d\right) \tag{4}$$

which is shown in Fig. 1.

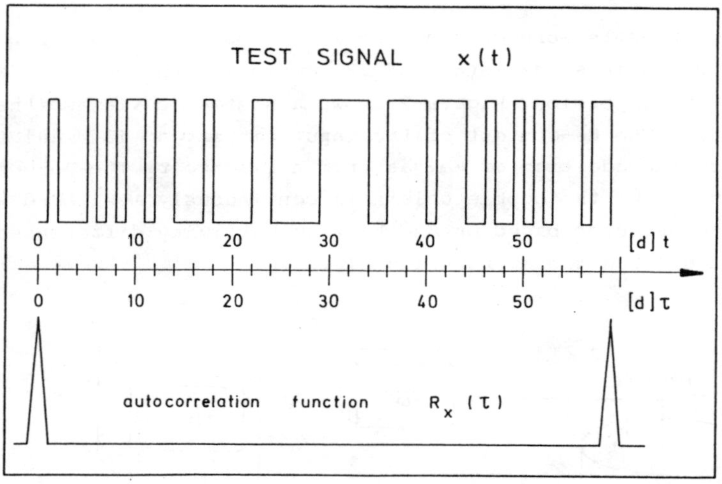

Fig. 1: Pseudostatistical binary (0,1) - sequence with rectangular pulse shape with corresponding auto-correlation function (lower part)

By using x(t) as an input function to a linear system it can be shown that the cross-correlation of x(t) with the measured output signal y(t) is proportional to the system response to a single rectangular pulse O(t) as used in conventional pulse response experiments plus a constant additive background. Compared to the conventional one-pulse experiment, the superiority of the pseudorandom method increases with the relative background level. The method is, therefore, predestined for experiments which require low tracer flow rates, and for which conventional one-shot experiments are unfeasible because of high noise levels.

EXPERIMENTAL

An experiment for measuring the residence time distribution of the gas phase in bubble column reactors requires the addition of a small amount of a gaseous tracer to the input gas stream, modulated by a function like eq. (4). This means that the tracer input must be periodically switched on or off according to x(t) during the entire experiment. The measured tracer concentration in the gas outlet must then be cross-correlated with the modulation function to give the impulse response of the system, i.e., the residence time distribution.

Test experiments were carried out in a laboratory-scale bubble column 14 cm in inner diameter and 220 cm in length, operated with an air-in-water dispersion. Figure 2 shows a schematic view of the experimental setup. The He-content of the input air stream is modulated pseudo randomly by the addition of He-gas from a reservoir. The He-content in the gas outlet of the bubble column is continuously monitored with an inexpensive detector based on the heat conductivity differences between the output gas and the surrounding air.

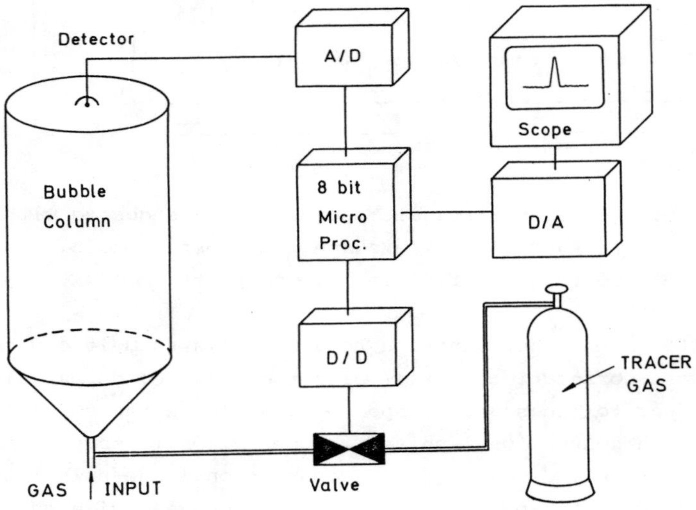

Fig. 2: Schematic view of the experimental setup

The central part of the electronics is an 8-bit microprocessor M6800 of Motorola, which controls the tracer input, samples the measuring data, makes the required calculations, and displays the resulting distributions on an oscilloscope.

The microprocessor program is based on interrupt processing. A system clock interrupts the program at constant time increments. In the interrupt service routine data are taken from the detector via an 8-bit analog-to-digital converter. The same clock impulse sets the control signal for the valve in the tracer input line according to a pseudo-statistical sequence stored in the memory of the microprocessor. This is done via an 8-bit digital output interface of the microprocessor and an appropriate relais. During the measurements the cross-correlation function is calculated and accumulated by segments in a buffer array. The current result on the residence time distribution is displayed simultaneously on an oscilloscope screen via a digital-to-analog converter interface.

For further analysis the digital data can be transferred to a process computer via another digital output interface not shown in Fig. 2. On the process computer a model function can be fitted to the data by a nonlinear regression procedure, or, if necessary, corrected for the finite width of the unit impulse.

REFERENCES

(1) F. Hossfeld, R. Amadori, R. Scherm, in: Instrumentation for neutron inelastic scattering research, Vienna 1970, 117

(2) J.S. Bendat, A.G. Piersol, Random data, New York 1971

Simulation of the Performance of a Flow System Consisting of Interconnected Reactors by Markov Processes

R. Nassar, J. R. Too*, L.T. Fan*

Department of Statistics, Kansas State University, Manhattan, KS 66506, U.S.A.

SUMMARY

A markov process (continuous time Markov chain) approach is used to model the residence time distribution of entities or molecules in a flow system consisting of interconnected reactors. This approach is capable of treating a system in which the reactant molecules undergo first-order reactions. An example is given to demonstrate the applicability of the approach.

INTRODUCTION

Applicability of Markov processes to the analysis, modeling and simulation of flow chemical reactor systems has been amply demonstrated recently (see, e.g., [1-3]). This work briefly reviews the theory and mathematical foundation of our approach based on Markov processes and presents a specific example for demonstrating the approach.

*Department of Chemical Engineering, Kansas State University.

MODEL

Consider a flow system with n compartments. Without loss of generality, suppose that entities or molecules of types, A_1, A_2, ..., A_m, enter the system through the first compartment and that linear transitions take place among the entities or molecules in the system. Such transitions (linear first-order processes) may be unimolecular reactions, polymerization reactions or crystallization processes.

In each compartment, an entity or molecule of type A_i may transfer to another type, remain in its present state, move to another compartment or exit from the system. For a system with n compartments and m types of entities, we have a Markov process with a sample space of mn states. The states may be designated as S_1, S_2, ..., S_{nm}, where $\{S_1, S_2, ..., S_m\}$ represents the set of states in compartment 1, $\{S_{m+1}, S_{m+2}, ..., S_{2m}\}$ the set in compartment 2 and so on. Formally, we let

$$p_{ij}(t,t+\Delta t)$$

$$= \Pr[\text{an entity or molecule in state } S_i \text{ at time } t \text{ will be in state } S_j (j \neq i) \text{ at time } (t+\Delta t)]$$

$$= k_{ij}(t)\Delta t + o(\Delta t) \tag{1}$$

and

$$p_{id}(t,t+\Delta t)$$

$$= \Pr[\text{an entity or molecule in state } S_i \text{ at time } t \text{ will exit from the system at time } (t+\Delta t)]$$

$$= \mu_i(t)\Delta t + o(\Delta t) \tag{2}$$

Here, $k_{ij}(t)$ and $\mu_i(t)$ are the so-called intensity functions of the Markov process. Obviously,

$$\sum_{j=1}^{nm} p_{ij}(t,t+\Delta t) + p_{id}(t,t+\Delta t) = 1 \tag{3}$$

Let

$$p_{ii}(t,t+\Delta t) \equiv 1 + k_{ii}(t)\Delta t + o(\Delta t) \tag{4}$$

Then, from Equations (1) through (4), we have

$$k_{ii}(t) = -[\sum_{\substack{j \\ (j\neq i)}} k_{ij}(t) + \mu_i(t)] \tag{5}$$

The intensity functions $\{k_{ij}(t)\}$ within a compartment may be interpreted as rate constants for linear first-order reactions [1]. The intensity functions between states in two different compartments may be interpreted as the rate of migration or movement of entities between the two compartments. If these intensity functions are time independent, the process is said to be a time homogeneous process. Otherwise, it is a time heterogeneous process.

For a time interval (τ,t), we define

$p_{ij}(\tau,t)$ = probability that an entity or molecule in state S_i at time τ will be in state S_j at time t, $i,j = 1,2,\ldots,nm$

Let $\underline{P}(\tau,t)$ be the matrix of transition probabilities $[p_{ij}(\tau,t)]$. It has been shown that these transition probabilities satisfy the Kolmogorov forward differential equations [4,5], i.e.,

$$\frac{d}{dt}\,\underline{P}(\tau,t) = \underline{P}(\tau,t)\,\underline{K}(t) \tag{6}$$

with the initial condition

$$\underline{P}(\tau,\tau) = \underline{I} = \text{identity matrix} \tag{6a}$$

The matrix $\underline{K}(t)$ in Equation (6) is the so-called intensity matrix defined as

$$\underline{K}(t) = [k_{ij}(t)] \tag{7}$$

For the time homogeneous process, the forward differential equation, Equation (6), becomes

$$\frac{d}{dt}\,\underline{P}(t-\tau) = \underline{P}(t-\tau)\,\underline{K} \tag{8}$$

with the initial condition

$$\underline{P}(0) = \underline{I} \tag{8a}$$

The solutions of Equations (6) and (8) for the transition probabilities, $\{p_{ij}(\tau,t)\}$ and $\{p_{ij}(t-\tau)\}$, are given in [1]. With these transition probabilities known, we can obtain, as in [1], the internal and exit transitional distributions, lifetime distribution and residence time distribution of entities or molecules in a flow chemical reactor system containing an arbitrary number of reactors, even under time heterogeneous conditions, including unsteady state conditions.

Of interest here is the distribution of lifetime in the whole system (total time spent by the entity or molecule in the mn states). Let the random variable T_i denote the lifetime or life-span of an entity or molecule which was originally in state S_i. The probability density function of T_i is given in [1] as

$$f_i(\theta) = -\sum_{j=1}^{mn} p'_{ij}(\theta), \quad 0 \leq \theta < \infty \tag{9}$$

For a given time interval (0,t), the mean of the lifetime of a molecule starting from state S_i at time 0 is obtained as

$$\sum_{j=1}^{mn} \int_0^t p_{ij}(\theta)\, d\theta \tag{10}$$

For a molecule in state S_i at time 0, let $a_{ij}(t)$ be the time spent in state S_j in the time interval (0,t). The mean and variance of $a_{ij}(t)$ are, respectively [1],

$$E[a_{ij}(t)] = \int_0^t p_{ij}(\tau)\, d\tau \tag{11}$$

and

$$Var[a_{ij}(t)] = 2\int_0^t ds \int_0^s p_{ij}(\tau)\, p_{ij}(s-\tau) d\tau - \{E[a_{ij}(t)]\}^2 \tag{12}$$

For a non-reacting system, the intensity matrix $\underline{K}$ reduces to an (n x n) matrix whose elements are the intensities of transition between any two compartments. Hence, Equations (9) and (10) become, respectively,

$$f_i(\theta) = -\sum_{j=1}^{n} p'_{ij}(\theta), \quad 0 \leq \theta < \infty \tag{13}$$

and

$$\sum_{j=1}^{n} \int_0^t p_{ij}(\theta)\, d\theta \tag{14}$$

Note that subscript j indicates the j-th compartment or reactor for this case. From Equations (11) and (12), we obtain the mean and variance of lifetimes of entities or molecules in the j-th compartment of a flow system, given that they started in the i-th.

APPLICATIONS

Let us consider the reactions

$$A_1 \rightleftharpoons A_2 \rightleftharpoons A_3$$

occurring in a flow system containing four well-mixed reactors, three of which are connected in series without backflow and one of which is located in the recycle loop as shown in Figure 1. Molecules enter the system through reactor 1 and exit from reactor 3. For this example, we have mn (=12) states. The sets $\{k_{12}, k_{21}, k_{23}, k_{32}\}$, $\{k_{45}, k_{54}, k_{56}, k_{65}\}$, $\{k_{78}, k_{87}, k_{89}, k_{98}\}$ and $\{k_{10,11}, k_{11,10}, k_{11,12}, k_{12,11}\}$ represent the intensity functions in the matrix $\underline{K}$, given in Equation (7), for the first order reactions among three types of molecules occurring in each reactor; they may be equated to the reaction rate constants [1]. The sets $\{k_{14}, k_{25}, k_{36}\}$, $\{k_{47}, k_{58}, k_{69}\}$, $\{k_{7,10}, k_{8,11}, k_{9,12}\}$ and $\{k_{10,1}, k_{11,2}, k_{12,3}\}$ represents the intensity functions for transition of entities (molecules) between pairs of two adjacent reactors and may be determined from the out-flow rate of one reactor to the other and the volume of the reactor. Since the entities (molecules) can exit only through the third reactor, we have

$$\mu_i = \begin{cases} \dfrac{q}{V_3}, & i = 7,\ 8,\ 9 \\ 0, & \text{otherwise} \end{cases} \tag{15}$$

Figure 2 shows the concentration profiles of A_i (i = 1, 2, 3) in the exit stream.

For the case without chemical reactions, the process reduces to 4 states (reactors) with the intensity matrix

$$\underline{K} = [k_{ij}]_{4x4} \tag{16}$$

By letting i = 1, Equation (13) gives the residence time distribution of the reactor system under consideration, as shown in Figure 3.

DISCUSSION

From the results presented in this work, we can recover the internal and exit transitional distributions, lifetime distribution and resi-

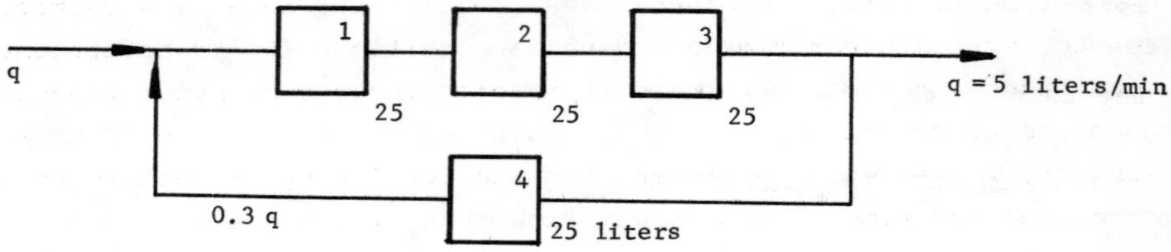

Figure 1. Schematic diagram of a recycle flow system.

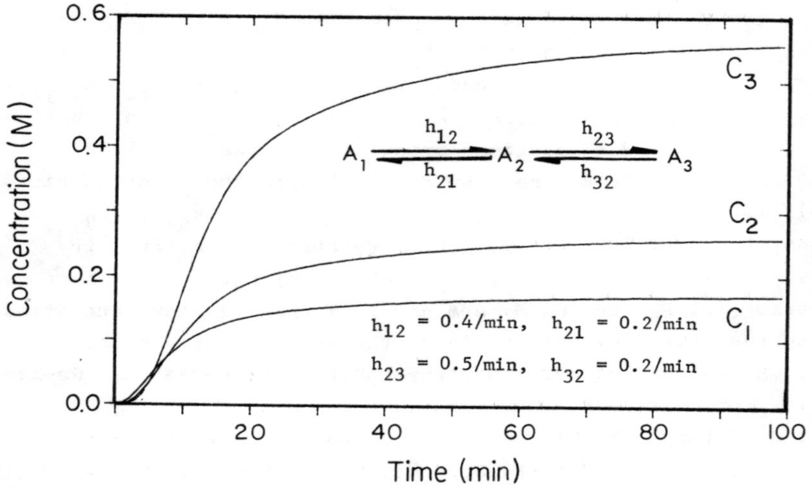

Figure 2. Concentration profiles of reactants in the exit stream for the complex reaction occurring in the recycle flow system shown in Figure 1.

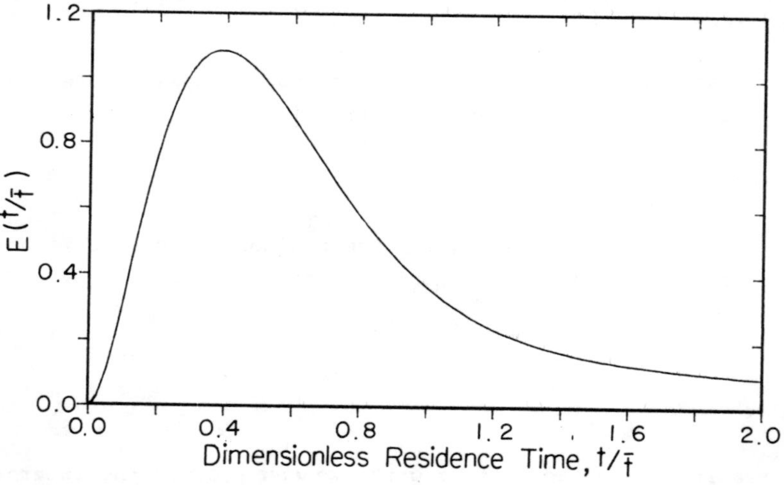

Figure 3. The residence time distribution for the recycle flow system shown in Figure 1.

dence time distribution of entities or molecules in a flow chemical reactor system under time homogeneous conditions [6] or heterogeneous conditions and those for a single reactor under time heterogeneous or homogeneous conditions. However, much remains to be done on this subject; for example, efficient computational schemes need to be developed for time heterogeneous flow reactor systems.

For further details, readers are referred to our lecture note [6] and earlier related works [1-3].

REFERENCES

1. R. Nassar, L. T. Fan, J. R. Too and L. S. Fan, Chem. Eng. Sci. 36 (1981) 1307.
2. R. Nassar, J. R. Too and L. T. Fan, J. Appl. Polym. Sci. 26 (1981) 3745.
3. R. Nassar, J. R. Too, C. H. Ahn and L. T. Fan, a paper submitted to AIChE J. for publication, 1982.
4. C. L. Chiang, An Introduction to Stochastic Processes and Their Applications, Krieger, New York, 1980.
5. N. T. J. Bailey, The Elements of Stochastic Processes with Applications to the Natural Science, Wiley, New York, 1964.
6. L. T. Fan, J. R. Too and R. Nassar, a lecture note to be presented at the Summer School on Residence Time Distribution Theory in Chemical Engineering, Bad Honnef, West Germany, Aug. 15-25, 1982.

Simulation of the Performance of a Flow Chemical Reactor by Markov Chains

J. R. Too, R. Nassar*, L.T. Fan

Department of Chemical Engineering, Kansas State University,
Manhattan, KS 66506, U.S.A.

SUMMARY

A procedure is described for simulating the performance of a flow chemical reactor by means of Markov chains. The procedure does not require the solution of differential equations governing the performance of the reactor. It is illustrated numerically with complex reactions.

INTRODUCTION

Markov chains have been shown to be effective tools for analyzing, modeling or simulating flow chemical reactor systems [1-4]. This work briefly reviews the statistical and mathematical foundations of our approach based on Markov chains and illustrates the applicability of the approach with examples. Some extensions of the approach are also described.

In our earlier stochastic studies of flow chemical reactors [5-7], we have resorted mainly to Markov processes, for which the sample space is discrete and the parameter (time) is continuous. Further-

---

*Department of Statistics, Kansas State University.

more, these studies have concentrated on systems without rate processes (chemical reactions) or with linear first-order rate processes. In this work, it is shown that the present Markov chain approach can deal not only with such systems but also with systems with non-linear chemical reactions or rate processes.

MARKOV CHAIN METHOD

Suppose that a sequence of consecutive trials, numbered m = 0,1,2,..., has been attempted. The outcome of the m-th trial is represented by the random variable X_m, which is assumed to be discrete. Let E_1, E_2,..., and E_ℓ represent the possible outcomes (states of the system) at each trial. It is customary to speak of X_m being in state E_i if $X_m = E_i$ (see, e.g. [8]).

A Markov chain is a sequence of random variables such that for a given X_m, X_{m+1} is conditionally independent of $X_0, X_1, \ldots, X_{m-1}$. In other words, the "next" state X_{m+1} of the process is independent of the "past" states provided that the "present" state X_m is known. The probability of X_{m+1} being in state E_j, given that X_m is in state E_i (called a one-step transition probability), is denoted by $p_{ij}(m)$, i.e.,

$$p_{ij}(m) = Pr[X_{m+1} = E_j \mid X_m = E_i] \tag{1}$$

The transition probabilities of a Markov chain can be conveniently exhibited in the form of a square matrix as shown below.

$$\underline{P}(m) = \begin{bmatrix} p_{11}(m) & p_{12}(m) & \cdots & p_{1\ell}(m) \\ p_{21}(m) & p_{22}(m) & \cdots & p_{2\ell}(m) \\ \cdot & \cdot & \cdot & \cdot \\ \cdot & \cdot & \cdot & \cdot \\ \cdot & \cdot & \cdot & \cdot \\ p_{\ell 1}(m) & p_{\ell 2}(m) & \cdots & p_{\ell\ell}(m) \end{bmatrix} \tag{2}$$

Notice that all elements are non-negative, and the elements in each row sum to unity.

The probability that the chain will be in state E_i at time m is given by

$$Pr[X_m = E_i] = p_i(m) \tag{3}$$

Suppose that we denote the probabilities $\{p_i(m),\ i = 1,2,\ldots,\ell\}$ at time m as the row vector, $\underline{p}(m)$, i.e.,

$$\underline{p}(m) = [p_1(m) \quad p_2(m) \quad \ldots \quad p_\ell(m)]$$

It has been shown (see, e.g., [8,9]) that

$$\underline{p}(m) = \underline{p}(0) \prod_{k=1}^{m} \underline{P}(k) \tag{4}$$

This expression states that the chain is completely determined once the initial distribution and the transition probability matrix for each step are specified.

Consider a flow chemical reactor initially containing $n_i(0)$ molecules of type $A_i (i = 1,2,\ldots,\ell)$. Each molecule of any type will reside in the flow reactor for a random length of time before it reacts in it or exits from it. The type of molecules, $A_1, A_2,\ldots,A_\ell$, are considered as different transient states of the system. The exit stream may be considered as an absorbing state (state of death); it is designated as state D. Once a molecule enters state D, it will never return to any of the transient states. Then, $p_{ij}(m)$ represents the probability that a molecule in state A_i at time m will be in state A_j at time (m + 1); the probability that a molecule in state A_i will remain unchanged at time (m + 1) is then $p_{ii}(m)$. Let $p_{id}(m)$ be the probability that a molecule will exit from the reactor during the transition. Naturally,

$$\sum_{j=1}^{\ell} p_{ij}(m) + p_{id}(m) = 1 \tag{5}$$

For illustration, let us consider the competitive reactions

$$A_1 \xrightarrow{k_1} A_3 \tag{6a}$$

$$A_1 + A_2 \xrightarrow{k_2} A_4 + A_5 \tag{6b}$$

occurring in a flow reactor with rate constants k_1 and k_2; the first reaction is of the unimolecular first-order, and the second is of the bimolecular second-order. The transition probability matrix, $\underline{P}(m)$, can be easily formulated as

$$\underline{P}(m) = [p_{ij}(m)]_{6x6} \tag{7}$$

For instance, the elements of the first row of this matrix are obtained as follows:

1. Since a molecule of type A_1 will not transform into type A_2, we have

$$p_{12}(m) = 0$$

2. The probability that a molecule in state A_1 at time m will be in state A_3 due to the reaction, Equation (6a), at time (m + 1) is

$$p_{13}(m) = \zeta_1(m)$$

Here, $\zeta_1(m)$ is independent to the number of molecules of type A_1 in the reactor and can be related to the rate constant as $\zeta_1(m) \simeq k_1\Delta t$ where Δt is the time interval between two transitions.

3. The probability that a molecule in state A_1 at time m will be in state A_4 due to the reaction, Equation (6b), at time (m + 1) is [3]

$$p_{14}(m) = \frac{1}{2}\zeta_2(m)n_2(m)$$

Similarly, we have

$$p_{15}(m) = \frac{1}{2}\zeta_2(m)n_2(m)$$

where $\zeta_2(m)$ is related to the rate constant as

$$\zeta_2(m) \simeq k_2\Delta t$$

4. The probability that a molecule of type A_1 in the flow reactor at time m will exit from it at time (m + 1) is

$$p_{id}(m) = \mu_1(m)$$

5. The probability for a molecule of type A_1 at time m to remain in the same state at time (m + 1) is, from Equation (3),

$$p_{11}(m) = 1 - \sum_{j=2}^{5} p_{1j}(m) - p_{1d}(m)$$

$$= 1 - \zeta_1(m) - \zeta_2(m)n_2(m) - \mu_1(m)$$

Note that the rate constants are dependent on the temperature in the reactor, and thus if it varies with time, $\zeta_1(m)$ and $\zeta_2(m)$ may be made functions of time by resorting to the Arrhenius expression.

The probability of a molecule exiting from a flow reactor, $\mu_i(m)$, is related to the flow pattern in the reactor. For example, if the reactor is completely mixed, $\mu_i(m)$ may be expressed as (see, e.g., [4])

$$\mu_i(m) \simeq \frac{q(m)\Delta t}{V(m)}, \quad i = 1, 2, \ldots, 5 \tag{8}$$

where q(m) is the volumetric flow rate, and V(m) is the volume of the reactor at time m. Furthermore, if the flow rate is fixed, we have

$$\mu_i(m) = \mu_i \simeq \frac{q\Delta t}{V} = \text{const.} \tag{8a}$$

Now, we are concerned with the estimation of the number of molecules of type A_i ($i = 1, 2, \ldots, 5$), n_i, at any moment. This can be accomplished by iterating over the following sequences;

$$n_i(m+1) = x_i(m) + \sum_{j=1}^{5} n_j(m)p_{ji}(m), \quad i = 1, 2, \ldots, 5 \tag{9}$$

where $x_i(m)$ is the number of molecules of type A_i fed into a reactor during the time interval (m, m+1). Figures 1 shows the simulated results based on Equation (9) for a continuous stirred tank reactor.

If the reactions, Equations (6a) and (6b), occur in a batch reactor, we have

$$\mu_i(m) = 0, \qquad i = 1, 2, \ldots, 5$$

The number of molecules of type A_i ($i = 1, 2, \ldots, 5$) in the reactor can be obtained by setting $x_i(m) = 0$ in Equation (9); the resultant expression is

$$n_i(m+1) = \sum_{j=1}^{5} n_j(m)p_{ji}(m), \qquad i = 1, 2, \ldots, 5 \tag{10}$$

This expression is illustrated in Figure 2.

The present technique can also be employed to generate the residence time distribution for a flow system which contains any number of completely mixed tanks or reactors connected in any fashion. For this case, each tank is considered as a transient state, and the exit stream is an absorbing state (state of death).

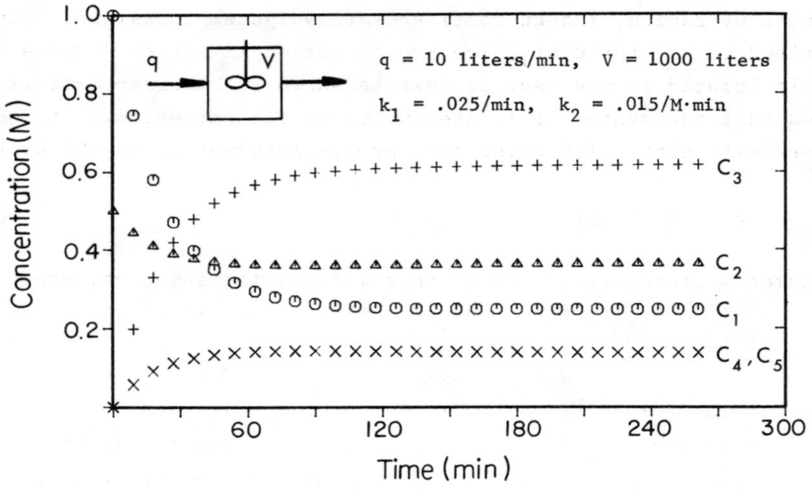

Figure 1. Concentrations as functions of time for the competitive reactions, Equations (6a) and (6b), occurring in a CSTR.

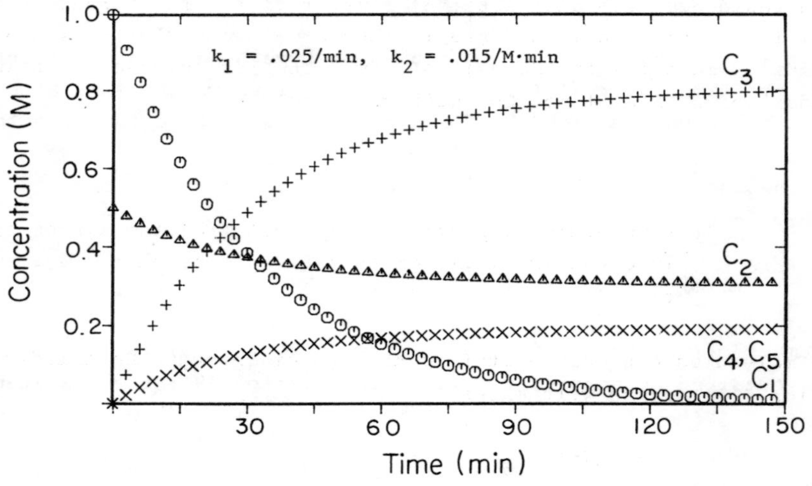

Figure 2. Concentrations as functions of time for the competitive reactions, Equations (6a) and (6b), occurring in a batch reactor.

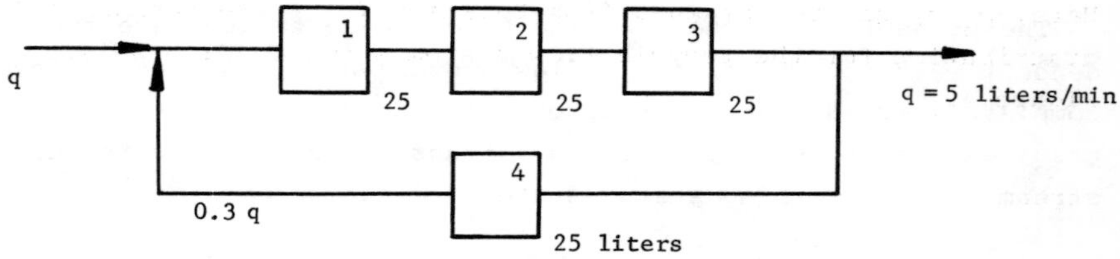

Figure 3. Schematic diagram of a recycle flow system.

For illustration, let us consider a flow system containing four well-mixed tanks, three of which are connected in series and one of which is located in the recycle loop as shown in Figure 3. It is assumed that the system is in steady state, i.e., the flow rate does not vary with time. The transition probability matrix may be written as

$$\underline{P}(m) = \underline{P} = [p_{ij}]_{5x5}$$

The elements of the first row of this matrix, for instance, are

$$p_{12} = \frac{(1+\alpha)q}{V_1}(\Delta t)$$

$$p_{13} = p_{14} = p_{15} = 0$$

and

$$p_{11} = 1 - \sum_{j=2}^{5} p_{1j} = 1 - \frac{(1+\alpha)q}{V_1}(\Delta t)$$

The residence time distribution of material flowing through a flow system is conventionally defined in such a way that $E(m)\Delta t$ is the fraction of material in the exit stream with ages between m and (m+1). In other words, $E(m)\Delta t$ may be interpreted as

$E(m)\Delta t$

= Pr[a molecule or particle will exit from the system in the interval (m, m+1), given that it entered the system at time 0] (11)

Since molecules can only exit from the system through the third tank, Equation (11) may be written as

$$E(m)\Delta t = p_3(m) \cdot p_{35}$$

or

$$E(m) = p_3(m)p_{35}/\Delta t \qquad (12)$$

Here, $p_3(m)$ can be obtained from Equation (4). The residence time distribution for the recycle flow system shown in Figure is given in Figure 4.

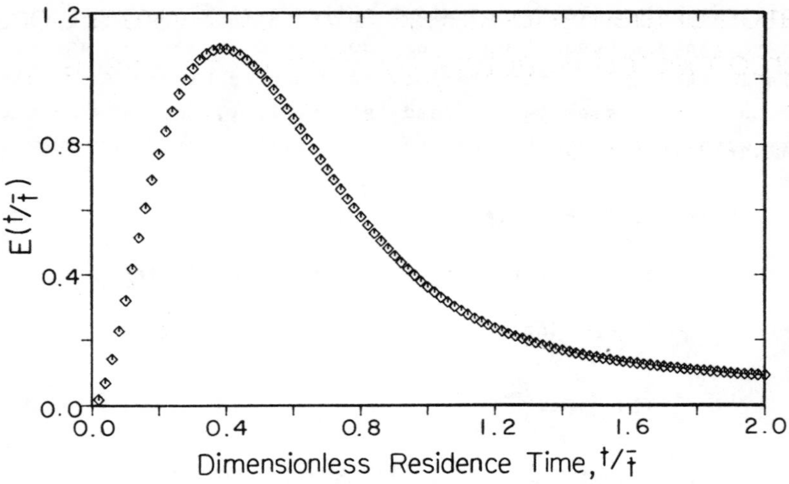

Figure 4. The residence time distribution for the recycle flow system shown in Figure 1.

DISCUSSION

In the present Markov chain model, an assumption is made that transitions occur instantaneously at each instant of the discretized time. To obtain accurate results, Δt must be sufficiently small to render the transition probability from one state to another occurring in this interval very small. Two factors, therefore, must be considered in choosing the size of Δt. The smaller the Δt, the closer the approximation of the discrete time model to the continuous time process; on the other hand, the computation time increases proportionally with decreasing Δt. For further details, readers are referred to our earlier work [4].

REFERENCES

1. L. G. Gibilaro, H. W. Kropholler and D. J. Spikins, Chem. Eng. Sci. 22 (1967) 517.
2. W. Pippel and G. Phillipp, Chem. Eng. Sci. 32 (1977) 1535.
3. S. J. Formosinho and M. M. Miguel, J. Chem. Educ. 56 (1979) 582.
4. J. R. Too, L. T. Fan and R. Nassar, a paper to appear in Comput. and Chem. Eng., 1982.

5. R. Nassar, L. T. Fan, J. R. Too and L. S. Fan, Chem. Eng. Sci. 36 (1981) 1307.
6. R. Nassar, J. R. Too and L. T. Fan, J. Appl. Polym. Sci. 26 (1981) 3745.
7. R. Nassar, J. R. Too, C. H. Ahn and L. T. Fan, submitted to AIChE J. for publication, 1982.
8. N. T. J. Bailey, The Elements of Stochastic Processes with Applications to the Natural Sciences, Wiley, New York, 1964.
9. E. Cinlar, Introduction to Stochastic Processes, Prentice-Hall, Englewood Cliffs, N.J., 1975.

A Macroscopic Model of a Continuous Emulsion Liquid Membrane Extraction System

J. D. Way, R. D. Noble

National Bureau of Standards
Center for Chemical Engineering, 773.1, Boulder, CO 80303

Introduction

The liquid surfactant or emulsion liquid membrane (ELM) separation technique is a highly selective method of separating organics, inorganics and metal ions. The technique is capable of simultaneous extraction and stripping. It was invented by Dr. Norman Li in 1968 (Li, 1968). Since that time, much work has been done by many authors to qualitatively demonstrate the feasibility of performing separations with specific formulations.

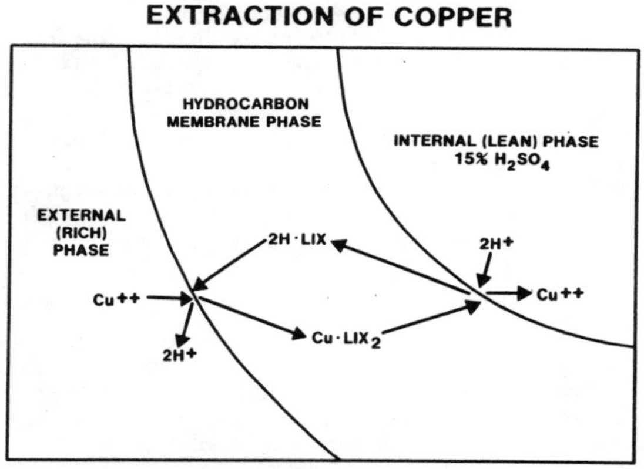

Figure 1. Idealized Cross Section of Emulsion Liquid Membrane for Copper Extraction

Figure 1 shows an idealized schematic diagram of a section of a liquid membrane globule. The membrane separates two miscible phases from each other while being insoluble in the outer continuous and inner droplet phase. The membrane can be either aqueous or organic, depending upon the nature of the separation.

Transport of a desired species from a mixture into liquid membranes can occur due to several mechanisms. In facilitated transport systems a carrier is incorporated into the membrane phase. At the membrane/continuous phase interface the carrier reacts with the permeant species forming a complex. Diffusion of the complex augments the diffusion of the unreacted permeant species (Ward, 1970). At the opposite membrane interface, the reverse reaction takes place, completing the transport of the permeate.

Coupled transport is a special case of facilitated transport in which the interaction between the permeant species and the carrier is an ion-exchange reaction. As shown in figure 1 for copper ion transport, the carrier, designated by LIX, exchanges hydrogen ions for the copper ion at the outer interface and the reverse reaction at the inner interface. Consequently, the transport of hydrogen ions is "coupled" to the copper ion transport. In coupled transport, the gradient of the coupled ion provides the driving force for the permeant species.

In ELM formulations for metal ion recovery, an aqueous trapping phase is mixed with an organic liquid containing oil soluble surfactants and a complexing agent selective for a specific metal ion forming a water-in-oil emulsion. The emulsion is contacted with the leach liquor containing the metal ions and the metal organic complex formed in the liquid membrane exchanges the metal ion for hydrogen ions in the trapping phase. The carrier diffuses back to the interface with the continuous phase and the process is repeated. In this way ELM "chemically pumps" the metal ion into the inner trapping phase and is not limited by equilibrium (Cussler, 1971). Emulsion liquid membranes are extremely well-suited to recovering metal ions from low concentration sources, such as leach liquors from low-grade ore bodies.

Background

While many recent experimental studies describe transport of Cu^{++} ions through both supported and emulsion liquid membranes (Frankenfeld et al., 1981; Lee et al., 1978; Baker et al., 1977), few published studies present mathematical models of the facilitated transport process in emulsion liquid membranes. Recent work by Ho et al. (1981) and Ho and Li (1981) on modeling emulsion liquid has been confined to transport due to solubility differences in the membrane phase between the transported species and others in a mixture. The model did not describe facilitated or coupled transport. Cussler (1971) developed the first mathematical treatment of the coupled transport of two ions. The model was applied to experimental data of sodium ion transport across immobilized liquid films. Further modeling work by Caracciolo et al. (1975) extended the work of Cussler (1971) by considering the effect of the association of the transported solutes to form ion pairs. Baker et al. (1977) developed a simplified mathematical treatment of coupled transport which relates the flux of the transported ion to the gradient of that ion and the gradient of the coupled ion. More recently, Danesi et al. (1981) have also presented mathematical models of the coupled transport of metal ions. However, these studies have been confined to an immobilized or supported liquid membrane configuration. The objective of this paper is to describe a preliminary macroscopic model of a copper ion transport in emulsion liquid membranes.

Problem Statement

The model presented in this paper will describe a continuous ELM extraction process for cuprous ions. The model will predict the steady state external phase copper concentration and the average copper concentration in the ELM globule. The residence time distribution of the globules in the extraction vessel was incorporated in the analysis. A diagram of the process is shown in figure 2.

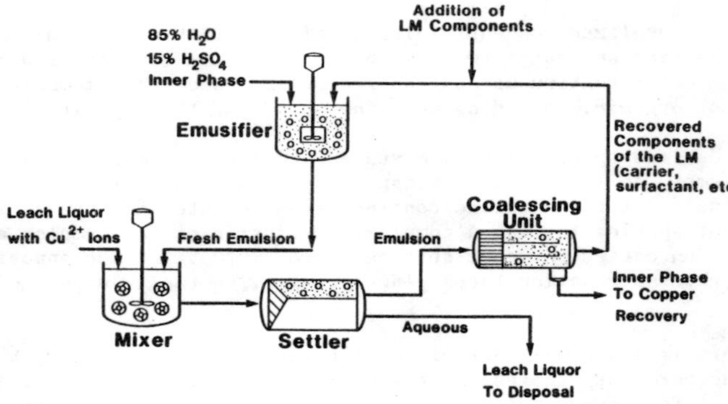

Figure 2. Flow Diagram of Extraction System

The hypothetical process consists of a mixer, settler, emulsion coalescer, and an emulsifier. The model will only describe the mixing vessel. The following assumptions were made:

(1) The system is at steady state

(2) The mixing vessel is a CSTR (continuous stirred tank reactor)

(3) No external mass transfer limitations in the external aqueous phase

(4) Transport is reaction rate limited

(5) The residence time distribution of the reactor is

$$\frac{dF(t)}{dt} = \frac{e^{-t/\theta}}{\theta} \tag{1}$$

$$\text{where } \theta = \frac{V_T}{q} \tag{2}$$

and V_T ≡ total mixer volume

q ≡ volumetric flowrate into mixer

(6) The mixer contents are a segregated system in which each emulsion globule behaves like a batch reactor (no coalescence).

(7) The emulsion globules are homogeneous with a constant radius.

The final assumption neglects the distribution of global sizes and effects of osmotic swell. Osmotic swell is an increase in the globule size by the diffusion of water into the globule because of an osmotic pressure gradient. These effects will be incorporated into the model at a later date when they can be quantified.

Mass Balance on the External Continuous Phase

The following reversible complexation reactor can occur at an aqueous phase/membrane interface:

$$LH_2^{+} + Cu^{++} \underset{k_{-1}}{\overset{k_1}{\rightleftharpoons}} LCu^{++} + 2H^{+} \tag{3}$$

where L ≡ carrier, LIX 64N, β-hydroxy-oxime (Merigold et al., 1971)

LCu^{++} ≡ cuprous ion complex

LH^{+} ≡ hydrogen ion complex

k_1 ≡ forward rate constant

k_{-1} ≡ reverse rate constant

Danesi et al. (1980) have measured the kinetics of the above reaction and report the following rate law for the forward reaction

$$r_{Cu} = -\frac{k_1\,[Cu^{++}]\,[\bar{L}]}{[H^{+}]} \tag{4}$$

where $k_1 = 2.86 \cdot 10^4$ cm/s

$[\bar{L}]$ ≡ carrier concentration in the membrane phase

$[H^{+}]$ = hydrogen ion concentration in aqueous phase

$[Cu^{++}]$ = cuprous ion concentration in aqueous phase

r_{Cu} = rate of forward reaction

The control volume for the material balance will be the contents of the mixing tank. A material balance for copper yields:

$$q\,[Cu^{++}]^{o} - q\,[Cu^{++}] = -r_{Cu}A_{I}N \tag{5}$$

where $[Cu^{++}]^{o} \equiv$ initial copper concentration
$A_I \equiv$ interfacial area/globule
$N \equiv$ number of globules

Substituting for r_{Cu} from equation (4) gives:

$$q\,[Cu^{++}]^{o} - q\,[Cu^{++}] = \frac{k_1\,[L]\,[Cu^{++}]\,A_I N}{[H^+]} \tag{6}$$

From stoichiometry the hydrogen ion concentration in the continuous phase is:

$$[H^+] = 2\,([Cu^{++}]^{o} - [Cu^{++}]) \tag{7}$$

The interfacial area and number of globules can be expressed in terms of system parameters:

$$A_I = 4\pi Rg^2 \tag{8}$$

$$N = \frac{\text{volume emulsion}}{\text{volume per globule}} = \frac{Ve}{4/3\pi Rg^3} \tag{9}$$

where Rg = globule radius
Ve = volume of emulsion

Substituting and simplifying we obtain:

$$([Cu^{++}]^{o} - [Cu^{++}])^2 = \frac{3k_1\,[\bar{L}]\,Ve\,[Cu^{++}]}{2qRg} \tag{10}$$

which can be written as

$$(a'-x)^2 = b'x \tag{11}$$

where $a' = [Cu^{++}]^{o}$ $\qquad x = [Cu^{++}]$

$$b' = \frac{3k_1\,[\bar{L}]\,Ve}{2qRg}$$

and $\quad x^2 - (2a' + b')x + a'^2 = 0 \qquad (12)$

Simplifying and making variable substitutions we obtain

$$x^2 - bx + c = 0 \tag{13}$$

where $b = 2[Cu^{++}]^{o} + \dfrac{3k_1 Ve\,[\bar{L}]}{2qRg}$

$$c = ([Cu^{++}]^{o})^2$$

This equation can easily be solved to obtain the steady state cuprous ion concentration in the continuous phase:

$$[Cu^{++}] = \frac{b - \sqrt{b^2 - 4c}}{2} \tag{14}$$

The sign on the discriminant in equation (14) must be negative or the copper concentration after extraction would exceed the initial copper concentration.

Material Balance on an Emulsion Globule

If an emulsion globule is taken to be the control volume, a material for copper gives

$$\frac{d\bar{N}_{Cu}}{dt} = -r_{Cu}A_I \tag{15}$$

where $\bar{N}_{Cu}$ = mass of copper in the globule

This equation assumes that transport is reaction rate limited and that there are no external mass transfer resistances. Substituting for N_{Cu}, r_{Cu}, and A_I we obtain:

$$\frac{d}{dt}\left([Cu^{++}]_g \ \frac{4}{3}\pi Rg^3\right) = \frac{k_1\ [\bar{L}]\ [Cu^{++}]\ 4\pi Rg^2}{2([Cu^{++}]^o - [Cu^{++}])} \tag{16}$$

where $[Cu^{++}]g \equiv$ copper concentration in the globule which simplifies to:

$$\frac{d}{dt}[Cu^{++}]g = \frac{3}{Rg}\left\{\frac{k_1\ [\bar{L}]\ [Cu^{++}]}{2([Cu^{++}]^o - [Cu^{++}])}\right\} \tag{17}$$

The right-hand side of equation 17 is a constant and subsequent integration gives:

$$[Cu^{++}]g = \alpha t \tag{18}$$

where

$$\alpha = \frac{3}{Rg}\left\{\frac{k_1\ [\bar{L}]\ [Cu^{++}]}{2([Cu^{++}]^o - [Cu^{++}])}\right\}$$

since $[Cu^{++}]g = 0$ at $t = 0$.

The ion-exchange reaction (4) requires that 2 hydrogen ions be exchanged for each Cu^{++} ion extracted. Consequently, the capacity for Cu^{++} extraction is limited by the amount of hydrogen ions present in the encapsulated aqueous phase. An equation was derived to calculate the time, t_{max}, corresponding to the maximum copper extraction:

$$t_{max} = \frac{([\bar{Cu}^{++}]g)_{max}}{\alpha} \tag{19}$$

$$t_{max} = \left(\frac{WT}{100}\right)\left\{\frac{63.54\ \frac{g\ Cu}{mol}}{98.078\ \frac{g\ H_2SO_4}{mol}}\right\}\left(\frac{1}{\alpha Ve}\right) \tag{20}$$

where WT ≡ weight percent sulfuric acid in the internal droplet phase.

Incorporation of Residence Time Distribution

An equation has been derived to predict the copper concentration within a globule as a function of time. In a segregated system, the time an aggregate spends in the mixer is a function of the residence time distribution of the particular vessel. In this preliminary model, the RTD of an ideal CSTR was assumed to describe the mixing vessel. From Levenspiel (1972) the following equation describes the fraction of the copper extracted:

$$\begin{pmatrix}\text{fraction of}\\ \text{the } Cu^{++} \text{ ion}\\ \text{extracted}\end{pmatrix} = \sum_{\substack{\text{all}\\ \text{globules}}} \begin{pmatrix}\text{fraction } Cu^{++}\\ \text{extracted for}\\ \text{globule of age}\\ \text{between t and}\\ t + \Delta t\end{pmatrix} \begin{pmatrix}\text{fraction of}\\ \text{exit stream}\\ \text{consisting of globules}\\ \text{of age between t and}\\ t + \Delta t\end{pmatrix} \quad (21)$$

Substituting into equation (21) we obtain

$$[\overline{Cu}^{++}]g = \frac{\alpha}{\theta} \int_0^{t_{max}} t e^{-t/\theta}\, dt \quad (22)$$

Integrating equation (22) gives

$$[\overline{Cu}^{++}]g = \frac{\alpha}{\theta} \left\{ e^{\frac{-t_{max}}{\theta}} (-\theta^2 - t_{max}\theta) + \theta^2 \right\} \quad (23)$$

which will predict the average cuprous ion concentration in the globules and the extent of separation which will be achieved.

Discussion of Model Prediction

Equation (23) can be non-dimensionalized as follows:

$$\frac{[\overline{Cu}^{++}]g}{[Cu^{++}]^{\circ}} = \frac{\alpha}{[Cu^{++}]^{\circ}\theta} \left\{ -e^{\frac{-t_{max}}{\theta}} (\theta + t_{max}\theta) + \theta^2 \right\} \quad (24)$$

Figure 3 is a plot of four sets of solutions to equation (24).

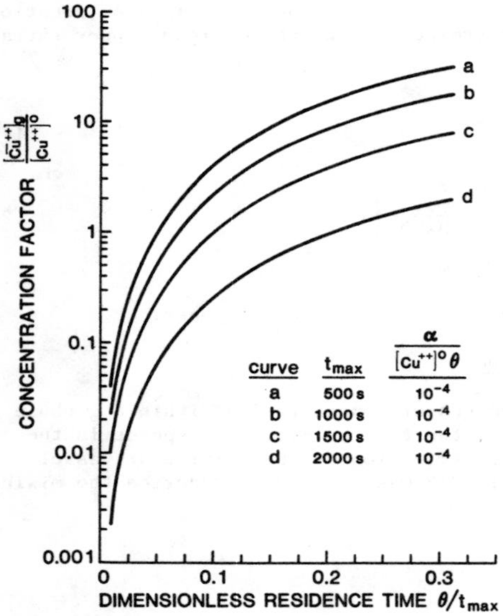

Figure 3.

Plot of Model Solution - Concentration Factor Versus Dimensionless Residence Time

The ratio $[\overline{Cu}^{++}]g/[Cu^{++}]^\circ$ is plotted as a function of dimensionless residence time θ/t_{max}. The ratio $[\overline{Cu}^{++}]g/[Cu^{++}]^\circ$ is the degree of concentration of the feed solution that is obtained in the globule phase. The curves show the dynamics of the process, with the globule concentration increasing sharply and then leveling out as the residence time increases. The four curves in figure 3 were calculated for $\alpha/[Cu^{++}]^\circ\theta = 10^{-4}$ and typical values of t_{max} of 500, 1000, 1500, and 2000 seconds. Values of the concentration factor from figure 3 can be used to calculate the concentration factor at other values of the group $\alpha/[Cu^{++}]^\circ\theta$ for any of the four t_{max} quantities. The following equation can be derived from equation (24):

$$CF_2 = CF_1 \frac{\beta_2}{\beta_1} \tag{25}$$

where CF ≡ concentration factor

$$\beta \equiv \frac{\alpha}{[Cu^{++}]^\circ\theta}$$

This calculational procedure can be used with figure 3 to describe the transport of other divalent metal cations which follow a complexation reaction similar to that of equation 3. The dimensionless group β would be recalculated reflecting different values of the rate constant, initial concentrations, etc., and the concentration factor could be determined for the values of t_{max} presented on figure 3.

Conclusions and Recommendations

This paper has presented a preliminary macroscopic model of an emulsion liquid membrane system for metal ion extraction. The results of the model indicate that the macroscopic approach is valuable when information concerning degree of separation, effect of operating variables, etc., is desired.

Several refinements are needed to more closely describe the actual separation process. The size distribution of the globules should be considered. Also, the present model completely neglects breakage of the emulsion globules and swelling of the globules due to diffusion of water into the globules because of osmotic pressure differences. Further work will incorporate these refinements into the model and they will be reported in future publications of this laboratory.

References

Baker, R. W., M. E. Tuttle, D. J. Kelly, and H. K. Lonsdale, "Coupled Transport Membranes I: Copper Separations," Journal of Membrane Science, 2, 213 (1977).

Caraciolo, F., E. L. Cussler, and D. F. Evans, "Membranes with Common Ion Pumping," AIChE Journal 21, 1, 160 (1975).

Cussler, E. L., "Membranes Which Pump," AIChE Journal 17, 6, 1300 (1971).

Danesi, P. R., E. P. Horowitz, G. F. Vandegrift, and R. Chiarizia, "Mass Transfer Rate Through Liquid Membranes: Interfacial Chemical Reactions and Diffusion as Simultaneous Permeability Controlling Factors," Separation Science and Technology, 16, 201 (1981).

Danesi, P. R., R. Chiarizia, and G. F. Vandegrift, "Kinetics and Mechanism of the Complex Formation Reactions Between Cu(II) and Fe(III) Aqueous Species and a beta-Hydroxy Oxime in Toluene," J. Phys. Chem., 84, 3455 (1980).

Frankenfield, J. W., R. P. Cahn, and N. N. Li, "Extraction of Copper by Liquid Membranes," Separation Sci. and Tech., 16, 4, 385 (1981).

Ho, W. S. and N. N. Li, "Modeling of Liquid Membrane Extraction," paper presented at the ACS National Meeting, New York, April 23-28, 1981.

Ho, W. S., T. A. Hatton, E. N. Lightfoot, and N. N. Li, "Extraction with Liquid Surfactant Membranes: A Diffusion Controlled Model," paper presented at the Second World Congress of Chemical Engineering, Montreal, Canada, October 4-9, 1981.

Lee, K., D. F. Evans, and E. L. Cussler, "Selective Copper Recovery with Two Types of Liquid Membranes," AIChE Journal 24, 5, 860 (1978).

Levenspiel, O., Chemical Reaction Engineering, second edition, Wiley, New York, 1972.

Li, N. N., U.S. Patent 3410 794 (1968).

Merigold, C. R., D. W. Agers, and J. E. House, "Lix 64N - The Recovery of Copper from Ammoniacal Leach Solutions," in Proceedings of the International Solvent Extraction Conference, Society Chemical Industries, p 1351, London, England (1971).

Ward, W. J., "Analytical and Experimental Studies of Facilitated Transport," AIChE J., 16, 405 (1970).

Models for Flow Systems and Chemical Reactors

C. Y. Wen

1. INTRODUCTION

The design, analysis and simulation of chemical reactors are of unique and prime interest to chemical engineers. Probably the discipline in this field, more than any other, distinguishes chemical engineering from other fields of engineering as a distinct and coherent branch of engineering. Yet, the study of chemical reactors - chemical reaction engineering, as it is often called - is comparatively new in spite of the early development of fundamental theories of chemical kinetics. This slow development stemmed from lack of understanding the intrusion of complex physical phenomena on chemical rate processes in chemical reactors.

Physical effects in chemical reactors, whether in the laboratory or on an industrial scale, are difficult to eliminate from the chemical rate processes. Non-uniformities in the velocity and temperature profiles, and interphase and intraparticle heat and mass transfer tend to distort the kinetic data and make the analyses and scale-up of a reactor difficult. Reaction rate data obtained from laboratory units without a proper account of the physical effects can result in an erroneous rate expression. Consequently, the mechanism and order of reaction, the activation energies and the selectivities determined are misleading and may cause disastrous plant operation if used in scale-up. In plant operations, non-chemical or physical aspects of reactor behavior could affect the stability and controllability of the entire unit. It is, therefore, important to make careful studies of interacting mechanisms and to isolate their effects from purely chemical processes.

Considerable information on the combined effects of chemical kinetics and interphase and intraparticle transport of heat and mass within chemical reactors is available in a large volume of literature and texts. In what follows we shall examine the effects of flow pattern and state of fluid mixing on chemical kinetics prevailing in reactors.

We shall employ mathematical models to represent both chemical and physical effects. The model must, therefore, represent the flow behavior of an actual reactor realistically enough to yield useful information for its design and analysis. However, a model can never represent a complete picture of reality. A simple model may be quite adequate in some instances, but a much more refined and elaborate model may be necessary in another circumstance. Figure 1 presents three levels of sophistication in modeling reactors. The simplest is the black box approach represented by residence time distribution model. The opaque box, on the other hand, represents the majority of phenomenological models and is used most frequently for reactor modeling. The glass box is the most comprehensive model with knowledge of the velocity distribution of the molecules and particles involved. Each model serves its purpose depending on the scale of interest and the type of chemical reactions that are taking place. A good model, therefore, must recognize its own inadequacies, so that it can serve as a means to develop a more complete picture of reality. Hence, in formulating a reactor model, it is imperative that we differentiate the major factors that are significantly important from the minor factors that may be safely neglected. By analyzing the behavior of the reactor model and comparing it with the actual reactor, we shall be able to learn how and in which direction the improvement of the model should be attempted.

Department of Chemical Engineering
West Virginia University, Morgantown, West Virginia 26506

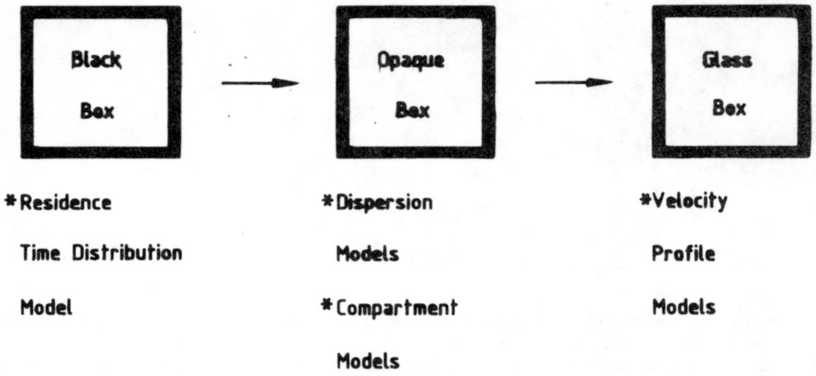

Figure 1. Level of Sophistication in Modeling

In this lecture, we concentrate our attention to the opaque box approach and present three examples of reactor models, namely the tubular reactor, the fixed bed reactor and the fluidized bed reactor.

2. DISPERSION MODELS

In general, the information necessary to describe velocity profile in a reactor is usually not available for complex reactors. Therefore, for description of the flow behavior in a complex reactor, we have to rely on a model which contains empirical parameters and approximates the actual behavior closely. This implies that for such a model to be generally useful for reactor design, the correlation of the parameters contained in the model must be developed as is common in other fields of chemical engineering.

One of the most widely used models is the dispersion model in which the diffusion is superimposed on plug-flow and, therefore, it is sometimes called the dispersed plug-flow model. The general mathematical expression is given below:

$$\frac{\partial c}{\partial t} = \nabla \cdot (E\nabla c) - \overline{u} \cdot \nabla c + \phi(c),$$

where $\phi(c)$ is the reaction rate and/or source term. For the isothermal, incompressible flow of fluids under a constant flow rate and in a cylindrical vessel, the above equation can be rewritten as

$$\frac{\partial c}{\partial t} = E_z \frac{\partial^2 c}{\partial z^2} + E_r \left(\frac{\partial^2 c}{\partial r^2} + \frac{1}{r}\frac{\partial c}{\partial r}\right) - \overline{u}\frac{\partial c}{\partial z} + \phi(c) \qquad (2\text{-}1)$$

E_z is termed the axial dispersion coefficient and E_r, the radial dispersion coefficient. They are assumed to be independent of concentration and position. This equation is used very frequently for turbulent flow of fluidis in pipes, flow through packed beds, flow of liquids through fluidized beds, etc. In fact, the equation has been applied to many other homogeneous and heterogeneous systems in which axial symmetry can be assumed and in which the flow behavior is not too far from that of plug-flow.

However, when the flow behavior deviates considerably from plug-flow such as in a stirred tank, in a bubbling fluidized bed, and in the two-phase flow of gas-liquid systems, the behavior can not always be represented by this model. This does not mean that the model can not be used in each phase when two phases are involved. Many investigators used a simplification of this model to represent gas-flow behavior in irrigated packed columns or liquid flow in extraction columns.

When radial dispersion can be neglected in comparison with axial dispersion, Equation (2-1) is reduced to

$$\frac{\partial c}{\partial t} = E_z \frac{\partial^2 c}{\partial z^2} - \bar{u}\frac{\partial c}{\partial z} + r, \tag{2-2}$$

where r is the rate of reaction.

This model is called the "axial-dispersed plug-flow model" or the "longitudinal-dispersed plug-flow model" or sometimes simply the "dispersion model". Usually radial dispersion can be neglected in comparison with the axial dispersion when the ratio of column diameter to length is very small and the flow is in turbulent regime. Perhaps this model is the most widely used model for chemical reactors and other contacting devices. As early as 1908, Langmuir [1908] discussed this model and obtained steady-state solutions using the following boundary conditions:

$$\bar{u}c_{z\to 0^-} = \bar{u}c_{z\to 0^+} - E_z\left(\frac{\partial c}{\partial z}\right)_{z\to 0^+}$$

$$\left(\frac{\partial c}{\partial z}\right)_{z=L} = 0 \qquad \text{for} \qquad \text{all } t.$$

Later, Danckwerts [1955] also obtained steady-state solutions based on the same boundary conditions. Validity of this set of boundary conditions has been re-examined from various points of view and approaches [Ahn (1962), Fan et al. (1962), Wehner et al. (1956)].

(A) FLOW OF FLUIDS THROUGH PIPES AND TUBES

The dispersion model has been successfully applied to single-phase flow of fluids through an empty tube or pipe. Following the classical study by Taylor [1954] and an extensive theoretical analysis by Aris et al. [1956], much work has been conducted to establish experimental correlations of the dispersion coefficients. In turbulent regimes, the Taylor-Aris solution considering only longitudinal dispersion has been well-substantiated experimentally for most of the part of the flow regimes. In this section, experimental correlation of the axial-dispersed plug-flow coefficient, E_z, is presented for regimes of Reynolds number less than 2,000 and larger than 2,000.

In laminar flow regimes, the Taylor-Aris solution of the axial dispersion coefficient is represented by

$$E_z = D_M + \frac{d^2\bar{u}^2}{192\ D_M}$$

or

$$\frac{1}{N_{Pe_a}} = \frac{1}{N_{Re}\cdot N_{Sc}} + \frac{N_{Re}\cdot N_{Sc}}{192} \tag{2-3}$$

Available experimental data confirm the accuracy of Equation (2-3). This equation is applicable for $1.0 < N_{Re} < 2{,}000$ and $0.23 < N_{Sc} < 1{,}000$.

Taylor [1954] derived the following expression for the dispersion coefficient in fully turbulent flow regime:

$$E_z \propto du^*, \tag{2-4}$$

where u* is the friction velocity and is related to the tube friction factor, f, by

$$u^* = \sqrt{f/2} \cdot \overline{u} \tag{2-5}$$

Substituting Equation (2-5) into Equation (2-4), we obtain

$$\frac{E_z}{\overline{u}d} \propto \sqrt{f/2}$$

If friction factors for smooth pipes in turbulent regime from the Blasius equation

$$f = 0.0791\ (N_{Re})^{-1/4}$$

are used, the Peclet number relation for turbulent regime becomes

$$\frac{1}{N_{Pe_a}} \propto \frac{1}{(N_{Re})^{1/8}}$$

Adding the term for the transition regime, an empirical correlation for the range of Reynolds numbers larger than 2,000 can be obtained as

$$\frac{1}{N_{Pe_a}} = \frac{3.0 \times 10^7}{(N_{Re})^{2.1}} + \frac{1.35}{(N_{Re})^{1/8}} \tag{2-6}$$

(B) AXIAL DISPERSION OF GASES IN PACKED BEDS

Unlike liquids, dispersion of gases in fixed or packed beds is affected by the molecular diffusion. Based on a typical value of molecular diffusivity for a liquid, 10^{-5} cm^2/sec, and a gas 0.5 cm^2/sec, Edwards [1966] showed that molecular diffusion becomes important at particle Reynolds number smaller than about 3 x 10^{-4} for liquids and smaller than about 1.8 for gases.

Let us consider the effect of molecular diffusion in the following way. If molecular diffusion is the only operating mechanism, the axial-dispersion coefficient, E_z, under extremely low flow rate is related to the molecular diffusivity D_M by the equation

$$E_z = \gamma D_M \tag{2-7}$$

where γ is known as the tortuosity factor. The value of γ probably ranges from 0.4 to 0.9 depending on the investigators and shape of the particles. Blackwell et al. [1959] obtained a value of 0.67 for γ and the results of Carberry and Bretton [1958] confirmed this value. While Evans and Kenney [1966] obtained a value of 0.69 for spherical particles, Edwards and Richardson [1968] obtained 0.73 for γ.

For any given shape of packings, γ may be considered essentially constant. The factors affecting γ can be discussed assuming that all flow has ceased and axial diffusion has taken place along the stilled fluid in the interstitial channels created by the packings. We may envision these channels to have two main characteristics which hinder diffusion. The tortuous zig-zag path of channels prevents the diffusion from taking place along the shortest and direct path. On the average, an element of fluid may be considered to move at about 45° to the direction of flow. When the fluid has traveled a net distance, L, it has traveled an actual average distance of about $\sqrt{2}$ L. Thus, Equation (2-7) may be approximated by

$$\frac{E_z}{D_M} \cong \frac{1}{\sqrt{2}} = 0.707$$

In addition, constriction and enlargement as well as branching of channels obstruct the diffusion. The constricted points create "traffic bottle-necks" for the diffusion. The combined tortuosity and constriction of channels provide the slowing down of diffusion by a factor of γ.

At the other extreme where the Reynolds number is very high, Aris and Amundson [1957] showed that the Peclet number, N_{Pe_a}, based on the particle diameter is given by

$$N_{Pe_a} = \frac{\bar{u}d_p}{E_z} = 2/\eta$$

The distance between the successive particle layers is represented by ηd_p. For different arrangements of spherical packings, η may vary from 0.817 to 1.0. Experimental data of McHenry and Wilhelm [1957] and DeMaria and White [1960] gave values to Peclet number in the region of 2 for high Reynolds numbers. Thus, for high Reynolds numbers, $E_z = \frac{1}{2}\bar{u}d_p$. If the mechanism of axial dispersion can be considered to be composed of molecular diffusion and turbulent mixing, and if we assume that the effects of these mechanisms are additive, then

$$E_z = \gamma D_M + \tfrac{1}{2}\,\bar{u}\,d_p \tag{2-8}$$

or

$$\frac{1}{N_{Pe_a}} = \frac{\varepsilon\gamma}{N_{Sc}\cdot N_{Re}} + \tfrac{1}{2} \tag{2-9}$$

The above equation will result in a curve with the Peclet number asymptotically reaching a maximum value of 2 as the Reynolds number is increased sufficiently. However, the experimental data plotted in terms of the Peclet number versus Reynolds number show a curve reaching a maximum greater than 2 after which the curve fails to approach the value of 2 asymptotically. This phenomenon was explained by Hiby [1963] and Giddings [1965] in the following manner. Because of the wide variation in voidage distribution in the packed bed, the tracer will flow at a greater velocity through some interstices than through others. This will set up a radial concentration gradient causing radial diffusion. This effect in turn tends to reduce the axial dispersion. The effect becomes of negligible importance at large Reynolds numbers because the time available for radial diffusion to take place is too short. In order to account for this phenomenon, Edwards and Richardson [1968] introduced an empirical correction factor modifying Equation (2-8) into

$$E_z = \gamma D_M + \frac{\bar{u}d_p/2}{1 + (\beta D_M/\bar{u}d_p)} \tag{2-10}$$

or

$$\frac{1}{N_{Pe_a}} = \frac{\varepsilon\gamma}{N_{Sc}\cdot N_{Re}} + \frac{0.5}{1 + \varepsilon\beta(N_{Re}\cdot N_{Sc})^{-1}} \tag{2-11}$$

The experimental data available on axial-dispersion coefficients in packed beds are correlated according to Equation (2-11). The coefficients appearing in Equation (2-11) are now seen to be approximately

$$\gamma \cong 0.75 \text{ and } \beta \cong 9.5$$

The resultant correlation for axial dispersion of gases flowing through a fixed bed can be expressed as

$$\frac{1}{N_{Pe_a}} = \frac{0.3}{N_{Sc}\cdot N_{Re}} + \frac{0.5}{1 + 3.8(N_{Re}\cdot N_{Sc})^{-1}} \tag{2-12}$$

for $0.008 < N_{Re} < 400$ and $0.28 < N_{Sc} < 2.2$

As discussed in the axial dispersion of liquids in fixed beds, the particle Reynolds number, $d_p u_o \rho/\mu$, is based on the superficial velocity, u_o, and the effective particle diameter (hydraulic diameter).

(D) RADIAL DISPERSION

In a fixed bed catalytic reactor, a radial temperature gradient exists within the bed because of the heat of reaction and heat transfer at the wall. The transverse variation of temperature must always be accompanied by a corresponding transverse diffusion of the reactant or tracer due to a steep transverse concentration gradient. Thus, it is necessary to solve the energy balance including dispersion terms and the reaction rate term containing heat of rejection in conjunction with mass balance, Equation (2-1). In this section, a correlation of radial-dispersion coefficients, E_r, is presented which is necessary for estimation of the transverse concentration gradient in packed bed reactors.

Equation (2-1) under steady-state conditions without a source term can be reduced to

$$E_z\left(\frac{\partial^2 c}{\partial z^2}\right) + E_r\left[\frac{\partial^2 c}{\partial r^2} + \frac{1}{r}\frac{\partial c}{\partial r}\right] - \bar{u}\frac{\partial c}{\partial z} = 0 \tag{2-13}$$

where $\bar{u}$ is interstitial velocity and is equal to u_o/ε. ε is the porosity of the bed.

The correlation for radial-dispersion coefficients in packed beds is represented by the following empirical equations.

For gaseous dispersion,

$$\frac{1}{N_{Pe_r}} = \frac{0.4}{(N_{Re} \cdot N_{Sc})^{0.8}} + \frac{0.09}{1 + \dfrac{10}{N_{Re} \cdot N_{Sc}}} \tag{2-14}$$

$$\text{where} \quad N_{Pe_r} = \frac{\bar{u} d_p}{E_r} = \frac{u_o d_p}{E_{r_o}}$$

$$0.4 < N_{Re} < 500$$

$$0.77 < N_{Sc} < 1.2$$

For liquid dispersion,

$$N_{Pe_r} = \frac{17.5}{(N_{Re})^{0.75}} + 11.4 \tag{2-15}$$

Like axial-dispersion correlation for fixed beds, the radial-dispersion coefficients for gases are affected by N_{Sc}, while the radial-dispersion coefficients for liquids are not sensitive to N_{Sc}.

NOMENCLATURE

c	concentration of the injected tracer in the exit stream
d_p	particle diameter
d	pipe diameter
D_M	molecular diffusivity
E	general-dispersion coefficient

E_r	radial-dispersion coefficient
E_z	axial-dispersion coefficient
f	tube friction factor
L	length of the tubular reactor, or BOD concentration
N_{Pe}	Peclet number; ud_p/E_z or $u_o dp/E_{zo}$ or $\bar{u}d/E_z$
N_{Sc}	Schmidt number; $\mu/\rho D_M$
t	time of interest
u*	friction velocity
$\bar{u}$	average fluid velocity
z	distance along the column

Greek Symbols

ε	voidage, void fraction of packing
γ	tortuosity factor
ρ	dimensionless radius; r/R

REFERENCES

Ahn, Y. K., M.S. Thesis, Kansas State University (1962).

Aris, R., Proc. Roy. Soc. (London), 235A, 67 (1956).

Aris, R., and Amundson, N. R., AIChE Journal, 3, 280 (1957).

Blackwell, R. J., Rayne, J. R., and Terry, W. M., J. Petrol. Technol., 11, 1 (1959).

Carberry, J. J., and Bretton, R. H., AIChE Journal, 4, 367 (1958).

Danckwerts, P. V., Chem. Eng. Sci., 2, 1 (1955).

De Maria, F., and White, R. R., AIChE Journal, 6, 473 (1960).

Edwards, M. F., Ph.D. Dissertation, University of Wales (1966).

Edwards, M. F., and Richardson, J. F., Chem. Eng. Sci., 23, 109 (1968).

Evans, E. V., and Kenny, C. N., Trans. Instn. Chem. Engrs., 44, T189 (1966).

Fan, L. T., and Ahn, Y. K., I.E.C. Proc. Design and Devel., 1, 190-195 (1962).

Giddings, J. C., Dynamics of Chromotography Part I, Principle and Theory, Marcel Dekker, Inc., New York, 1965.

Hiby, J. N., Interaction Between Fluids and Particles, Institution of Chemical Engineers (London), 312 (1963).

Langmuir, I., J. Amer. Chem. Soc., 30, 1742 (1908).

McHenry, K. W., and Wilhelm, R. H., AIChE Journal, 3, 83 (1957).

Taylor, G. J., Proc. Roy. Soc. (London), 223A, 446 (1954).

Wehner, J. F., and Wilhelm, R. H., Chem. Eng. Sci., 6, 89 (1956).

3. FLOW REGIMES AND FLOW MODELS FOR FLUIDIZED BED REACTORS

Fluidized bed technology has been widely applied to the chemical, petroleum, and mineral processing industries since their advent during World War II. Fluidized bed cat crackers considerably aided the Allied victory by producing large quantities of cheap aviation fuel.

Applications of this technology include: cracking and reforming of hydrocarbons, Fischer-Tropsch synthesis, coal carbonization and gasification, ore roasting, aniline production, acrylonitrile production, phthalic anhydride production, polyethylene production, calcining, coking, aluminum production, drying, granulation, etc.

Intensive research in new fluidized bed processes directed towards gasification, liquefaction and combustion of coal, oil shale and other fuels may enable us to turn away from imported oil and back to indigenous fossil fuels. In addition, as the supply of essential raw materials gradually decreases, application of fluidization technology to these fields can certainly be accelerated.

In spite of its importance and wide application, knowledge of the basic fluidization phenomena is still very rudimentary and the design of fluidized bed reactors is, at best, difficult, imprecise, and based mainly on experience and know-how. This is because the flow behavior of fluidized beds is sensitive to geometry, scale and operating conditions. Going to commercial-scale units usually provides surprises for which data from laboratory units are often inadequate and misleading. The common procedure for the scale-up of fluidized bed reactors has been to build a sequence of large prototype reactors. This procedure is costly and time-consuming and has led to the over-design of reactors. Therefore, there is critical need for developing a reliable scale-up method for fluidized bed reactors based primarily on first principles with minimum pilot planting. In order to achieve this goal, more fundamental information, particularly data on the flow of gas and solids in a large-scale fluidized bed operating at reactor conditions, is needed. As more is learned about the scale-up problems of fluidized bed reactors, less risk will be incurred in new applications. This paper reviews the current state of the art on the development of flow models for design and scale-up of fluidized bed reactors. Although a number of fluidized bed reactor models have appeared in literature, it is still difficult to identify which one of these models represents the fluidized bed behavior most closely and can be confidently used for scale-up purposes. In this review, emphasis is therefore made on representative flow models preferred by this reviewer. As more information becomes available, refinement of the models and model parameters to represent the behavior of large fluidized beds would be made. Only through such an iterative approach can design and scale-up of fluidized bed reactors be eventually achieved on a priori basis.

FLUIDIZED BED REACTOR MODELS

Fluidized bed reactors operating under different flow regimes require different models to represent their flow behavior. Flow models devised for a given flow regime can not be directly used for other flow regimes. In addition, the rates of chemical reactions taking place in a fluidized bed have a significant effect on the level of sophistication required in the model. If chemical reaction is slow (say, k is less than 0.5 per sec for the first order reaction), the system is limited by chemical reaction rather than by mass transfer or by hydrodynamic considerations when the conversion requirement is not very high. However, even in this case if the conversion requirement is very high, namely if a near complete conversion is required, bed hydrodynamics must be carefully considered. If chemical reaction is intermediate or fast (say, k is greater than 0.5 per sec for the first order reaction), mass transfer and hydrodynamics can become very sensitive and a sophisticated model is needed, particularly when high conversion is required.

(A) BUBBLELESS FLUIDIZED BED REACTOR

Application of fluidized bed reactors to this flow regime is rare and the flow model representing this flow regime, namely bubbleless fluidized bed reactors, has not been well established.

Since this flow regime is characterized by relatively uniform expansion of the bed without formation of bubbles, the bubbleless fluidized bed can be approximated as an expanded packed bed. Thus a dispersion model may be used for the modeling of the bed in this flow regime (Potter, 1971). The material balance equation for the dispersion model in this flow regime can be represented by:

$$E_z \frac{d^2C_i}{dz^2} + E_r \left(\frac{d^2C_i}{dr^2} + \frac{1}{r}\frac{dC_i}{dr}\right) - U_o \frac{dC_i}{dz} + R_i = 0 \quad (3\text{-}1)$$

Where R_i is the production rate of species i, E_z is the axial dispersion coefficient and E_r is the radial dispersion coefficient.

E_z is usually much greater than E_r. For beds with large height to diameter ratio, the radial dispersion, and hence E_r, can be neglected. Hence,

$$E_z \frac{d^2C_i}{dz^2} - U_o \frac{dC_i}{dz} + R_i = 0 \quad (3\text{-}2)$$

The values of the axial dispersion coefficients, E_z, can be estimated from the following equations (Wen and Fan, 1975).

$$\frac{1}{N_{Pe}} = \frac{0.75\varepsilon}{N_{Sc} \cdot N_{Re}} + \frac{0.5}{1 + 9.5\varepsilon\,(N_{Re} \cdot N_{Sc})^{-1}} \quad (3\text{-}3)$$

for $0.008 < N_{Re} < 400$, and $0.28 < N_{Sc} < 2.2$

where $N_{Pe} = U_o\, d_p/E_z$, $N_{Re} = d_p\, U_o\, \rho/\mu$ and $N_{Sc} = \mu/(D_M\rho)$

The bed voidage ε can be estimated from the correlation proposed by Wen and Yu [1966] as follows. Based on the analysis of forces acting on the suspending particles, a relation between the drag coefficient of a constituent particle in a multiple particle suspension, C_D and the drag coefficient of a single particle in an infinite expanse of fluid, C_{DS}, is established as follows:

$$C_D = C_{DS}\, \varepsilon^{-4.7} \quad (3\text{-}4)$$

Combination of Equation (3-4) with the correlations for C_{DS} (Grace and Clift [1974], Schiller and Naumann [1935], and the pressure drop of the bed, $\Delta P = (\rho_s - \rho) g (1-\varepsilon) L_f$, the following equation for the bed voidage of a bubbleless fluidized bed is obtained.

$$\varepsilon = \left(\frac{N_{Ar}}{18\, N_{Re} + 2.7\, N_{Re}^{1.69}}\right)^{4.7} \quad (3\text{-}5)$$

where $$N_{Ar} = \frac{d_p^{\,3}\, (\rho_s - \rho)\, \rho \cdot g}{\mu^2}$$

Experimental data are lacking for validation of the flow model in this flow regime for gas-solid reaction systems. For a liquid-solid system, E_z is nearly independent of the molecular diffusivity of the liquid species and can be estimated by (Wen and Fan, 1975)

$$\frac{E_z\, U_{mf}\, \rho}{U_o \mu} = \frac{N_{Re}}{0.20 + 0.011\, N_{Re}^{0.48}} \quad (3\text{-}6)$$

U_{mf} is the minimum fluidization velocity which can be estimated from (Wen and Yu, 1966)

$$\frac{d_p U_{mf} \rho}{\mu} = [(33.7)^2 + 0.0408 N_{Ar}]^{\frac{1}{2}} - 33.7 \qquad (3\text{-}7)$$

(B) BUBBLING FLUIDIZED BED REACTOR MODELS

A large number of bubbling fluidized bed models with varying complexity and sophistication have been proposed (Shen and Johnstone [1955], May [1959], Lewis et al. [1959], van Deemter [1961], Orcutt et al. [1962], Davidson and Harrison [1963], Kobayashi and Arai [1965], Partridge and Rowe [1966], Toor and Calderbank [1971], Kunii and Levenspiel [1969], Kato and Wen [1969], Gwyn et al. [1970], Orcutt and Carpenter [1971], Mori and Muchi [1972], Behie and Kehoe [1973], Miyauchi [1974], Mori and Wen [1975], Fryer and Potter [1976], Potter [1978], Werther [1978], DeLasa and Grace [1979], Kuhne and Wippen [1980]).

These models are critically evaluated and compared by several authors (e.g. Rowe [1972], Pyle [1972], Grace [1971], Horio and Wen [1977], Barreteau et al. [1978]). Seventeen models have been classified by Horio and Wen [1977] into three groups.

Essentially all of the models developed are two-phase models; bubble phase and emulsion (dense) phase with gas exchange between the two phases. The simplest models, or Level I, consider that the excess gas above minimum fluidization velocity flows through the bed in the form of bubbles in the bubble phase. The gas flow in the emulsion phase is therefore at the minimum fluidization velocity and the voidage of the emulsion phase is also at the minimum fluidization condition. However, the parameters are not related to bubble size. The next level of fluidized bed models, Level II, introduces bubble size either as a constant or an adjustable parameter. Extension of the Level II bubbling bed models to include varying bubble size as a function of bed height and bed diameter leads to the Level III bubbling models (Horio and Wen, 1977).

A general expression of bubbling bed models containing all the parameters proposed in all of the three levels of fluidized bed models can be formulated as follows:

For a first order reaction, the material balance around the bubble, cloud, wake and emulsion phase of a Comprehensive Bubbling Fluidized Bed Model can be written as:

Bubble Phase (b)

$$U_b\delta_b \frac{dC_b}{dh} - F_{bc}\delta_b(C_b - C_c) - F_{bw}\delta_b(C_b - C_w) - k_r a_b C_b = 0 \qquad (3\text{-}8)$$

Cloud Phase (c)

$$E_z\delta_c\varepsilon_e \frac{d^2C_c}{dh^2} - U_c\delta_c\varepsilon_e \frac{dC_c}{dh} + F_{bc}\delta_b(C_b - C_c) - F_{ce}\delta_c(C_c - C_e) - k_r\delta_c(1 - \varepsilon_e)C_c = 0 \qquad (3\text{-}9)$$

Wake Phase (w)

$$E_z\delta_w\varepsilon_e \frac{d^2C_w}{dh^2} - U_w\delta_w\varepsilon_e \frac{dC_w}{dh} + F_{bw}\delta_b(C_b - C_w) - F_{we}\delta_w(C_w - C_e) - k_r\delta_w(1 - \varepsilon_e)C_w = 0 \qquad (3\text{-}10)$$

Emulsion Phase (e)

$$E_z\delta_e\varepsilon_e \frac{d^2C_e}{dh^2} - U_e\delta_e\varepsilon_e \frac{dC_e}{dh} + F_{ce}\delta_c(C_c - C_e) + F_{we}\delta_w(C_w - C_e) - k_r\delta_e(1 - \varepsilon_e)C_e = 0 \qquad (3\text{-}11)$$

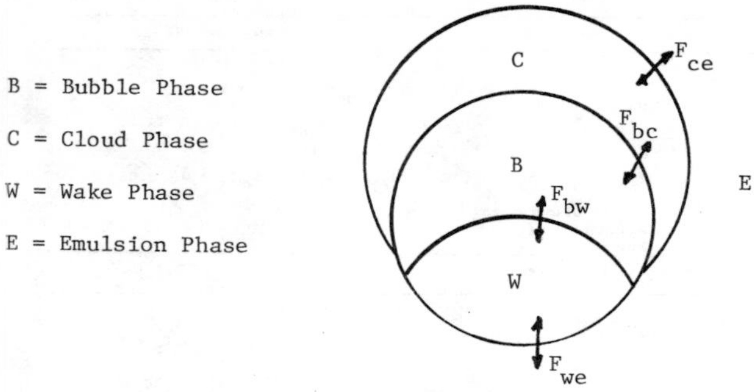

Figure 2. The Gas Exchange Per Bubbling Fluidized Bed Model

As can be seen from Table 1, practically all of the models proposed can be shown as a simplified form reducible from this comprehensive general expression. The major differences among these models are the ways by which the model parameters are selected. Careful examinations of these models reveal that although some conceptual differences in the structure of the models exist, they are nevertheless relatively minor. These models are basically structured around the two-phase theory or some variations of the theory. The two-phase theory of fluidization postulates that:

(1) The volumetric gas flow rate due to bubbles is equal to the excess velocity or $V_b/A_T = U_b \cdot \delta_b = U_o - U_{mf}$; and (2) local emulsion phase velocity, U_e, is equal to $(U_{mf}/\varepsilon_{mf})$. The underlying assumption of the two-phase theory and the consequences of its interpretation are examined below.

Based on a material balance for gas flow through the bed we have

(Total Gas Flow) = (Net Flow of Gas Through Bubble) + (Net Flow of Gas Through Cloud) + (Net Flow of Gas Through Emulsion) (3-12)

Table 1. Some Typical Fluidized Bed Reactor Models

Model	Regions	Assumption	Equations
Shen & Johnstone (1955)	B ↔ C + W + E	$E_z = 0$, $a_b = 0$ $U_c = U_w = U_e$ $C_c = C_w = C_e$ $F_{be} = F_{bc} + F_{bw}$ Parameters are constant.	$U_b \frac{dC_b}{dh} + F_{be}(C_b - C_e) = 0$ $U_e(1 - \delta_b)\varepsilon_e \frac{dC_e}{dh} - F_{be}\delta_b(C_b - C_e) +$ $k_r(1 - \delta_b)(1 - \varepsilon_e)C_e = 0$
Davidson & Harrison* (1963)	B ↔ C + W + E	$E_z = 0$, $a_b = 0$ $U_c = U_w = U_e$ $C_c = C_w = C_e$ $F_{be} = F_{bc} + F_{bw}$ Parameters are determined by an effective bubble diameter	$U_b \frac{dC_b}{dh} + F_{be}(C_b - C_e) = 0$ $U_e(1 - \delta_b)\varepsilon_e \frac{dC_e}{dh} - F_{be}\delta_b(C_b - C_e) +$ $k_r(1 - \delta_b)(1 - \varepsilon_e)C_e = 0$

Table 1. (cont'd)

Model	Regions	Assumption	Equations
Calderbank & Toor* (1967)	B $\leftrightarrow$ C + W + E	$E_z = 0,\ a_b = 0$ $U_c = U_w = U_e$ $C_c = C_w + C_e$ $F_{be} = F_{bc} + F_{bw}$ Bubble diameter is a function of bed height.	$U_b \frac{dC_b}{dh} + F_{be}(C_b - C_e) = 0$ $U_e(1 - \delta_b)\varepsilon_e \frac{dC_e}{dh} - F_{be}\delta_b(C_b - C_e) + k_r(1 - \delta_b)(1 - \varepsilon_e)C_e = 0$

*Case with perfect mixing in emulsion phase is omitted.

Lewis (1959)	B $\leftrightarrow$ C + W + E	$E_z \to \infty$ $C_c = C_w = C_e$ $F_{be} = F_{bc} + F_{bw}$ Parameters are constant.	$U_b\delta_b \frac{dC_b}{dh} + F_{be}\delta_b(C_b - C_e) + k_r a_b C_b = 0$ $F_{be}\delta_b(C_b - C_e) - k_r(1 - \delta_b)(1 - \varepsilon_e)C_e = 0$
Van Deemter (1961)	B $\leftrightarrow$ C + W + E	$a_b = 0$ $U_c = U_w = U_e$ $C_c = C_w = C_e$ $F_{be} = F_{bc} + F_{bw}$ Parameters are constant.	$U_b \frac{dC_b}{dh} + F_{be}(C_b - C_e) = 0$ $E_z(1 - \delta_b)\varepsilon_e \frac{d^2C_e}{dh^2} - U_e(1 - \delta_b)\varepsilon_e \frac{dC_e}{dh} + F_{be}\delta_b(C_b - C_e) - k_r(1 - \delta_b)(1 - \varepsilon_e) = 0$
Kato & Wen (1969)	B + C $\leftrightarrow$ W + E	$E_z = 0,\ a_b = 0$ $U_w = U_e,\ U_b = U_c$ $C_b = C_c,\ C_w = C_e$ $F_{be}\delta_b = F_{bw}\delta_b + F_{ce}\delta_c$	$U_b(\delta_b + \delta_c\varepsilon_e) \frac{\Delta C_b}{\Delta h} + F_{be}\delta_b(C_b - C_e) + k_r\delta_c(1 - \varepsilon_e) = 0$ $F_{be}\delta_b(C_b - C_e) = k_r(\delta_w + \delta_e)(1 - \varepsilon_e)C_e$
Kunii & Levenspiel (1969)	B $\leftrightarrow$ C $\leftrightarrow$ E	$E_z = 0$ $U_c = U_w = U_e = 0$ $C_c = C_w$ $F'_{bc} = F_{bc} + F_{bw}$ $F'_{ce}\delta_b = F_{ce}\delta_c + F_{we}\delta_w$ Parameters are constant.	$U_b\delta_b \frac{dC_b}{dh} + F'_{bc}\delta_b(C_b - C_c) + k_r a_b C_c = 0$ $F'_{bc}\delta_b(C_b - C_c) - F'_{ce}\delta_b(C_c - C_e) - k_r \cdot (\delta_c + \delta_w)(1 - \varepsilon_e)C_c = 0$ $F'_{ce}\delta_b(C_c - C_e) - k_r\delta_e(1 - \varepsilon_e)C_e = 0$
Werther (1977)	B $\leftrightarrow$ C + W $\leftrightarrow$ E	$E_z = 0,\ a_b = 0$ $U_c = U_w = U_e = 0$ $C_c = C_w$ But $-D_G dA \frac{\partial C_c}{\partial y}\Big\vert_{y=0} = (F_{bc} + F_{bw})\delta_b A_T dh \cdot (C_b - C_c)$ $-D_G dA \cdot \frac{\partial C_c}{\partial y}\Big\vert_{y=\delta} = [F_{ce}\delta_c + F_{we}\delta_w] A_T dh (C_c - C_e)$	$U_b\delta_b A_T dh \frac{dC_b}{dh} - D_G\, dA \frac{\partial C_c}{\partial y}\Big\vert_{y=0} = 0$ $D_G dA \frac{\partial^2 C_c}{\partial y^2} - k_r A_T dh(\delta_c + \delta_w)(1 - \varepsilon_e)C_c = 0$ $-D_G dA \frac{\partial C_c}{\partial y}\Big\vert_{y=\delta} - k_r A_T\, dh\,\delta_e\varepsilon_e C_e = 0$
Fryer & Potter (1976)	B $\leftarrow$ C + W + E	$E_z = 0,\ a_b = 0$ $U_c = U_w,\ U_e < 0$ $C_c = C_w$ $F'_{bc} = F_{bc} + F_{bw}$ $F'_{ce}\delta_b = F_{ce}\delta_c + F_{we}\delta_w$	$U_b \frac{dC_b}{dh} + F'_{bc}(C_b - C_c) = 0$ $-U_c(\delta_c + \delta_w)\varepsilon_e \frac{dC_c}{dh} + F'_{bc}\delta_b(C_b - C_c) - F'_{ce}\delta_b(C_c - C_e) - k_r(\delta_c + \delta_w)(1 - \varepsilon_e)C_c = 0$ $F'_{ce}\delta_b(C_c - C_e) - k_r\delta_e(1 - \varepsilon_e)C_e = 0$

Table 1. (cont'd)

Model	Region	Assumption	Equations
Miyauchi & Morooka (1969)	$B \leftrightarrow C + W + E$	$E_z = 0$ $U_c = U_w = U_e = 0$ $C_c = C_w$ $F'_{bc} = F_{bc} + F_{bw}$ $F'_{ce}\delta_b = F_{ce}\delta_c + F_{we}\delta_w$ Parameters are constant.	$U_b\delta_b\frac{dC_b}{dh} + F_{bc}\delta_b(C_b - C_c) + k_r a_b C_b = 0$ $F'_{bc}\delta_b(C_b - C_c) - F'_{ce}\delta_b(C_c - C_e) - k_r(\delta_c + \delta_w)(1 - \varepsilon_e)C_c = 0$ $F'_{ce}\delta_b(C_c - C_e) - k_r\delta_e(1 - \varepsilon_e)C_e = 0$
Gwyn et al. (1970)	$B \leftrightarrow C + W + E$	$E_z = 0,\ a_b = 0$ $U_c = U_w,\ U_e < 0$ $C_c = C_w$ $F'_{bc} = (F_{bc} + F_{bw})$ $F'_{ce} = F_{ce}(\delta_c + A_c) + F_{wo}(\delta_w + A_w)$ Parameters are constant.	$U_b\frac{dC_b}{dh} + F_{bc}(C_b - C_c) = 0$ $-U_c(\delta_c + \delta_w)\varepsilon_e\frac{dC_c}{dh} + F'_{bc}\delta_b(C_b - C_c) - F'_{ce}\delta_b(C_c - C_e) - k_r(\delta_c + \delta_w)(1 - \varepsilon_e)\cdot C_c = 0$ $-U_e\delta_e\varepsilon_e\frac{dC_e}{dh} + F'_{ce}\delta_b(C_c - C_e) - k_r\delta_e(1 - \varepsilon_e)\cdot C_e = 0$

If the net flow rate of gas through bubbles is taken as the visible bubble flow rate, the above equation becomes,

$$U_o = U_b\delta_b + U_b\delta_b(R + fw - 1)\ \varepsilon_{mf} + \{1 - \delta_b(R + fw)\}\cdot U_e\varepsilon_{mf} \tag{3-13}$$

where fw is the ratio of volume of wake to volume of bubble, and R is the ratio of volume of cloud sphere to volume of a bubble.

Based on a material balance for solids flow and taking into consideration the solid circulation due to the bubble's dragging a wake of solids up the bed, we have

$$U_s = \frac{U_b\delta_b \cdot fw}{1 - \delta_b(1 + fw)} \tag{3-14}$$

The gas velocity in the emulsion phase, U_e, can be expressed as

$$U_e = (U_{mf}/\varepsilon_{mf}) - U_s \tag{3-15}$$

If the effect of solids circulation is neglected, that is, $U_s = 0$, Equation (3-15) becomes,

$$U_o - U_{mf} = U_b\delta_b + \delta_b\ [(U_b\ \varepsilon_{mf} - U_{mf})\ R - U_b\ \varepsilon_{mf}] \tag{3-16}$$

Based on the hydrodynamic models of bubbles proposed by various investigators, various forms of the two-phase theory emerge:

Davidson and Harrison's [1963] three-dimensional bubble:

$$U_o - U_{mf} = \delta_b U_b + 2\delta_b\ U_{mf}$$

Davidson and Harrison's [1963] two-dimensional bubble:

$$U_o - U_{mf} = \delta_b U_b + \delta_b U_{mf}$$

Murray's [1965, 1966] two and three-dimensional bubble:

$$U_o - U_{mf} = \delta_b U_b$$

Partridge and Rowe's [1966] experimental three-dimensional bubble:

$$U_o - U_{mf} = \delta_b U_b + 0.17\delta_b U_{mf}$$

The above analysis shows that when the particle is small and U_{mf} is negligible compared to U_b, all the bubble models reduce to the original postulation of the two-phase theory, namely $U_o - U_{mf} = \delta_b U_b$. The deviation becomes greater as δ_b and U_{mf} become greater, indicating that the deviation could be significnt near the distributor and for large particles.

Horio and Wen [1977] examined the validity of the two-phase theory and concluded that:

(a) Measured values of visible bubble flow velocity, $\delta_b U_b$, are generally less than postulated by the two-phase theory, have the smallest value at the bottom of the bed and increase with height approaching the value $U_o - U_{mf}$ in deep beds where slugging conditions prevail. Thus, the two-phase theory seems to be better suited for tall beds having a small diameter.

(b) As shown in Fig. 3, gas can pass through the permeable boundaries of the bubble and flow through it particularly for slow bubbles. When bubbles rise slower than the gas velocity in the emulsion phase, they are called slow bubbles. This occurs when bubbles are small or when fluidizing particles are large (Fig. 4).

In addition, it is possible for the gas in the emulsion phase to reverse its direction of flow when the emulsion solids descend faster than the gas can percolate through the solids. Fryer and Potter [1975] presented profiles of the average axial concentration of ozone from a three-dimensional bed, showing a minimum ozone concentration within the bed at high gas velocities. The authors attributed the change of concentration profiles to the reversal of the direction of gas flow and estimated what they termed the critical velocity, U_{cr}.

Here, U_{cr} can be estimated from

$$\frac{U_{cr}}{U_{mf}} = (1 + \frac{1}{\varepsilon_{mf}\, fw})\ [1 - \delta_b\ (1 + fw)] \tag{3-17}$$

where

U_{cr} = value of superficial gas velocity, U, to give the back-mix flow of emulsion gas ($U_e < 0$).

For typical values of ε_{mf}, fw and δ_b, Equation (3-17) gives

$$\frac{U_{cr}}{U_{mf}} > 6 \sim 11 \tag{3-18}$$

The reverse flow of gas in the emulsion phase is caused by the downward flow of solids in a portion of the emulsion phase.

This downflow of solids can lead to the surprising result that under certain conditions the gas in the emulsion phase is also flowing downwards (Stephens et al., 1967; Kunii et al., 1967; Latham et al., 1968; Nguyen and Potter, 1974; Nguyen, 1975). Nguyen et al. [1977] and their experiments with 1.22 m square bed showed that the solid movement is clearly related to the bubble patterns, and that the gas movement in the particulate (emulsion) phase is related to the solids movement. They observed that the stable bubble pattern in the upper region of the bed leaves a persistent central area relatively bubblefree; a pronounced solids downflow in this area is associated with strong gas backmixing, illustrated in Figures 5a and 5b. By use of radioactive tracers, gross solids circulation patterns have been examined by Chen et al. [1981] and are shown in Figure 6. This figure shows how the solids flow pattern changes as the gas velocity is increased. Therefore, the reverse flow associated with solid circulation in the emulsion phase needs to be introduced in the bubbling bed model to describe the concentration profile of a fluidized bed reactor when the flow is above U_{cr}.

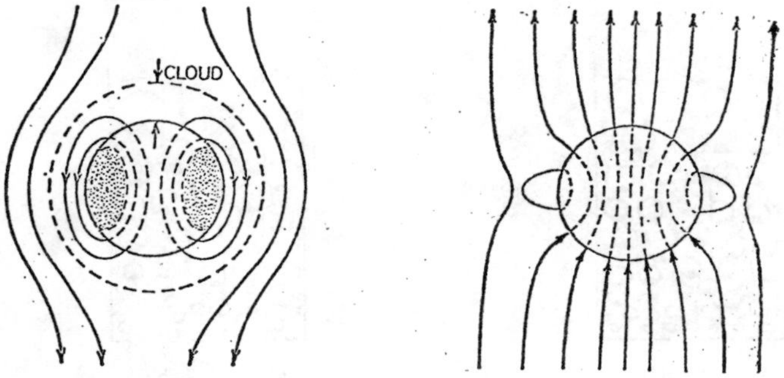

(a) Fast Bubble (b) Slow Bubble

Figure 3. Differences in Gas Streamlines Between a Fast Bubble and a Slow Bubble (Catipovic et al., 1978)

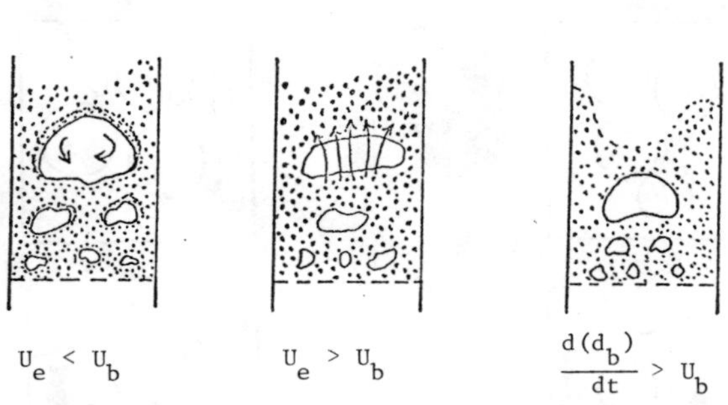

Figure 4. Flow Regime for the Bubbling Bed

(C) <u>SCALE-UP PROBLEMS OF FLUIDIZED BED REACTORS</u>

A vivid illustration of problems associated with the scale-up of fluidized bed reactors is shown in Figure 7 by Werther [1980] based on the Shell Chlorination Process of catalytic oxidation of HCl. In order to reach 90% of the HCl equilibrium conversion, a fluidized bed of 1.5 m in height is sufficient for the laboratory size reactor, but 2.8 m is required for a pilot scale and 10 m is required for a full-scale plant. Such an enormous scale-up effect is explained by the fact that the gas residence time in the small scale reactor is much longer than larger reactors and that the mass transfer or gas exchange between the bubble phase and the emulsion

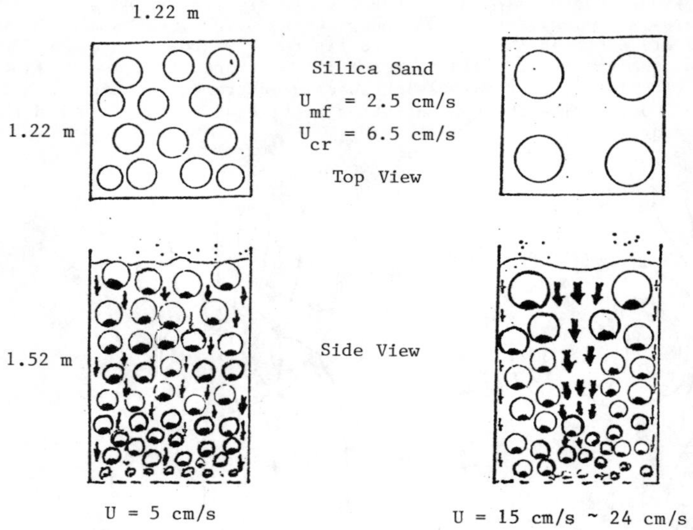

Bubbles rise uniformly at the velocity 5 cm/s. Bubbles tend to rise along the corners at velocity 15 to 24 cm/s. At this velocity the solids circulate downward in the center portion of the bed dragging some of the gas down into the bed (back-mixing of gas).

Figure 5a. Bubble Movement and Solids Movement in a Tubeless Fluidized Bed at CSIRO (Nguyen et al., 1977)

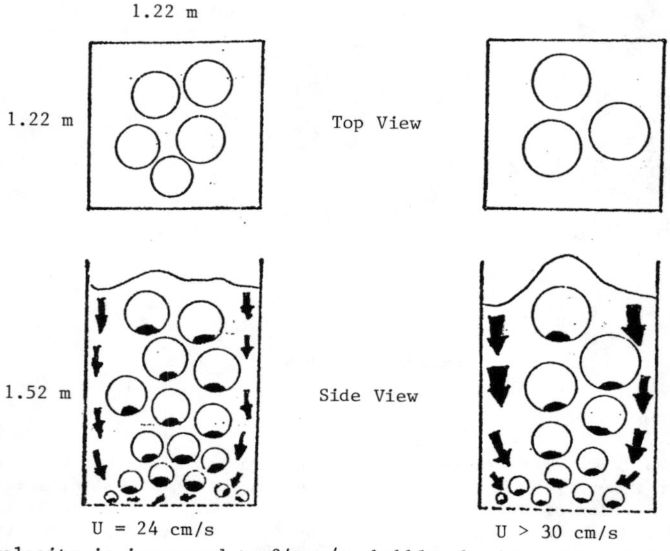

As gas velocity is increased to 24 cm/s, bubbles begin to rise in the center of the bed. At a velocity greater than 30 cm/s gas bubbles predominantly rise in the center and solids move downward along the wall

Figure 5b. Bubble Movement and Solids Movement in a Tubeless Fluidized Bed at CSIRO

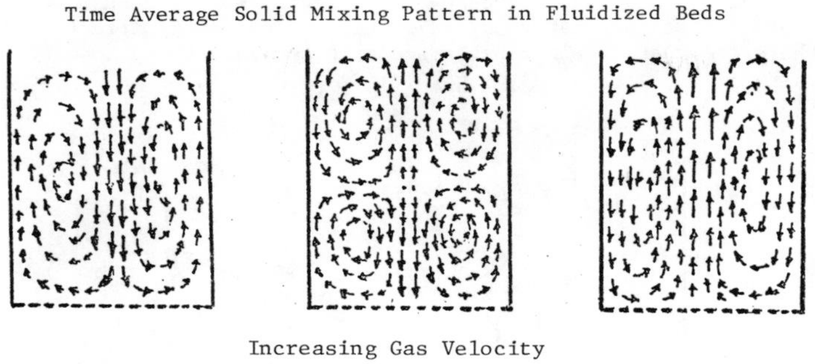

Figure 6. Gross Solid Particle Flow Pattern in Fluidized Beds

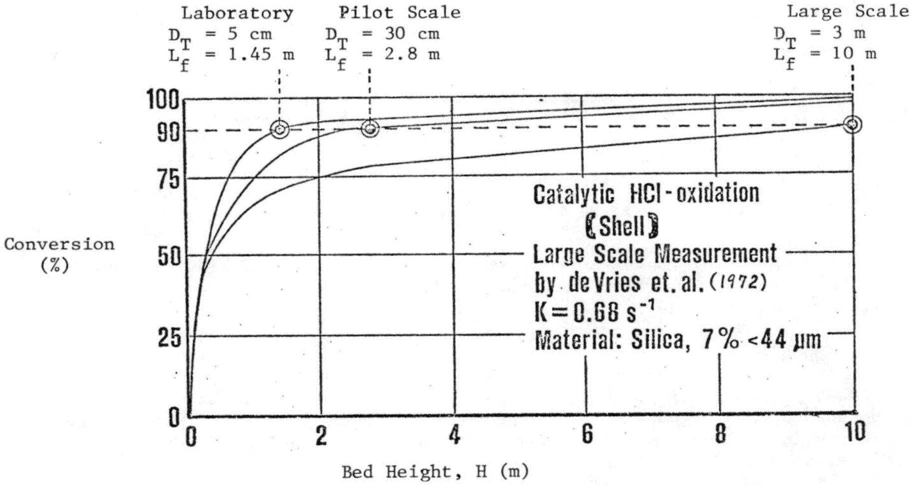

Figure 7. Scale-Up Problem of Catalytic Oxidation of HCl

phase is more favorable for the small reactor. It is clear that the bubble size of 5 cm diameter for the laboratory scale reactor can not grow bigger than 5 cm (when the bubble diameter reaches a size near the column diameter, the bed is in the slugging state) (Figure 8). Consequently, the bubble velocity for the small scale laboratory reactor is much slower and the gas exchange is much more favorable than in the larger scale reactor.

This is primarily the reason why direct scale-up to commercial scale using experimental results from small laboratory units often encounters unexpected failure.

It is now clear that any fluidized bed reactor model must be able to address the effect of bed geometry if the model is to be used for design and scale-up of the reactor.

Examination of the models of bubbling fluidized bed reactors listed in Table 1 reveals that there appear to be at least four key parameters that could affect the behavior of the models significantly. They are bubble diameter, d_b, bubble velocity,

U_b, bubble fraction, δ_b, and gas interchange rate, F, between the bubble phase and the emulsion phase. These parameters are directly or indirectly affected by the bed geometry and therefore must be the clue in scale-up considerations.

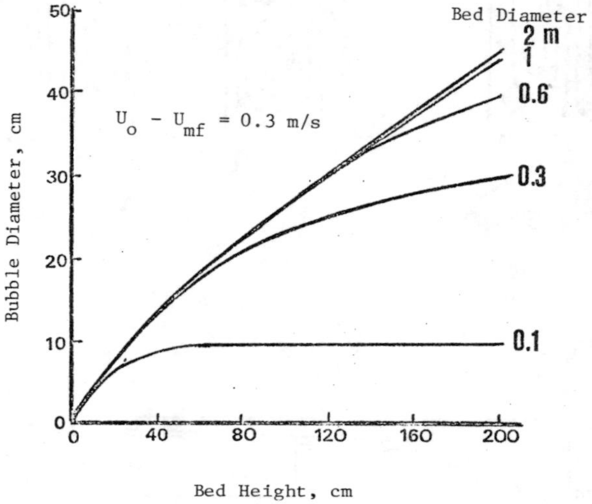

Figure 8. Effect of Bed Diameter on Bubble Diameter

A brief review of these four key parameters is presented below in order to assess the state-of-the-art in the understanding of these parameters and to recommend the future research needs.

(a) Bubble Size

Probably the most important parameter for bubbling bed models is the bubble size because other key parameters, namely the bubble velocity, the bubble fraction and the gas interchange, are all directly or indirectly tied to the bubble size. Therefore, accurate estimation of bubble size is essential for design and scale-up of a fluidized bed reactor based on any bubbling bed model. Many correlations on bubble size are available in the literature and are summarized in Table 2. In order to use these correlations for bubble size estimation an initial bubble size at the surface of the distributor must be known. The correlations of the initial bubble size, d_{bo}, are summarized in Table 3. A detailed discussion of gas distributors and the phenomena near the distributor region will be presented later.

Among the correlations listed in Table 2, none relates the bubble size with bed diameter except Mori and Wen's correlation [1975]. The accuracy of these correlations is unfortunately not very high and careful examination of the limits of application of individual correlations should be made so that the correlation is not applied beyond the range of the operating conditions recommended.

Examining the available bubble size correlations and comparing them with the existing experimental data, the equations proposed by Darton et al. [1979] and that of Mori and Wen [1975] appear more consistent and are recommended here for a rough estimation of bubble size in fluidized beds. In practice, bubble shape tends to dilate periodically as bubbles rise and this is accompanied by the fact that bubble diameter along radial (or horizontal) direction is not a constant value but has a size distribution. Consequently, the bubble diameter from any of the correlations is only a statistical average value. Further studies are needed to formulate a more

Table 2. Summary of Bubble Diameter Correlations

Investigator	Equations	Range of Data
Yasui and Johanson (1958)	$d_b = 2.05\,\rho_p d_p\,(\frac{U}{U_{mf}} - 1)^{0.63}\,h$	$D_T = 10,\ 15$ cm Glass beads, FCC $d_p = 20 \sim 580\ \mu m$
Whitehead and Young (1967)	$d_b = 0.34\,(\frac{U}{U_{mf}})^{0.33}\,h^{0.54}$	Square beds 0.1 0.37 1.5, 5.9 m^2 Silicuous sand $d_p = 70 \sim 300\ \mu m$
Park et al. (1969)	$d_b = 33.3\,d_p^{1.5}\,(\frac{U}{U_{mf}} - 1)^{0.77}\,h$	$D_T = 10$ cm Coke $d_p = 70 \sim 450\ \mu m$
Kato and Wen (1969)	$d_b = 1.4\,\rho_p d_p\,(\frac{U}{U_{mf}})\,h + d_{bo}$ $d_{bo} = (6\,G/\pi)^{0.4}/g^{0.2}$ $G = (U - U_{mf})/N$	Modification of Kobayashi's Correlation
Geldart (1972)	$d_b = 0.027\,(U - U_{mf})^{0.94}h + d_{bo}$ $d_{bo} = 1.43\,G^{0.4}/g^{0.2}$	$D_T = 30.8$ cm Sand $d_p = 40 \sim 350\ \mu m$
Chiba et al. (1973)	$d_b = d_{bo}\{(2^{7/6}-1)(h-h_{bo})/d_{bo}+1\}^{2/7}$ $d_{bo} = (6\,G/\pi k_b g^{\frac{1}{2}})^{2/5}$	$D_T = 10,\ 20$ cm Silica gel, MS, Micro Beads Cat. $d_p = 67 \sim 443\ \mu m$
Mori and Wen (1975)	$d_b = d_{bM}-(d_{bM}-d_{bo})\exp(-0.3\,h/D_T)$ $d_{bM} = 0.652\,\{A_T\,(U - U_{mf})\}^{2/5}$ $d_{bo} = 0.347\,G^{2/5}$ [for perforated plate] $d_{bo} = 0.00376\,(U - U_{mf})^2$ [for porous plate]	$0.5<U_{mf}<20$ cm/s $60< d_p < 450\ \mu m$ $U-U_{mf} < 48$ cm/s $D_T < 130$ cm
Rowe (1976)	$d_b = (U - U_{mf})^{\frac{1}{2}}\,(h + h_o)^{3/4}/g^{1/4}$ $h_o = 0$ [for porous plate]	Alumina $d_p = 210\ \mu m$
Darton et al. (1977)	$d_b = 0.54(U-U_{mf})^{0.4}(h+4\sqrt{A_o})^{0.8}/g^{0.2}$	
Werther (1978)	$d_b = 0.853[1+0.272(U-U_{mf})]^{1/3}$ $(1+0.684\,h)^{1.21}$	

Table 3. Initial Bubble Size Above the Distributor (in CGS Units)

Investigator	Investigator	Remarks
Davidson and Schuler (1960)	$D_{bo} = 1.381\ G^{0.4}/g^{0.2}$	Based on analogy of gas bubble formation from an orifice in a liquid
Davidson and Harrison (1963)	$D_{bo} = 1.295\ G^{0.4}/g^{0.2}$	G = volumetric flow rate of gas per orifice.
Kato and Wen (1969)	Perforated plate $D_{bo} = 1.295\ (\frac{U - U_{mf}}{N})^{0.4}/g^{0.2}$	N = number of orifices per unit area
Geldart (1972)	Perforated plate $D_{bo} = 1.43\ (\frac{U - U_{mf}}{N})^{0.4}/g^{0.2}$	For porous plate use N = 0.1 hole/cm² of bed cross section
Chiba et al. (1972)	$D_{bo} = 1.295\ (\frac{G}{k_b})^{0.4}/g^{0.2}$	Initial bubbles are formed at the end of a spout of gas. k_b depends on the bed material ≈ 0.60~0.95.
Miwa et al. (1972)	Perforated plate $D_{bo} = 0.347\ (\frac{U - U_{mf}}{N})^{0.4}$ Porous plate $D_{bo} = 0.00376\ (U - U_{mf})^2$	Perforated plate: Davidson and Shuler's correlation (1960)
Fryer and Potter (1976)	Bubble cap $D_{bo} = 1.08\ (U - U_{mf})^{0.33}$	A plate with 61 caps on 2.78 cm spacing; each cap is 1.8 cm high and 0.9 cm in diameter with four 0.08 cm diameter holes.
Rowe (1976)	Porous plate $D_{bo} = 0$	
Darton et al. (1977)	$D_{bo} = 1.63\ \{(U - U_{mf})A_o/g^{1/2}\}^{2/5}$	A_o = the area of plate per hole, For porous plate, A_o = 0.56 cm²

reliable correlation for bubble size which can represent a wider range of operating conditions. The information is particularly in need for estimation of the maximum stable bubble size. As the gas bubbles ascend to the surface of the bed they grow bigger mostly due to coalescence. However, they soon reach the maximum size and cease to grow since if too large bubbles are formed, the break up into smaller bubbles. There has been controversy over how large the maximum stable bubble size should be. Harrison et al. [1961] postulated that bubbles split from the rear if the bubble rising velocity exceeds the terminal velocity of the particles. They argued that when this happens, the particles will be drawn into the bubble from below causing bubbles to break up. This criterion unfortunately predicts the maximum size too small and has been modified (Matsen, 1973; Clift et al., 1978) as:

The terminal velocity, U_t, of the particle is calculated based on a fictitious particle size of 2.7 times $\bar{d}_p$. Then the maximum bubble diameter is estimated by:

$$d_{b\ max} = 2.0\ U_t^{\ 2}/g \qquad (3\text{-}19)$$

Equation (3-19) is good for a rough estimation of the maximum bubble size, although the mechanism of bubble splitting appears to be inconsistent.

Another approach is to use bubble size correlation to calculate bubble diameter, assigning the bubble size at 1.0 m from the distributor to the maximum bubble size.

Since the maximum bubble size affects the residence time and mixing of the reacting gas in the fluidized bed reactor, an accurate estimate of this quantity is very important for estimation of the extent of reaction and establishing scale-up procedure.

(b) Bubble Velocity

Following the theoretical derivation of Davis and Taylor [1950] for a large spherical cap bubble rising in a liquid, Davidson and Harrison [1963] obtained the following expression for the velocity of rising of a single bubble:

$$U_{bs} = 0.711 \ (g \ d_b)^{1/2} \tag{3-20}$$

The bubble velocity in a fluidized bed is then expressed as:

$$(U_b)_{DH} = U_o - U_{mf} + 0.711 \ (g \ d_b)^{1/2} \tag{3-21}$$

Werther [1978] conducted experimental measurement in fluidized beds of diameters up to 1.00 m and obtained a correlation with a wall effect correction for bubble velocity as:

$$(U_b)_W = \phi \ (g \ d_b)^{1/2} \tag{3-22}$$

where

$$\phi = \begin{cases} 0.64 & \text{for } D_T < 0.1 \text{ m} \\ 1.6 \ D_T^{0.4} & \text{for } 0.1 < D_T < 1.0 \text{ m} \\ 1.6 & \text{for } D_T > 1.0 \text{ m} \end{cases}$$

Examination of Equations (3-21) and (3-22) reveals that when the bed diameter is less than 10 cm, the predicted bubble rise velocity based on Equation (3-21) is much greater than that based on Equation (3-22) particularly for small d_b. On the other hand, when the bed diameter is greater than 100 cm, the predicted bubble velocity based on Equation (3-21) is much smaller than, and often as small as one-half of, that calculated based on Equation (3-22). Hence, for the model to be useful for scale-up purposes, it is necessary to relate the bubble velocity to the bed geometry. Further refinement of Equation (3-22) is needed to improve the reliability of the correlation.

(c) Interchange of Gas Between Bubble Phase and Emulsion Phase

As a bubble rises through a gas-fluidized bed, it exchanges gas with the emulsion phase. Experimental evidence shows that slow and small bubbles serve merely as a bypass for emulsion phase gas, whereas larger and fast bubbles carry with them a cloud of recirculating gas. The relative size of the cloud decreases as the bubble increases in velocity. Most bubbles are large enough to have an associated cloud phase, except in the grid region where embryonic bubbles or jets occur or when large particles are fluidized. The grid region is dealt with separately later.

As discussed previously, gas exchange between the bubble void and the cloud plays a significant role in reaction and mass transfer in fluidized beds. Coupled with convective exchange between the bubble void and the cloud is diffusive exchange at the cloud-emulsion interface. A further complicating factor in bubbling beds is that bubbles split, interact, and coalesce, and inevitably disturb the integrity of the cloud phase. The coalescence, therefore, leads to enhanced exchange between the cloud and emulsion. A number of correlations for bubble-to-emulsion gas exchange have been proposed and are summarized in Table 4. Experimental data (Kobayashi et al. [1967], Calderbank et al. [1976], Rietema and Hoebink [1976], Kunii and Levenspiel [1969] and Bohle and Van Swaaij [1978]) are plotted in Figure 9 for comparison with the correlations available from the literature. The simplest form of correlation proposed by Kobayashi et al. [1967] indicated by line 5 seems to represent experimental data as well as any other correlations.

Table 4. The Models for the Mass Transfer from Bubbles to Emulsion Phase

Investigator	Experimental Conditions				Equations
	D_T (cm)	d_p (μm)	U (cm/s)	U_{mf} (cm/s)	
Davidson & Harrison (1963)					$K_{be} = 0.75\, U_{mf} + 0.975\, \left(\frac{D_G^{1/2}\, g^{1/4}}{d_b^{1/4}}\right)$
Partridge & Rowe (1966)					$\frac{K_{be} d_c}{D_G} = 2 + 0.69\, N_{sc}^{1/3} \left(\frac{d_c U_b \rho_g}{\mu_g}\right)^{1/2}$
Davies & Richardson (1967)	--	65 ~ 142	3 - 15	--	$K_{be} = 0.303\, D_G^{1/2}\, g^{1/4}/d_b^{1/4}$
Kunii & Levenspiel (1969)					$K_b = 0.75\, U_{mf} + 0.975\, (D_G^{1/2}\, g^{1/4}\, d_b^{-1/4})$ $K_e = 1.128\, \left(\frac{\varepsilon^2_{mf} D_G U_{bo}}{d_b}\right)^{1/2}$ $\frac{1}{K_{be}} = \frac{1}{K_b} + \frac{1}{K_e}$; $U_{bo} = U - U_{mf} + 0.711\sqrt{g d_b}$
Toei et al. (1968)	2-D 40 x 2 Height of 1.3 m	149 ~ 710			$K_c = \frac{1}{1 + 2\varepsilon_{mf}/(\alpha - 1)} \cdot \frac{\lambda\, \varepsilon_{mf}\, A}{\pi d_b}$ $K_D = \frac{1.02\, \varepsilon_{mf}}{1 + 2\varepsilon_{mf}/(\alpha - 1)} \left(\frac{U_b D_G}{d_b} \cdot \frac{\alpha - 1}{\alpha} \sqrt{\frac{\alpha + 1}{\alpha - 1}}\right)^{1/2}$ $K_{be} = K_c + K_D$; $\alpha = \frac{U_b \varepsilon_{mf}}{U_{mf}}$
Kobayashi et al. (1967)	84	177 ~ 250	3 ~ 18	2.1	$K_{be} = 1.833$
Miyauchi & Morooka (1969)					$K_b = 1.128\, (D_G U_b/d_b)^{1/2}$ $K_e = 1.128\, (m D_{eff} U_b/d_b)^{1/2}$ $K_{be}^{-1} = K_b^{-1} + (\beta_r Ke)^{-1}$
Chiba & Kobayashi (1970)	10	140 ~ 210	≈ U_{mf}	3.1 ~ 5	$K_{be} = 1{,}128\, \left(\frac{\varepsilon^2_{mf} D_G U_b}{d_b}\right)^{1/2} \left(\frac{\alpha - 1}{\alpha}\right)^{2/3}$
Calderbank et al. (1976)	15.4	80 - 105		0.58	$K_{be} = \frac{3\pi d_b^2 U_{mf}}{4 s_b} + 1.128\, (D_G U_b/L_b)^{1/2}$
Drinkenburg & Rietema (1972)	18.9	66	= U_{mf}	0.2	Numerical model
Mori & Muchi (1972)					$K_{be} = \frac{9\delta\xi U_{mf}}{4 d_b}$: for bubble growth region $K_{be} = \left(\frac{\sqrt{\pi}}{2}\sqrt{\frac{\delta D_T}{D_G \varepsilon_b U_b}} + \frac{4}{3 U_{mf}}\right)^{-1}$ for non-bubble growth region $\xi = 1$ cm, $\delta = 1.4\, d_p\, \rho_p\, U/U_{mf}$
Zenz (1960)					$K_{be} = 1.05$
Davidson et al. (1977)					$K_{bo} = 1.19\, U_{mf} + 0.91\, \left(\frac{D_G^{1/2}\, g^{1/4}}{d_b^{1/4}}\right) \frac{\varepsilon_{mf}}{1 + \varepsilon_{mf}}$

* Dimensions in C.G.S. Units

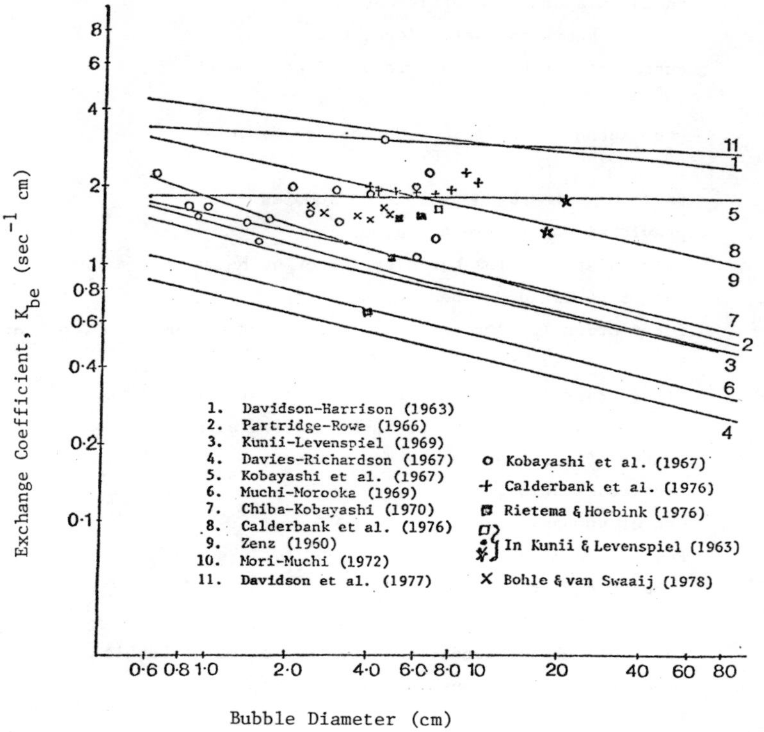

Figure 9. Previous Models for Mass Transfer Between Bubble and Emulsion Phase

NOMENCLATURE

a_b	ratio of solids dispersed in bubbles to the volume of the bed
C_b, C_c, C_e, C_w	molar concentration in bubbles, cloud, emulsion phase, and wake, respectively, Mol L^{-3}
C_D	drag coefficient of a particle in a suspension
C_{DS}	drag coeffient of a single particle in an infinite expanse of fluid
C_i	molar concentration of species i, Mol L^{-3}
d_b	bubble diameter, L
d_{bo}	initial bubble diameter, L
$d_{b\ max}$	maximum bubble diameter, L
d_p	particle diameter, L
D_c	column diameter, L
D_G	gas diffusivity, L^2T^{-1}
D_T	reactor diameter, L

E_r	radial dispersion coefficient, L^2T^{-1}
E_Z	axial dispersion coefficient, L^2T^{-1}
F	entrainment rate in the freeboard at a height $ML^{-2}T^{-1}$
F_{bc}, F_{be}, F_{ce}, F_{bw}, F_{we}	gas exchange coefficient between phases, T^{-1}
fw	ratio of wake to the volume of bubbles
g	gravitational acceleration, LT^{-2}
h	axial distance from the distributor or height above the bed surface, L
L_f	height of fluidized bed, L
k	first order (gas) reaction rate constant per unit vol. of settled bed, T^{-1}
k_r	first order (gas) reaction rate constant per unit vol. of solids, T^{-1}
K_{be}	gas exchange coefficient (bubble to emulsion), LT^{-1}
N	number of orifices in the distributor
N_{Ar}	Archimedes number
N_{Pe}	Peclet number
N_{Re}	Reynolds number
N_{Sc}	Schmidt number
r	distance from the center of reactor, L
R	ratio of bubble-cloud region to the volume of bubble
R_i	production rate of species i, Mol $L^{-3}T^{-1}$
U_b	bubble velocity, LT^{-1}
U_{bs}	velocity of a bubble with respect to the emulsion phase, LT^{-1}
U_c	gas velocity in cloud or critical gas velocity through each orifice, LT^{-1}
U_{cr}	critical gas velocity for gas backmixing, LT^{-1}
U_e	gas velocity in the emulsion phase, LT^{-1}
U_{mf}	minimum fluidization velocity, LT^{-1}
U_o	superficial gas velocity, LT^{-1}
U_s	solids velocity, LT^{-1}
U_t	terminal velocity of the particle, LT^{-1}
U_w	gas velocity in wake, LT^{-1}
V_b	volume of bubbles
z	height, L

Greek Letters

δ_b	volume of bubbles/total bed volume
δ_c	volume of cloud/total bed volume
δ_e	volume of emulsion/total bed volume
δ_w	volume of wake/total bed volume
ε	voidage
ε_b	bubble fraction

ε_e	voidage in the emulsion phase
ε_{mf}	voidage at minimum fluidization
λ	solid friction coefficient
μ_G	gas viscosity, $ML^{-1}T^{-1}$
ρ_G	gas viscosity, ML^{-3}
ρ_s	solid density, ML^{-3}
ρ_p	particle density, ML^{-3}

REFERENCES

Barreteau, D., Lagureria, C., and Angelino, H., "Fluidization", Cambridge University Press, 292 (1978).

Behie, L. A., and Kehoe, P., AIChE J., 19 (5) 1070 (1973).

Bohle, W. and Van Swaaij, W. P. N., "Fluidization", eds. J. F. Davidson and D. L. Keairns, p. 167, Cambridge University Press, Cambridge, England (1978).

Calderbank, PH. H., Pereira, J., and Burgess, M. M., "Fluidization Technology", International Fluidization Conf., Pacific Grove, Calif., p. 261 (1976).

Chen, M. M., Lin, J., and Chao, B. T., AIChE Annual Meeting, New Orleans, LA, Nov. (1981).

Chiba, T., and Kobayashi, H., Chem. Eng. Sci., 25, 1375 (1970).

Chiba, T., Terashima, K., and Kobayashi, H., Chem. Eng. Sci., 27, 965 (1972).

Chiba, T., Terashima, K., and Kobayashi, H., J. Chem. Eng. Japan, 6, 78 (1973).

Clift, R., Grace, J. R., and Weber, M. E., "Bubbles, Drops and Particles", Academic Press, New York, (1978).

Darton, R. C., LaNanze, R. D., Davidson, J. F., and Harrison, D., Trans. Inst. Chem. Eng., 57, 134 (1979).

Darton, R. C., LaNanze, R. D., Davidson, J. F., and Harrison, D., Trans. Inst. Chem. Eng., 57, 134 (1979).

Davidson, J. F., and Harrison, D., "Fluidized Particles", Cambridge University Press, Cambridge, England (1963).

Davidson, J. F. et al., "Chemical Reactor Theory, A Review," eds. L. Lapidus and N. R. Amudson, Chap. 10, Prentice-Hall, Englewood Cliffs, NJ (1977).

Davidson, J. F., and Schuler, B. O. G., Trans. Instn. Chem. Eng., 38, 335 (1960).

Davies, L., and Richardson, J. F., Brit. Chem. Eng., 12, 1223 (1967).

Davies, R. M., and Taylor, G. I., Proc. Roy. Soc., A200, 375 (1950).

DeLasa, H. I., and Grace, J. R., AIChE J., 25 (6) 984 (1979).

Drinkenburg, A. A. H., and Rietema, K., Chem. Eng. Sci., 27, 1765 (1972).

Fryer, C., and Potter, O. E., Preprints of the International Fluidization Conference, Pacific Grove, III-1 (1975).

Fryer, C., and Potter, O. E., AIChE J., 22, 38 (1976).

Geldart, D., Powder Technol., 6, 201 (1972).

Grace, J. R., Chem. Eng. Prog., Symp. Ser., 67 (116) 159 (1971).

Grace, J. R., and Clift, R., Chem. Eng. Sci., 29, 327 (1974).

Gwyn, J. E., Moser, J. H., and Parker, W. A., Chem. Eng. Prog. Symp. Ser., 66 (101) 19 (1970).

Harrison, D., Davidson, J. F., and deKock, J. W., Trans. Instn. Chem. Engr., 39, 202 (1961).

Horio, M., and Wen, C. Y., AIChE Symp. Ser., 73 (161) 9 (1977).

Kato, K., and Wen, C. Y., Chem. Eng. Sci., 24, 1351 (1969).

Kobayashi, H., Arai, F., and Chiba, T., Kagaku Kogaku, 31, 239 (1967).

Kobayashi, H., and Arai, F., Kagaku Kogaku, 29, 885 (1965).

Kuhne, J., and Wippern, D., Can. J. Chem. Eng., 58, 527 (1980).

Kunii, D., Yoshida, Y., and Hiraki, I., Proc. International Symp. on Fluidization, Netherlands Univ. Press, 243 (1967).

Kunii, D., and Levenspiel, O., Fluidization Engineering, Wiley & Sons, NY (1969).

Latham, R. L., Hamilton, C. J., and Potter, O. E., Brit. Cem. Eng., 13, 666 (1968).

Lewis, W. K., Gilliland, E. R., and Glass, W., AIChE J., 5, 419 (1959).

May, W. G., Chem. Eng. Prog., 55 (12) 49 (1959).

Miwa, K., Mori, S., Kato, T., and Muchi, I., Int. Chem. Eng., 12, 187 (1972).

Miyauchi, T., J. Chem. Eng. Japan, 7, 201, 207 (1974).

Miyauchi, T., and Morooka, S., J. Chem. Eng. Japan, 33, 369 (1969).

Mori, S., and Muchi, I., Kagaku Kogaku, 5, 251 (1972).

Mori, S., and Wen, C. Y., AIChE J., 21, 109 (1975).

Murray, J. D., J. Fluid. Mech., 21, 465 (1965).

Murray, J. D., Cem. Eng. Prog. Symp. Ser., 62 (62) 71 (1966).

Nguyen, H. V., and Potter, O. E., Chem. React. Eng., 11 in Advance in Chemistry Series, 133, ACS, 290 (1974).

Nguyen, H. V., Ph.D. Thesis, Monash Univ., Australia (1975).

Nguyen, H. V., Whitehead, A. B., and Potter, O. E., AIChE J., 23, 913 (1977).

Orcutt, J. C., Davidson, J. F., and Pigford, R. L., Chem. Eng. Prog. Symp. Ser., 58 (38) 1 (1962).

Orcutt, J. C., and Carpenter, B. H., Chem. Eng. Sci., 26, 1049 (1971).

Park, W. H., Kang, W. K., Capes, C. E., and Osberg, G. L., Chem. Eng. Sci., 24, 851 (1969).

Partridge, B. A., and Rowe, P. N., Trans. Inst. Chem. Engrs., 44, T347 (1966).

Potter, O. E., "Fluidization", eds. Davidson, J. F., and Harrison, D., p. 293, Academic, NY (1971).

Potter, O. E., Catal. Rev. Sci. Eng., 17 (2) 155 (1978).

Pyle, D. L., Avd. Chem. Series, 109, 106 (1972).

Rietema, K., and Hoebink, J., "Fluidization Technology", ed. Keairns, D. L., Vol. 1, pp. 279, Hemisphere, Washington, DC (1976).

Rowe, P. N., Proc. Second Internat. Symp. on Chem. Reaction Eng., A9 (1972).

Rowe, P. N., Chem. Eng. Sci., 31, 285 (1976).

Schiller, L., and Naumann, A., Z. Ver. Dtsch. Ing., 77 , 318 (1935).

Shen, C. Y., and Johnstone, H. F., AIChE J., 1, 349 (1955).

Stephens, G. K., Sinclair, R. J., and Potter, O. E., Powder Technol., 1, 157 (1967).

Toei, R., Matsuno, R., Nishitani, K., Miyagawa, H., and Komagawa, Y., Kagaku Kogaku, 32, 565 (1968).

Toor, F. D., and Calderbank, P. H., "Fluidization", eds. Davidson, J. F., and Harrison, D., p. 383, Academic Press, London (1971).

Van Deemter, J. J., Chem. Eng. Sci., 13, 143 (1961).

Wen, C. Y., and Fan, L. T., "Models for Flow Systems and Chemical Reactors", Dekker, NY (1975).

Wen, C. Y., and Yu, Y. H., Chem. Eng. Prog. Symp. Ser., 62, 100 (1966).

Werther, J., Chem. Ing. Tech., 50, 850 (1978).

Werther, J., Intern. Chem. Eng., 20 , 529 (1980).

Whitehead, A. B., and Young, A. D., Proc. of Int. Sym. on Fluidization, Eindhoren, p. 284, Netherlands Univ. Press (1967).

Yasui, G., and Johanson, L. N., AIChE J., 4, 445 (1958).

Zenz, F. A., and Othmer, D. F., "Fluidization and Fluid-Particle Systems", Reinhold Publishing Corp., NY (1960).

Two Abstracts

E. Bruce Nauman

Rensselaer Polytechnic Institute, Department of Chemical Engineering, Troy, New York 12181, U. S. A.

DIFFUSION, DISPERSION, AND OPEN SYSTEMS

After nearly thirty years of literature controversy, the long-sought residence time distribution in an open, diffusive system has been shown identical to that for a closed system. Random walk theory provides an unambiguous distinction between residence times and transient response functions and shows the impossibility of measuring residence times in open systems using inert tracer experiments. It also points out the inherent difficulties in a strictly continuum approach to residence time theory.

RECENT DEVELOPMENTS IN RESIDENCE TIME THEORY

Asymptotic results have been found for the residence time distribution in any flow system having a zero slip boundary condition. In the absence of molecular diffusion, all distributions will have slowly decaying tails and infinite second moments. With diffusion, all distributions have exponentially decaying tails and finite moments of all orders.

Other recent results include pathological recycle systems where increasing the recycle rate gives limiting distributions other than the exponential and diffusive systems where inert and reactive molecules have different residence times.

Subject Index

adsorption 153ff., 182ff.
– nonlinear 168
age distribution 1, 148
back mixing 103
catalyst 155ff.
cell model 104, 107
compartments-in-series (*see also* stirred tank) 85
contact time 153
cracking 25
diffusion
– binary 41
– bulk 52
– Knudsen 51
– molecular 258
– pore 46
diffusion-cell 55
dispersion 105, 151, 256
– axial 53, 113ff., 130, 257
– heat 103
– longitudinal (*see also* dispersion, axial) 198
– radial 130, 260
extinction 104
F-curve 149
F-diagram 1
fixed bed 103, 160ff.
flow
– plug 2, 36f.
– laminar 2, 257
– turbulent 256
fluidized bed 181
– bubbleless 262
– bubbling 264
holdback 2
ignition 104
integral transforms 124
intensity function 1
Kolmogorov equations 79ff., 231
life expectancy 7, 14
life expectation (*see also* life expectancy) 148
life time (*see also* residence time) 90, 232
linear process 3
liquid membrane 247
Markov chain (*see also* Markov process) 76, 237
Markov process 13, 229
mixing 7, 152
moments 3, 15, 32, 150
operator, differential 121ff.
packed bed (*see also* fixed bed) 42, 258
percolation 178
piston-flow (*see also* plug-flow) 105
pressure drop 49
pseudorandom input 223ff.
reaction 192
– catalytic 104
– consecutive 97
– first order 8, 29, 75, 114ff., 150, 170, 230
– non-linear 238
– parallel 23
– transform 9
reactor
– biological 217

– conversion 151
– heterogeneous 153ff.
– tubular 113, 257
residence time 3, 88, 148ff.
– joint 30ff.

segregation 2, 9, 24, 152
sorption (*see also* adsorption) 191
steady state 105ff., 260
Stieltjes transform 10
stirred tank 12, 14, 30, 119
– network 75

tortuosity 258
tracer 2, 29, 149
transfer function 150ff.